Differential Algebra

by

JOSEPH FELS RITT
Late Professor of Mathematics
in Columbia University

Dover Publications, Inc.
New York

Published in Canada by General Publishing Company, Limited, 30 Lesmill Road, Don Mills, Toronto, Ontario.
Published in the United Kingdom by Constable and Company, Limited, 10 Orange Street, London W.C. 2.

This Dover edition, first published in 1966, is an unabridged and unaltered republication of the work originally published by the American Mathematical Society in 1950 as Volume XXXIII of the Society's Colloquium Publications.
This edition is published by special arrangement with the American Mathematical Society, P. O. Box 6248, Providence, Rhode Island 02904.

Library of Congress Catalog Card Number: 66-23746

Manufactured in the United States of America
Dover Publications, Inc.
180 Varick Street
New York, N. Y. 10014

PREFACE

In 1932, the author published *Differential equations from the algebraic standpoint,*[1] a book dealing with differential polynomials and algebraic differential manifolds. In the sixteen years which have passed, the work of a number of mathematicians has given fresh substance and new color to the subject. The complete edition of the book having been exhausted, it has seemed proper to prepare a new exposition.

The title *Differential algebra* was suggested by Dr. Kolchin. The body of algebra deals with the operations of addition and multiplication. We are concerned here with three operations—addition, multiplication and differentiation.

If I am not mistaken, the general nature of the subject here treated is now well enough known among mathematicians to permit me to dispense with a detailed introduction, such as was given in A. D. E. My principal task is to show how much the present book owes to my associates. I am referring to H. W. Raudenbush, W. C. Strodt, E. R. Kolchin, Howard Levi, Eli Gourin and Richard M. Cohn.

Cohn's constructive proof of the theorem of zeros will be found in Chapter V. The theorem on embedded manifolds due to Gourin is contained in Chapter II. Chapter VI contains a discussion of Strodt's work on sequences of manifolds.

In Chapters I, III and IX, there are presented portions of Levi's work on ideals of differential polynomials and on the low power theorem. Of Kolchin's investigation of exponents of differential ideals, I have been able to give only a bare idea. Other work of Kolchin, for instance, proofs for the abstract case of results previously established for the analytic case, is given in Chapter II. His work on the Picard–Vessiot theory, which employs the methods of differential algebra, has just appeared in the Annals of Mathematics,[2] and may be permitted to speak for itself.

The contributions of Raudenbush can only be described as fundamental. The basis theorem of Chapter I was, in the analytic case, implicitly contained in A. D. E. It exists there in two parts; the first, the theorem on the completeness of infinite systems; the second, the theorem of zeros. Only casually had I noticed that the two theorems amounted to a basis theorem. I was acquainted with the fact that the theorem on the decomposition of manifolds amounted, in virtue of the theorem of zeros, to a theory of perfect and prime ideals of differential polynomials. In the summer of 1933, I suggested to Raudenbush the problem of constructing a theory of perfect ideals which would be valid in the abstract case. This he accomplished, and, in the course of his work, he brought the basis theorem to its present complete and abstract form. In the proof of

[1] These Colloquium publications, vol. 14. Called below A. D. E.

[2] Kolchin, 14. (See Bibliography, p. 180.)

the basis theorem, the procedure of taking powers is due to Raudenbush. The chains, characteristic sets and methods of reduction existed in the older theorem of completeness.

Raudenbush introduced generic zeros of prime ideals. Here he adapted a method of van der Waerden, which can be traced back to König. Raudenbush gave the first example of a system of differential polynomials with a weak basis. Systems with no strong bases were later produced by Kolchin.

The problems which this book treats are very concrete problems. They deal with situations of the classical theory of differential equations. Seldom would much be lost, as far as the results are concerned, if one limited oneself to the material of classical analysis. The abstract method which we generally employ has, however, a definite utility. It serves to separate algebraic methods from analytic methods. On the whole, it contributes to simplicity, although at times an abstract treatment is less natural than an analytical one. The form in which the results of differential algebra are being presented has thus been deeply influenced by the teachings of Emmy Noether, a prime mover of our period, who, in continuing Julius König's development of Kronecker's ideas, brought mathematicians to know algebra as it was never known before.

In this connection, I should like to say something concerning basis theorems. The basis theorem of Chapter I will be seen to play, in the present theory, the role held by Hilbert's theorem in the theories of polynomial ideals and of algebraic manifolds. When I began to work on algebraic differential equations, early in 1930, van der Waerden's excellent *Moderne Algebra* had not yet appeared. However, Emmy Noether's work of the twenties was available, and there was nothing to prevent one from learning in her papers the value of basis theorems in decomposition problems. Actually, I became acquainted with the basis theorem principle in the writings of Jules Drach[3] on logical integration, writings which date back to 1898. How a basis theorem is employed by him will now be described.

There are two distinct methods for characterizing an irreducible algebraic equation. On the one hand, an equation $f(x) = 0$ is irreducible if $f(x)$ cannot be factored. On the other, there is irreducibility if every equation which is satisfied by a single solution of $f(x) = 0$ is satisfied by all such solutions. The first formulation of irreducibility leads to the notion of irreducible algebraic manifold and to that of irreducible algebraic differential manifold. The second leads to the concept of irreducible system of algebraic differential equations which was employed by Koenigsberger and by Drach. A system of such equations, ordinary or partial, is irreducible if every differential equation which admits a single solution of the system admits all solutions. Drach undertakes to show that, given a system of partial differential equations, the repeated adjunction of new equations will eventually produce an irreducible system. For this he invokes a theorem of Tresse,[4] which states that, in every infinite system

[3] Drach, 4, pp. 292–296.

[4] Acta Mathematica, vol. 18 (1894), p. 4.

of partial differential equations, there is a finite subsystem from which the infinite system can be derived by differentiations and eliminations. A study of Tresse's paper will quickly convince one that he claims for his work a generality which it does not have. The statement of his theorem, and his argument, have a definite meaning only for linear systems.

It has not been possible for me to present all of the material which has been developed since the publication of A. D. E. Thus, I have had to pass by most of Kolchin's study of exponents and a good deal of Levi's work on ideals. Of Strodt's paper, only a sketch is given. My own work on general solutions of equations of the second order in one unknown, and of equations of the first order in two unknowns, is also omitted.

I have tried to give, to the present book, the elementary quality which is possessed by A. D. E. Essentially, no previous knowledge of abstract algebra is necessary. As in A. D. E., a treatment is given of Riquier's existence theorem for orthonomic systems of partial differential equations.

New York, N. Y.
January, 1948.

CONTENTS

CHAPTER VII

INTERSECTIONS OF ALGEBRAIC DIFFERENTIAL MANIFOLDS 133

Dimensions of components of intersections, orders of components of an intersection, intersections of general solutions, intersections of components of a differential polynomial, analogue of a theorem of Kronecker.

CHAPTER VIII

RIQUIER'S EXISTENCE THEOREM FOR ORTHONOMIC SYSTEMS 147

Monomials, dissection of a Taylor series, marks, orthonomic systems, passive orthonomic systems.

CHAPTER IX

PARTIAL DIFFERENTIAL ALGEBRA 163

Partial differential polynomials, ideals and manifolds, components of a partial differential polynomial, the low power theorem, characteristic sets of prime ideals, algorithm for decomposition, the theorem of zeros.

APPENDIX

QUESTIONS FOR INVESTIGATION 177

BIBLIOGRAPHY 180

INDEX 183

CHAPTER I

DIFFERENTIAL POLYNOMIALS AND THEIR IDEALS

Differential fields

1. We deal with an algebraic field of characteristic zero, denoting the field by $\mathfrak{F}$. $\mathfrak{F}$, then, is a collection of elements of one type or another, upon which can be performed the operations of addition, subtraction, multiplication and division, except that division by a certain element 0 of $\mathfrak{F}$ is excluded. Addition and multiplication are commutative and associative, and multiplication is distributive with respect to addition. Subtraction and division are one-valued operations. $\mathfrak{F}$ contains a subset which is isomorphic, as regards addition and multiplication, with the system of rational numbers; this subset we consider, as we may, actually to be the system of rational numbers.

We are going to work with fields $\mathfrak{F}$ of characteristic zero in which an operation of *differentiation* is performable. This operation, which replaces every element a of $\mathfrak{F}$ by its *derivative*, an element a' of $\mathfrak{F}$, must be such that, for a and b in $\mathfrak{F}$,

$$(a + b)' = a' + b' \tag{1}$$

and

$$(ab)' = ba' + ab'. \tag{2}$$

When such an operation of differentiation exists for $\mathfrak{F}$, we shall call $\mathfrak{F}$ a *differential* field.

From (1) with $b = 0$, we see that $0' = 0$. From (2) with $b = 1$ and $a \neq 0$, it follows that $1' = 0$. It is easy to show that the derivative of every rational number is zero. An element with zero for derivative is called a *constant.*

The system of rational numbers, with derivatives taken, as they must be taken, equal to zero, is a differential field. So are the system of real numbers and the system of complex numbers. Further examples are the totality of rational functions of a variable x, with complex coefficients, and the totality of elliptic functions with a given period parallelogram; in these examples, differentiation is supposed to be performed as in analysis.

If $\mathfrak{F}$ and $\mathfrak{F}_1$ are differential fields and if $\mathfrak{F}_1$ contains $\mathfrak{F}$, $\mathfrak{F}_1$ is called an *extension* of $\mathfrak{F}$. It is understood that, when $\mathfrak{F}$ is considered by itself, the rational operations and differentiation are performed in it just as when $\mathfrak{F}$ is regarded as part of $\mathfrak{F}_1$.

Hereafter the term *field* will be used as an abbreviation for *differential field.* When an ordinary algebraic field is used, a proper announcement will be made. We repeat that the characteristic will always be zero.

Indeterminates

2. We shall be given frequently a letter such as y, the first of an infinite sequence of symbols

$$y, y', y'', \cdots, y^{(p)}, \cdots. \tag{3}$$

The symbols in (3) will be used for building polynomials, each polynomial involving, of course, only a finite number of the symbols. We shall call y a *differential indeterminate* or an *indeterminate*, and $y^{(p)}$ the pth *derivative* of y. Furthermore, for every p, and for every $q > 0$, $y^{(p+q)}$ will be called the qth derivative of $y^{(p)}$. It is to be emphasized that only y in (3) is an indeterminate; the $y^{(p)}$ are not indeterminates, but derivatives of an indeterminate.

Our problems will deal with any finite number n of indeterminates $y_1, \cdots, y_n$. The jth derivative of y_i will be written y_{ij}. We shall call y_i its own derivative of order zero and shall sometimes write y_{i0} for y_i. Where unsubscripted letters $u, v, \cdots, w$ are used for indeterminates, derivatives will be written with subscripts rather than with superscripts. Thus, u being an indeterminate, u_j is the jth derivative of u.

Differential polynomials

3. In what follows, we work with an arbitrary field $\mathfrak{F}$, which, in every question treated, is assigned in advance. Let there be given indeterminates $y_1, \cdots, y_n$. By a *differential polynomial* (d.p., singular and plural), we shall mean a polynomial in the y_{ij} with coefficients in $\mathfrak{F}$.

Two d.p. are considered equal if, and only if, their coefficients of like power products in the y_{ij} are equal. This is part of the basis for calling the y indeterminates.

In describing a d.p. A, it is at times desirable to refer to the field $\mathfrak{F}$, underlying the discussion, in which A has its coefficients. This is done by calling A a d.p. *over* $\mathfrak{F}$.

The totality of d.p. in $y_1, \cdots, y_n$ over $\mathfrak{F}$ will be denoted by $\mathfrak{F}\{y_1, \cdots, y_n\}$. At each stage of our work, $\mathfrak{F}$, as has been observed, is supposed to be known. $\mathfrak{F}$ is not changed without an explicit statement being made.

Let A be a d.p. By the *derivative of* A, we shall mean the d.p. obtained from A with the use of (1) and (2) of §1.

Thus, if $\mathfrak{F}$ is the totality of rational functions of a variable x and if

$$A = xy_1^2 + x^2y_{21},$$

the derivative of A is $y_1^2 + 2xy_1y_{11} + 2xy_{21} + x^2y_{22}$.

Higher derivatives are defined in the expected way.

Until further notice, capital italics will denote d.p.

By the *class* of A, if A is not merely an element of $\mathfrak{F}$, we shall mean the greatest p such that some y_{pj} is present in a term of A whose coefficient is distinct from zero. If A is an element of $\mathfrak{F}$, A will be said to be of class 0.

We shall at times speak of a d.p. A as involving a certain y_i effectively. We shall mean by this that at least one y_{ij} appears effectively in A.

By the *order of A with respect to y_i*, if A involves y_i effectively, we shall mean the greatest j such that y_{ij} appears effectively in A. If A does not involve y_i, the order of A in y_i will be taken as zero.

Let A_1 and A_2 be two d.p. Suppose that some indeterminate y_p appears effectively in both of them. If A_2 is of higher order in y_p than A_1, A_2 will be said to be of *higher rank than* A_1 and A_1 *of lower rank than* A_2, in y_p. If A_1 and A_2 are of the same order, say q, in y_p and if A_2 is of higher degree than A_1 in y_{pq}, then, also, A_2 will be said to be of higher rank than A_1 in y_p. Finally, A_2 will be of higher rank than A_1 in y_p if A_2 involves y_p and A_1 does not. Two d.p. for which no difference in rank is established by the foregoing criteria will be said to be of the same rank in y_p.

If A_2 is of higher class than A_1, A_2 will be said to be of *higher rank* than A_1, or to be *higher* than A_1. If A_1 and A_2 are of the same class $p > 0$, and if A_2 is of higher rank than A_1 in y_p, then, again, A_2 will be said to be higher than A_1. Two d.p. for which no difference in rank is created by what precedes will be said to be of the same rank. Thus, all d.p. of class zero are of the same rank.[1]

If A_2 is higher than A_1 and A_3 higher than A_2, then A_3 is higher than A_1.

Where unsubscripted indeterminates $u, v, \cdots, w$ are used, class and relative rank are established by giving to the pth indeterminate from the left the role of y_p above.

The following simple fact will be important in our later work.

Every aggregate of d.p. contains a d.p. which is not higher than any other d.p. of the aggregate.

If the aggregate contains a d.p. of class zero, any such d.p. answers our requirement. Otherwise, let p be the least of the classes of the d.p. From the d.p. of class p, we select those which are of a least order, say q, in y_p and from the d.p. just selected we pick one, A, which is of a lowest degree in y_{pq}. Then no d.p. in the aggregate is lower than A.

Chains

4. If A_1 is of class $p > 0$, A_2 will be said to be *reduced with respect to* A_1 if A_2 is of lower rank than A_1 in y_p.

The system

$$A_1, A_2, \cdots, A_r \tag{4}$$

will be called a *chain* if either

(a) $\qquad r = 1 \quad$ *and* $\quad A_1 \neq 0,$

or

(b) $r > 1$, A_1 *is of positive class and, for* $j > i$, A_j *is of higher class than* A_i *and reduced with respect to* A_i.

[1] As will be seen in Chapter IX, there are other ways of ordering d.p.

Of course, $r \leqq n$.

The chain (4) will be said to be of *higher rank* than the chain

$$(5) \qquad B_1, B_2, \cdots, B_s$$

if either

(a) *there is a j, exceeding neither r nor s, such that A_i and B_i are of the same rank for $i < j$ and that A_j is higher than*[2] B_j

or

(b) $s > r$ *and A_i and B_i are of the same rank for $i \leqq r$.*

Two chains for which no difference in rank is created by what precedes will be said to be of the same rank. For such chains, $r = s$ and A_i and B_i are of the same rank for every i.

Let Φ_1, Φ_2, Φ_3 be chains such that Φ_1 is higher than Φ_2 and Φ_2 higher than Φ_3. We write $\Phi_1 > \Phi_2$, $\Phi_2 > \Phi_3$. We shall prove that $\Phi_1 > \Phi_3$.

Let Φ_1 and Φ_2 be represented by (4) and (5) respectively and let Φ_3 be

$$C_1, C_2, \cdots, C_t.$$

Suppose first that $\Phi_1 > \Phi_2$ for the reason (a) and that $\Phi_2 > \Phi_3$ for the reason (a). Let j be the smallest integer such that B_j is higher than C_j. Then either A_i is of the same rank as B_i for $i \leqq j$ or there is a $k \leqq j$ such that A_k is higher than B_k. In either case, $\Phi_1 > \Phi_3$ by (a). Suppose now that $\Phi_1 > \Phi_2$ by (b), while $\Phi_2 > \Phi_3$ by (a). Let j be taken as above. If $j > r$, $\Phi_1 > \Phi_3$ by (b). If $j \leqq r$, $\Phi_1 > \Phi_3$ by (a). Now let $\Phi_1 > \Phi_2$ by (a) while $\Phi_2 > \Phi_3$ by (b). Let j be the smallest integer for which A_j is higher than B_j. Then A_j is higher than C_j and A_i is of the same rank as C_i for $i < j$. Thus $\Phi_1 > \Phi_3$ by (a). Finally, if $\Phi_1 > \Phi_2$ by (b) and $\Phi_2 > \Phi_3$ by (b), then $\Phi_1 > \Phi_3$ by (b).

We shall use later the following fact:

In every aggregate of chains, there is a chain which is not higher than any other chain of the aggregate.

Let α be the aggregate. We form a subset α_1 of α, putting a chain Φ into α_1 if the first d.p. in Φ is not higher than the first d.p. of any other chain in α (§3). If the chains in α_1 all consist of one d.p., any chain in α_1 meets our requirements. Suppose that there are chains in α_1 which have more than one d.p. We form the subset α_2 of them whose second d.p. are of a lowest rank. If the chains in α_2 all have just two d.p., any of those chains serves our purpose. If not, we continue, reaching lowest chains in no more than n steps.

Characteristic sets

5. Let Σ be a finite or infinite set of d.p. in $\mathfrak{F}\{y_1, \cdots, y_n\}$ (§3). We do not assume the d.p. in Σ to be distinct from one another.[3] Suppose that the d.p. in Σ are not all zero.

---

[2] If $j = 1$, this is to mean that A_1 is higher than B_1.

[3] What we are really considering then, is a system of distinct marks, each mark being associated with a d.p. Two marks may be associated with identical d.p.

It is possible to form chains with d.p. in Σ; for instance, every nonzero d.p. in Σ is a chain. Among all chains in Σ, there are some, by §4, which have a lowest rank. Any such chain will be called a *characteristic set* of Σ.

If A_1 in (4) is of positive class, a d.p. F will be said to be *reduced with respect to the chain* (4) if F is reduced with respect to A_i, $i = 1, \cdots, r$.

Let A_1 in (4) be of positive class and let Σ be a system containing (4). We shall prove that, *for* (4) *to be a characteristic set of* Σ, *it is necessary and sufficient that* Σ *contain no nonzero d.p. reduced with respect to* (4). Suppose that (4) is not a characteristic set of Σ, while (5) is. Suppose that (5) is lower than (4) by (b) of §4. Then B_{r+1} is reduced with respect to (4). If (5) is lower by (a), there is some B_i with $i \leqq r$ which is reduced with respect to (4). Suppose now that (4) is a characteristic set and that Σ contains a nonzero d.p. F which is reduced with respect to (4). If the class of F is higher than that of A_r, we get a chain lower than (4) by adjoining F to (4); otherwise, if the rightmost A whose class is not exceeded by that of F is A_j, the chain $A_1, \cdots, A_{j-1}, F$ is lower than (4).[4]

Let Σ be a system for which (4), with A_1 of positive class, is a characteristic set. We see that, *if a nonzero d.p., reduced with respect to* (4), *is adjoined to* Σ, *the characteristic sets of the resulting system are lower than* (4).

Let Σ be a system of d.p. which are not all zero. The following method for constructing a characteristic set of Σ can actually be carried out when Σ is finite. Of the nonzero d.p. in Σ, let A_1 be one of least rank. If A_1 is of class zero, it is a characteristic set for Σ. Let A_1 be of positive class. If Σ contains no nonzero d.p. reduced with respect to A_1, then A_1 is a characteristic set. Suppose that such reduced d.p. exist; they are all of higher class than A_1. Let A_2 be one of them of least rank. If Σ has no nonzero d.p. reduced with respect to A_1 and A_2, then A_1, A_2 is a characteristic set. If such reduced d.p. exist, let A_3 be one of them of least rank. Continuing, we arrive at a chain (4) which is a characteristic set.

Until further notice, large Greek letters not used as symbols of summation or of multiplication will denote systems of d.p.

Reduction

6. In this section, we deal with a chain (4) with A_1 of positive class.

If a d.p. G is of class $p > 0$ and of order m in y_p, we shall call $\partial G/\partial y_{pm}$ the *separant*[5] of G. The coefficient of the highest power of y_{pm} in G will be called the *initial* of G.[6]

The separant and initial of G are both lower than G.

---

[4] When $j = 1$, we use the chain F.

[5] If G, arranged as a polynomial in y_{pm}, is $\sum_{i=0}^{q} C_i y_{pm}^i$, the separant is $\sum_{i=1}^{q} i C_i y_{pm}^{i-1}$. As $\mathfrak{F}$ has characteristic zero, the separant does not vanish identically.

[6] If the indeterminates are $u, v, \cdots, w$, then w will play the role of y_p above, in the definitions of separant and initial of a d.p. actually involving w.

In (4), let S_i and I_i be respectively the separant and initial of A_i, $i = 1, \cdots, r$. We shall prove the following result.

Let G be any d.p. There exist nonnegative integers s_i, t_i, $i = 1, \cdots, r$, *such that, when a suitable linear combination of the A, and of a certain number of their derivatives, with d.p. for coefficients, is subtracted from*

$$S_1^{s_1} \cdots S_r^{s_r} I_1^{t_1} \cdots I_r^{t_r} G,$$

the remainder, R, is reduced with respect to (4).

We limit ourselves, as we may, to the case in which G is not reduced with respect to (4).

Let j be the greatest value of i such that G is not reduced with respect to A_i. Let A_j be of class p, and of order m in y_p. Let G be of order h in y_p.

We suppose first that $h > m$. If $k_1 = h - m$, then $A_j^{(k_1)}$, the k_1th derivative of A_j, will be of order h in y_p. It will be linear in y_{ph}, with S_j for coefficient of y_{ph}. Using the algorithm of division, we find a nonnegative integer v_1 such that

$$S_j^{v_1} G = C_1 A_j^{(k_1)} + D_1$$

where D_1 is of order less than h in y_p. In order to have a unique procedure, we take v_1 as small as possible.

Suppose, for the moment, that $p < n$. Let a be an integer with $p < a \leqq n$. We shall show that D_1 is not of higher rank than G in y_a. We may limit ourselves to the case in which $D_1 \neq 0$. Also, since S_j is free of y_a, we need only treat the case in which y_a is present in G. Let G be of order g in y_a. Then the order of D_1 in y_a cannot exceed g. If D_1 were of higher degree than G in y_{ag}, C_1 would have to involve y_{ag} to the same degree as D_1 and $C_1 A_j^{(k_1)}$ would contain terms involving y_{ag} and y_{ph} which would be balanced neither by D_1 nor by $S_j^{v_1} G$. This proves our statement.

If D_1 is of order greater than m in y_p, we find a relation

$$S_j^{v_2} D_1 = C_2 A_j^{(k_2)} + D_2$$

with D_2 of lower order than D_1 in y_p and not of higher rank than D_1 (or G) in any y_a with $a > p$. For uniqueness, we take v_2 as small as possible.

We eventually reach a D_u, of order not greater than m in y_p, such that, if

$$s_j = v_1 + \cdots + v_u,$$

we have

$$S_j^{s_j} G = E_1 A_j^{(k_1)} + \cdots + E_u A_j^{(k_u)} + D_u.$$

Furthermore, if $a > p$, D_u is not of higher rank than G in y_a.

If D_u is of order less than m in y_p, D_u is reduced with respect to A_j (as well as to any A_i with $i > j$). If D_u is of order m in y_p, we find, with the algorithm of division, a relation

$$I_j^{t_j} D_u = H A_j + K$$

with K reduced with respect to A_j, as well as to $A_{j+1}, \cdots, A_r$. For uniqueness, we take t_j as small as possible.

If K is not reduced with respect to (4), we treat K as G was treated. For some $l < j$, there are s_l, t_l such that $S_l^{s_l} I_l^{t_l} K$ exceeds, by a linear combination of A_l and its derivatives, a d.p. L which is reduced with respect to $A_l, A_{l+1}, \cdots, A_r$. Then

$$S_l^{s_l} S_j^{s_j} I_l^{t_l} I_j^{t_j} G$$

exceeds L by a linear combination of A_l, A_j and their derivatives.

Continuing, we reach a d.p. R as described in the italicized statement.

Our procedure determines a *unique* R. We call this R *the remainder of* G *with respect to the chain* (4).

Ideals of differential polynomials

7. Let Σ be a system of d.p. in $\mathfrak{F}\{y_1, \cdots, y_n\}$, any two d.p. in Σ being distinct from each other. We shall call Σ a *differential ideal of differential polynomials* if Σ satisfies the following two conditions:

(a) *If* $A_1, \cdots, A_r$ *is any finite subset of d.p. in* Σ,

$$C_1A_1 + \cdots + C_rA_r$$

where the C *are any d.p. at all in* $\mathfrak{F}\{y_1, \cdots, y_n\}$, *is contained in* Σ.

(b) *The derivative of every d.p. in* Σ *is contained in* Σ.

Condition (a) makes Σ an algebraic ideal in $\mathfrak{F}\{y_1, \cdots, y_n\}$. Together, (a) and (b) state that, given any finite subset of d.p. in Σ, every linear combination of the d.p. of the subset, and of their derivatives of any orders, belongs to Σ. The coefficients in the linear combination may be any d.p.

Throughout our work, unless some other indication is made, the term *ideal* will stand for *differential ideal of d.p.*

An ideal contains an infinite number of d.p. unless it consists of the single d.p. 0. The intersection of any finite or infinite number of ideals is an ideal.

An ideal Σ will be called *perfect* if, whenever a positive integral power of a d.p. A is contained in Σ, A is contained in Σ. The intersection of any finite or infinite number of perfect ideals is a perfect ideal.

An ideal Σ will be called *prime* if, whenever a product AB is contained in Σ, at least one of A and B is in Σ. Every prime ideal is perfect.

Let Λ be any system of (not necessarily distinct) d.p. There exist ideals, for instance $\mathfrak{F}\{y_1, \cdots, y_n\}$, which contain all d.p. in Λ. The intersection of all ideals containing Λ will be called the *ideal generated by* Λ and will be denoted by $[\Lambda]$. A d.p. A is contained in $[\Lambda]$ if, and only if, A is a linear combination of d.p. in Λ and of derivatives, of various orders, of such d.p.[7]

The intersection of all perfect ideals containing Λ will be called the *perfect ideal determined by* Λ and will be denoted by $\{\Lambda\}$. One sees that $\{\Lambda\}$ contains $[\Lambda]$.

[7] Unless other indications are given, the coefficients in a linear combination may be any d.p.

8. We represent by (Λ) the totality of linear combinations of d.p.[8] in Λ and, when we wish to express the fact that a difference $A - B$ is in (Λ), we shall write

$$A \equiv B, \qquad (\Lambda).^{9}$$

The statements

$$A \equiv B, \qquad [\Lambda] \qquad ; \qquad A \equiv B, \qquad \{\Lambda\},$$

will mean, respectively, that $A - B$ is contained in $[\Lambda]$ or in $\{\Lambda\}$.

9. We are going to prove that $\{\Lambda\}$ *consists of those d.p. which have positive integral powers in* $[\Lambda]$. We use the following lemma, in which the field is the field of rational numbers.

LEMMA: *For u an indeterminate and for every positive integer p,*

$$u_1^{2p-1} \equiv 0, \qquad [u].^{10} \tag{6}$$

Differentiating u^p and dividing by p, we have

$$u^{p-1}u_1 \equiv 0, \qquad [u^p], \tag{7}$$

which gives (6) if $p = 1$. Suppose that $p > 1$. By (7),

$$(p - 1)\, u^{p-2}u_1^2 + u^{p-1}u_2 \equiv 0, \qquad [u^p].$$

Multiplying by u_1 and using (7), we find that

$$u^{p-2}u_1^3 \equiv 0, \qquad [u^p]$$

and we have (6) for $p = 2$. Continuing, we find (6) to hold for every p.

We return now to $\mathfrak{F}\{y_1, \cdots, y_n\}$ and to $\{\Lambda\}$. As $\{\Lambda\}$ contains $[\Lambda]$, $\{\Lambda\}$ contains every d.p. which has a power in $[\Lambda]$. If we can show that the totality of such d.p. is an ideal, we shall recognize that totality to be $\{\Lambda\}$. If A has a power in $[\Lambda]$, CA, for every C, has a power in $[\Lambda]$. If A^p and B^q are in $[\Lambda]$, $(A + B)^{p+q-1}$ is seen, on being expanded, to be in $[\Lambda]$. Thus the set of those d.p. which have powers in $[\Lambda]$ is closed with respect to linear combination. The lemma above shows that, if A^p is in $[\Lambda]$, then $(A')^{2p-1}$ with A' the derivative of A, is in $[\Lambda]$. Our statement is proved.

10. We prove the following lemma, in which the field is that of the rational numbers.

LEMMA: *If u and v are indeterminates and if j is a nonnegative integer,*[11]

$$u^{j+1}v_j \equiv 0, \qquad (uv, (uv)_1, \cdots, (uv)_j)$$

where $(uv)_k$ *is the kth derivative of uv.*

---

[8] Note that we do not use derivatives of d.p. in Λ.

[9] If, for instance, Λ consists of d.p. $C_1, \cdots, C_r$, we may write

$$A \equiv B, \qquad (C_1, \cdots, C_r).$$

[10] See remarks on notation in §2.

[11] $v_0 = v$.

The statement is true for $j = 0$. We make an induction to $j = r$, where $r > 0$, supposing lower values of j to have been treated. We have

$$(8) \qquad u^r v_{r-1} \equiv 0, \qquad (uv, \cdots, (uv)_{r-1}).$$

Then

$$u^r v_r + r u^{r-1} u_1 v_{r-1} \equiv 0, \qquad (uv, \cdots, (uv)_r).$$

We multiply by u and use (8). The induction is seen to be accomplished.

Suppose now that, $\mathfrak{F}$ being any field, we are given a perfect ideal Σ in $\mathfrak{F}\{y_1, \cdots, y_n\}$. Let AB belong to Σ. By the lemma, with $j = 1$,[12] A^2B', with B' the derivative of B, is in Σ. This puts AB' in Σ. In general, we see that *if Σ is a perfect ideal, and if AB is in Σ, every $A^{(i)} B^{(j)}$, superscripts indicating differentiation, is in Σ.*

11. We denote the union[13] of systems Σ_1 and Σ_2 by $\Sigma_1 + \Sigma_2$. The intersection of Σ_1 and Σ_2 will be denoted by $\Sigma_1 \cap \Sigma_2$.

Let Σ be any system of d.p. and $F_1, \cdots, F_p$ any finite set of d.p. We shall prove that

$$(9) \quad \{\Sigma + F_1F_2 \cdots F_p\} = \{\Sigma + F_1\} \cap \{\Sigma + F_2\} \cap \cdots \cap \{\Sigma + F_p\}.$$

It suffices to treat the case of $p = 2$. The first member of (9) is easily seen to be contained in each $\{\Sigma + F_i\}$. It is enough, then, to consider an A which is contained in $\{\Sigma + F_1\}$ and in $\{\Sigma + F_2\}$ and to prove that A is in $\{\Sigma + F_1F_2\}$. By §9, there is a q such that

$$(10) \qquad A^q = S_1 + G_1; \qquad A^q = S_2 + G_2$$

with S_1 and S_2 in $[\Sigma]$, G_1 in $[F_1]$ and G_2 in $[F_2]$. Multiplying the two equations of (10), we have

$$(11) \qquad A^{2q} = S_3 + G_1G_2$$

with S_3 in $[\Sigma]$. Let

$$(12) \qquad \begin{aligned} G_1 &= MF_1 + M_1F_1' + \cdots + M_rF^{(r)}, \\ G_2 &= NF_2 + N_1F_2' + \cdots + N_rF_2^{(r)}, \end{aligned}$$

where superscripts indicate differentiation. Now F_1F_2 is in $\{F_1F_2\}$. By §10, every $F_1^{(i)} F_2^{(j)}$ is in $\{F_1F_2\}$. By (12) G_1G_2 is in $\{F_1F_2\}$, thus in $\{\Sigma + F_1F_2\}$. By (11), A^{2q}, and therefore also A, must be in $\{\Sigma + F_1F_2\}$.

Bases

12. Let Σ be an infinite system of (not necessarily distinct) d.p. We shall call a finite subset Φ of Σ a *basis* of Σ if $\{\Phi\}$ contains every d.p. in Σ. Thus, if Φ is a basis of Σ, there is, for every A in Σ, a positive integer p, depending on A, such that A^p is linear in the d.p. in Φ and their derivatives of various or-

[12] The complete lemma will be used in Chapter III.

[13] Where other indications are not given, we use d.p. in $\mathfrak{F}\{y_1, \cdots, y_n\}$, with $\mathfrak{F}$ any field.

ders. If Φ is a basis of Σ, and if Φ_1 is a finite subset of Σ which contains Φ, then Φ_1 is also a basis of Σ.

We shall prove the

THEOREM: *Every infinite system of differential polynomials in* $\mathfrak{F}\{y_1, \cdots, y_n\}$ *has a basis.*

The fundamental role played by Raudenbush in bringing the basis theorem to its present complete form has been described in the preface.

We assume the existence of infinite systems without bases and work towards a contradiction.

13. LEMMA: *Let Σ be an infinite system with no basis. Let* d.p. $F_1, \cdots, F_p$ *exist such that, when each d.p. in Σ is multiplied by a suitable product of powers of the F, one secures a system Λ which has a basis. Then at least one of the systems* $\Sigma + F_i$, $i = 1, \cdots, p$, *has no basis.*

Let us suppose that each $\Sigma + F_i$ has a basis. Since a basis may be enlarged (§12), we may assume that we have a finite subset Φ of Σ such that $\Phi + F_i$ is a basis for $\Sigma + F_i$, $i = 1, \cdots, p$. We suppose, furthermore, enlarging Φ if necessary, that when each d.p. in Φ is multiplied by a suitable product of powers of the F, we secure a basis of Λ.

For each i, $\{\Sigma + F_i\}$, the smallest perfect ideal containing $\Sigma + F_i$, is contained in $\{\Phi + F_i\}$. Let $K = F_1F_2 \cdots F_p$. By §11, $\{\Sigma + K\}$ is the intersection of the $\{\Sigma + F_i\}$ and so is contained in every $\{\Phi + F_i\}$. As $\{\Phi + K\}$ is the intersection of the $\{\Phi + F_i\}$, $\{\Sigma + K\}$ is contained in $\{\Phi + K\}$. Thus $\Phi + K$ is a basis for $\Sigma + K$.

It follows that, for every d.p. A in Σ, there is a relation

$$A^q = G + MK + M_1K' + \cdots + M_rK^{(r)}$$

with G in $[\Phi]$. Then

$$A^{q+1} = GA + MKA + M_1K'A + \cdots + M_rK^{(r)}A. \tag{13}$$

We shall prove that KA is in $\{\Phi\}$. We know that Λ has a basis Ψ, each d.p. in Ψ being obtained from one in Φ by a multiplication by a power product in the F. We see immediately that $\{\Phi\}$ contains $\{\Psi\}$; also that some power of KA is in $\{\Psi\}$. Then KA is in $\{\Psi\}$ and hence in $\{\Phi\}$.

By §10, each $K^{(j)}A$ is in $\{\Phi\}$. As GA is in $\{\Phi\}$, we see from (13) that A^{q+1} is in $\{\Phi\}$. Thus A is in $\{\Phi\}$, that is, Φ is a basis for Σ. This proves the lemma.

14. From among all infinite systems which lack bases, we select one, Σ, whose characteristic sets (§5) are not higher than those of any other system which lacks a basis (§4). Let (4) be a characteristic set of Σ. Then A_1 is not of class zero; otherwise A_1, an element of $\mathfrak{F}$, would be a basis of Σ.

For every d.p. in Σ which is not in (4), let a remainder with respect to (4) be found as in §6. Let Λ be the system composed of the d.p. in (4) and of the products of the d.p. of Σ not in (4) by the products $S_1^{s_1} \cdots I_r^{t_r}$ used in their reduction. Let Ω be the system composed of (4) and of the remainders of the d.p. of Σ not in (4).

Now Ω must have a basis. Otherwise it would certainly have nonzero d.p. not in (4). As such a d.p. would be reduced with respect to (4), (4) could not be a characteristic set of Ω (§5). This means that the characteristic sets of Ω would be lower than (4), and Σ would not be a system, lacking a basis, of lowest characteristic sets.

We may suppose that Ω has a basis Φ composed of d.p.

$$A_1, \cdots, A_r; \qquad R_1, \cdots, R_s.$$

Let H_i be the d.p. of Λ which corresponds to R_i, $i = 1, \cdots, s$. Let Ψ be the set

$$A_1, \cdots, A_r; \qquad H_1, \cdots, H_s.$$

We wish to see that Ψ is a basis for Λ.

We know that $\{\Phi\}$ contains $[A_1, \cdots, A_r]$.

Because

$$H_i \equiv R_i, \qquad [A_1, \cdots, A_r], \qquad i = 1, \cdots, s,$$

we have $H_i \equiv R_i$, $\{\Phi\}$. As each R_i is in $\{\Phi\}$, each H_i is in $\{\Phi\}$. Hence $\{\Phi\}$ contains $\{\Psi\}$. Reciprocally, $\{\Psi\}$ contains $\{\Phi\}$, so that $\{\Phi\}$ and $\{\Psi\}$ are identical. Now if H is any d.p. of Λ and R the corresponding d.p. of Ω, we see as above that H, like R, is in $\{\Phi\}$, therefore in $\{\Psi\}$. Thus Ψ is a basis for Λ.

The lemma of §13 informs us that at least one of the systems $\Sigma + S_i$, $\Sigma + I_i$ has no basis. But, for each i, S_i and I_i are distinct from zero and reduced with respect to (4). Then, by §5, the characteristic sets of $\Sigma + S_i$ and $\Sigma + I_i$ are lower than (4). This produces a final contradiction and the truth of the basis theorem of §12 follows.

Strong and weak bases

15. A basis Φ of a system Σ will be called a *strong* basis if there exists a positive integer p such that the pth power of every d.p. in Σ is in $[\Phi]$. Bases which are not strong may be called *weak.*

We are going to give an example of a system which has no strong basis.[14]

Let Σ_1 and Σ_2 be ideals. Let Σ be the totality of products AB where A is any d.p. of Σ_1 and B any d.p. of Σ_2. We shall call $[\Sigma]$ the *product* of Σ_1 and Σ_2 and shall write $[\Sigma] = \Sigma_1 \cdot \Sigma_2$. Multiplication as thus defined is commutative and associative.

We use a single indeterminate y and any field $\mathfrak{F}$. We shall prove that the ideal $[y]^2$ has no strong basis. Suppose that there is a strong basis. Then there is one, Φ, made up of d.p.

[14] Raudenbush, 23, and Kolchin, 9. See bibliography on page 180.

(14) $$y_i y_j, \qquad 0 \leqq i \leqq j \leqq s,$$

where s is some integer.

Let p be such that the pth power of every d.p. in $[y]^2$ is in $[\Phi]$. We shall prove that the product of any p d.p. in $[y]^2$ is in $[\Phi]$.

For any A and B, and for any positive integer r, the $r + 1$ powers $(A + iB)^r$, $i = 0, \cdots, r$, are linear in the $r + 1$ products A^iB^j, $i + j = r$, with a nonvanishing determinant. It follows that AB^{r-1} is linear in the $(A + iB)^r$ with rational coefficients. Thus, for instance, AB is a sum of three terms $a_iM_i^2$ with rational a and with M which are linear, with integral coefficients, in A and B. This implies, by what precedes, that for any A, B, C, the product ABC is a sum of terms $a_iM_i^3$ with M which are linear, with integral coefficients, in A, B, C.

In this way, we find that the product of any p d.p. in $[y]^2$ is linear in pth powers, and is therefore in $[\Phi]$.

Let α be a positive integer, which will be fixed at a large value later. We consider all d.p.

(15) $$y_{i_1}y_{i_2} \cdots y_{i_{2p}}$$

for which $i_1 + i_2 + \cdots + i_{2p} = \alpha$. Each d.p. in (15) is the product of p d.p. in $[y]^2$. If we define the weight of a product of y_j as the sum of the subscripts, the weight of each d.p. in (15) is α.

By the nature of (14) and by the homogeneity and isobaricity of the d.p. in (14) and (15), each d.p. in (15) is linear, with coefficients in $\mathfrak{F}$, in the d.p.

(16) $$(y_iy_j)_k\, y_{j_1} \cdots y_{j_{2p-2}}$$

where the subscript k indicates k differentiations and where one uses all nonnegative i, j, k, j_q for which

$$0 \leqq i \leqq j \leqq s, \qquad i + j + k + j_1 + \cdots + j_{2p-2} = \alpha.$$

A set of distinct d.p. (15) is a linearly independent set; we mean by this that there is no nonidentical linear relation, with coefficients in $\mathfrak{F}$, among the d.p. Thus the number of distinct d.p. (15) does not exceed the number of distinct d.p. (16).

Let α be divisible by $2p$. Let us consider these d.p. (15) which are obtained by assigning to $i_1, \cdots, i_{2p-1}$ arbitrary values from 0 to $\alpha/(2p)$ inclusive. When such assignments are made i_{2p} is determined. The number of times which any one d.p. can be secured from such assignments is at most $(2p)!$. Then there are at least

(17) $$\frac{1}{(2p)!}\left(\frac{\alpha}{2p} + 1\right)^{2p-1}$$

distinct d.p. (15).

In (16) when all subscripts except k are selected, k is determined. As the number of d.p. in (14) is $(s + 1)(s + 2)/2$, the number of distinct d.p. (16) is not more than

$$\tag{18} \tfrac{1}{2}(s + 1)(s + 2)(\alpha + 1)^{2p-2}.$$

For α large, the quantity in (17) exceeds that in (18). This furnishes a contradiction which proves that $[y]^2$ has no strong basis.

Decomposition of perfect ideals

16. We prove the following theorem:[15]

Theorem: *Every perfect ideal of differential polynomials in $\mathfrak{F}\{y_1, \cdots, y_n\}$ has a representation as the intersection of a finite number of prime ideals.*

We suppose that we have a perfect ideal Σ with no such representation. Then Σ is not prime.[16] Let A and B be d.p. which are absent from Σ while AB is contained in Σ. By §11, Σ is the intersection of $\{\Sigma + A\}$ and $\{\Sigma + B\}$. At least one of the latter two ideals must fail to be the intersection of a finite number of prime ideals. Suppose that $\{\Sigma + A\}$, which we denote by Σ_1, so fails. Repeating our argument, we find Σ_1 to be a proper part of a perfect ideal Σ_2 which is not an intersection of a finite number of prime ideals. Continuing, we form, with the help of the axiom of selection, an infinite sequence of perfect ideals

$$\tag{19} \Sigma, \Sigma_1, \cdots, \Sigma_p, \cdots$$

each a proper part of its successor. Let Ω be the union of the ideals in (19) and let Φ be a basis for Ω.[17] Then Φ is contained in some ideal in (19), say in Σ_q. Then Σ_q contains $\{\Phi\}$, hence Ω and thus Σ_{q+1}. This contradiction proves the theorem.

17. If an ideal Σ_2 contains an ideal Σ_1, Σ_2 will be called a *divisor* of Σ_1.

Let a perfect ideal Σ have a representation

$$\tag{20} \Sigma = \Sigma_1 \cap \Sigma_2 \cap \cdots \cap \Sigma_p$$

as an intersection of prime ideals.

If Σ_1 is a divisor of any other Σ_i, we may suppress Σ_1 in (20). On this basis, we suppose that Σ_1 is not a divisor of any other Σ_i. By repeated purging, we obtain a representation (20) with no Σ_i a divisor of any Σ_j with $j \neq i$.

Let Σ' be any prime divisor of Σ. We shall prove that Σ' is a divisor of some Σ_i in (20). Let this be false, and let A_i, for each i, be a d.p. in Σ_i which is not in Σ'. Then $A_1 A_2 \cdots A_p$ is not in Σ'. This contradicts the fact that the product is in Σ.

A prime divisor of Σ which is not a divisor of any other prime divisor of Σ

[15] Raudenbush, 21.

[16] We understand the "intersection" of a single aggregate to be that aggregate.

[17] Note that Σ, as it is not prime, does not consist of the single d.p. 0.

will be called an *essential prime divisor* of Σ. The only essential prime divisors of Σ are the Σ_i in (20). Every prime divisor of Σ is a divisor of an essential prime divisor. Our discussion of (20) shows that, in every representation of a perfect ideal Σ as the intersection of a finite number of prime ideals, every essential prime divisor of Σ appears; the other prime divisors are redundant.

We partially summarize what precedes as follows: *Every perfect ideal has a finite number of essential prime divisors, and is the intersection of those divisors.*

Relatively prime ideals

18. Two ideals Σ_1 and Σ_2 will be said to be *relatively prime* if there are an A_1 in Σ_1 and an A_2 in Σ_2 such that $A_1 + A_2 = 1$.

Let Σ_1 and Σ_2 be ideals and suppose that $\{\Sigma_1\}$ and $\{\Sigma_2\}$ are relatively prime. We shall prove that Σ_1 and Σ_2 are relatively prime. Let $A_1 + A_2 = 1$ with A_1 in $\{\Sigma_1\}$ and A_2 in $\{\Sigma_2\}$. Let q be such that A_1^q and A_2^q are in Σ_1 and Σ_2 respectively. In the expansion of $(A_1 + A_2)^{2q-1}$, we let B_1 be the sum of these terms in which the exponent of A_1 is at least q and B_2 the sum of the remaining terms. Then B_1 is in Σ_1, B_2 in Σ_2 and

$$B_1 + B_2 = 1. \tag{21}$$

We show that the intersection of two relatively prime ideals is their product (§15). The product is in the intersection. Let G be in the intersection. Then $G = GB_1 + GB_2$ with B_1 and B_2 as above. GB_1 and GB_2 are in the product; so then is G.

An ideal which is relatively prime to each of several ideals is easily seen to be relatively prime to their intersection.[18] It follows that, given several ideals, every one of which is relatively prime to every other, the intersection of the ideals is their product.

19. We derive a theorem of decomposition whose significance will be seen after the theory of algebraic differential manifolds is developed in the following chapter.

Theorem: *Let Σ be an ideal. Suppose that $\{\Sigma\}$ has a representation*

$$\{\Sigma\} = \Omega_1 \cap \Omega_2 \cap \cdots \cap \Omega_p \tag{22}$$

where the Ω are perfect ideals,[19] *every one of which is relatively prime to every other. Then Σ has a unique representation,*

$$\Sigma = \Sigma_1 \cap \Sigma_2 \cap \cdots \cap \Sigma_p, \tag{23}$$

where the Σ_i are ideals such that $\{\Sigma_i\} = \Omega_i$.

By §18, the Σ_i are relatively prime in pairs and the intersection in (23) is a product.

---

[18] One multiplies the equations which express the relative primeness.

[19] Not necessarily prime.

We treat first the case of $p = 2$. Let $A_1 + A_2 = 1$ with A_1 in Ω_1 and A_2 in Ω_2. As A_1A_2 is in $\{\Sigma\}$, some $(A_1A_2)^q$ is in Σ. In $(A_1 + A_2)^{2q-1}$, let B_1 be the sum of those terms in which the exponent of A_1 is at least q and B_2 the sum of the remaining terms. Then B_1 is in Ω_1 and B_2 in Ω_2. B_1B_2 is in Σ and $B_1 + B_2 = 1$.

We shall prove that B_1' and B_2', accents indicating differentiation, are in Σ. As B_1B_2 is in Σ,

$$(24) \qquad B_1'B_2 + B_1B_2' \equiv 0, \qquad (\Sigma).$$

As $B_1 = 1 - B_2$ and $B_2' = -B_1'$, (24) gives $B_1' \equiv 2B_2B_1'$, (Σ). Then $B_1' \equiv 4B_2^2B_1'$, (Σ). We know from §10 that $B_2^2B_1'$ is in Σ. Thus B_1' is in Σ; so also is B_2'.

Let $\Sigma_i = [\Sigma + B_i]$, $i = 1, 2$. We prove that $\{\Sigma_1\} = \Omega_1$. Because B_1 is in Ω_1, that ideal contains $\{\Sigma_1\}$. It suffices then to show that if a d.p. G is in Ω_1, G is in $\{\Sigma_1\}$. Now B_2G is in $\{\Sigma\}$ and therefore in $\{\Sigma_1\}$. Again, B_2G equals $G - B_1G$. As B_1 is in Σ_1, G is in $\{\Sigma_1\}$. Similarly $\{\Sigma_2\} = \Omega_2$.

We prove now that $\Sigma = \Sigma_1 \cap \Sigma_2$. It suffices to show that if G is any d.p. common to Σ_1 and Σ_2, G is in Σ. As G is in Σ_1 and B_1' is in Σ, we have

$$(25) \qquad G = C + DB_1$$

with C in Σ. Because G is in Σ_2, DB_1 is in Σ_2. As $B_1 = 1 - B_2$ and B_2 is in Σ_2, D is in Σ_2. Let $D = E + FB_2$ with E in Σ. As B_1B_2 is in Σ, DB_1 is in Σ. This puts G in Σ.

We have obtained a representation (23). We have to prove uniqueness. Let a second representation be $\Sigma = \Sigma_1' \cap \Sigma_2'$. Let G be any d.p. in Σ_1'. As B_2 is in Ω_2, some B_2^t is in Σ_2'. Then GB_2^t is in Σ. As $B_2 = 1 - B_1$ and B_1 is in Σ_1, G is in Σ_1. Again, let H be any d.p. in Σ_1. For some t, Σ_1' contains B_1^t and therefore HB_1^t. As $B_1 = 1 - B_2$ and HB_2 is in Σ, Σ_1' contains H. We have proved that Σ_1 and Σ_1' are identical. So also are Σ_2 and Σ_2'. This settles the question of uniqueness.

We now consider any $p > 2$ and perform an induction. Let Ω' be the intersection of the Ω_i with $i > 1$. By §18, Ω_1 and Ω' are relatively prime. In a unique way, $\Sigma = \Sigma_1 \cap \Sigma'$ with $\{\Sigma_1\} = \Omega_1$ and $\{\Sigma'\} = \Omega'$. Also Σ' is a unique intersection of ideals $\Sigma_2, \cdots, \Sigma_p$ with $\{\Sigma_i\} = \Omega_i$ so that we have a representation (23). We have to prove uniqueness. Consider any representation (23) and let Σ'' be the intersection of $\Sigma_2, \cdots, \Sigma_p$. Obviously, $\{\Sigma''\}$ is in the intersection of $\Omega_2, \cdots, \Omega_p$. If A is in that intersection, some A^t is in each of $\Sigma_2, \cdots, \Sigma_p$, hence in Σ''. Then $\{\Sigma''\}$ is identical with Ω' as above. It follows that $\Sigma'' = \Sigma'$ and that (23) is unique.

If the Ω are not relatively prime, there may be no decomposition (23) with $\{\Sigma_i\} = \Omega_i$. Thus, in $\mathfrak{F}\{u, v\}$, $\{uv\} = \{u\} \cap \{v\}$. Levi has shown that $[uv]$ has no representation $\Sigma_1 \cap \Sigma_2$ or $\Sigma_1 \Sigma_2$ where Σ_1 and Σ_2 are ideals with $\{\Sigma_1\} = \{u\}$ and $\{\Sigma_2\} = \{v\}$.[20]

[20] Levi, 17.

20. Each Σ_i in (23) is of the form $[\Sigma + B_i]$ with B_i' in Σ. Suppose now that Σ *has a strong basis* Φ and that *the qth power of every d.p. in* Σ *is in* $[\Phi]$. Let G be any d.p. in Σ_1. Then (25) holds with C in Σ. It follows that G^q is in $[\Phi + B_1]$. Thus, *for every i,* $\Phi + B_i$ *is a strong basis for* Σ_i *and the qth power of every d.p. in* Σ_i *is in* $[\Phi + B_i]$.

We would state in conclusion that it is possible to generalize the theory of ideals of d.p. into a theory which applies to algebraic rings of any type in which operations of differentiation exist.[21]

The ideal $[y^p]$

21. We work in $\mathfrak{F}\{y\}$.[22] The ideal $[y^p]$, where p is any positive integer, has properties which will be useful in Chapters III and VII.

We consider any power product

$$P = y_0^{q_0} y_1^{q_1} \cdots y_r^{q_r} \tag{26}$$

where r and the q are any nonnegative integers. The degree and weight of P will be

$$d = q_0 + \cdots + q_r, \qquad w = q_1 + 2q_2 + \cdots + rq_r,$$

respectively. We are going to find a condition on d and w which will be sufficient for P to belong to $[y^p]$.

If $p = 1$, every P of positive degree is in $[y^p]$. In what follows, we assume that $p > 1$.

Let d be any positive integer. One can express d in one and only one way in the form

$$d = a\,(p - 1) + b \tag{27}$$

where a and b are integers with $a \geqq 0, 0 < b \leqq p - 1$. Let

$$f(p, d) = a(a - 1)\,(p - 1) + 2\,ab.$$

The function $f(p, d)$ has the property that, if $d > p - 1$,

$$f(p, d) - f(p, d - p + 1) = 2(d - p + 1). \tag{28}$$

We prove the following theorem, which is due to Levi.[20]

Theorem: *Let* $p > 1$ *and let* P *be a power product in the* y_i, *of positive degree* d *and of weight* w. *If* $w < f(p, d)$, *then* $P \equiv 0, [y^p]$.

22. P of (26), distinct from[23]

$$Q = y_0^{q_0'} \cdots y_r^{q_r'},$$

---

[21] Raudenbush 21, and Kolchin, 10, 11.

[22] One understands that $\mathfrak{F}$ is any field.

[23] When two products have distinct r, the r may be made equal by the adjunction of zero powers.

will be said to be lower than Q if the nonzero difference $q_i - q_i'$ of greatest i is negative. This is a transitive relation and, if P is lower than Q, RP, with R any power product, is lower than RQ.

23. Let $A = y^p$. We denote the jth derivative of A by A_j. Then A_j is a sum of terms c_iR_i where the c are positive integers and the R are power products of degree p and weight j. Every power product of degree p and weight j is an R in A_j; this is easily proved by induction.

Let j, any nonnegative integer, be written in the form $rp + s$ where r and s are nonnegative integers and $s < p$. We shall show that the lowest power product in A_j is

$$L_j = y_r^{p-s}\, y_{r+1}^s.$$

Suppose that some power product P in A_j is not higher than L_j. Then P involves no y_i with $i > r + 1$ and the degree t of P in y_{r+1} does not exceed s. P has $p - t$ factors y_i with $i \leqq r$. Their total weight does not exceed $r(p - t)$. Then the weight of P is no more than $rp + t$. Hence $t = s$ and each factor y_i of P with $i \leqq r$ is y_r. Thus $P = L$.

24. P in (26) will be called a *weak product* if, for $i = 0, \cdots, r - 1$, one has $q_i + q_{i+1} < p$. Thus P is weak if and only if there is no A_j whose L_j is a factor of P. If P is not weak, it will be called *strong*.

We prove that *if F is a d.p. with rational coefficients, homogeneous, of degree $d > 0$, and isobaric, of weight w, either $F \equiv 0$, $[A]$, or*

$$F \equiv \sum_{k=1}^{t} a_kQ_k, \qquad [A], \tag{29}$$

where t is a positive integer, the a rational numbers and the Q weak products of degree d and weight w.

If the power products in F are all weak, there is nothing to prove. Otherwise, let $F = gG + R$ where G is the lowest strong product in F and R is free of G. Let $G = HL_j$ with L_j the lowest product in A_j. Then

$$A_j = rL_j + \sum_{i=1}^{m} c_iP_i,$$

with r and m integers and the P higher than L_j. We have

$$F = \frac{g}{r} H\,(A_j - \sum c_iP_i) + R,$$

so that

$$F \equiv -\frac{g}{r} \sum c_iHP_i + R, \qquad [A]. \tag{30}$$

The strong products in the second member of (30) are higher than G. A finite number of repetitions of this process will remove the strong products, so that either $F \equiv 0$, $[A]$, or a relation (29) holds.

25. Now let d be any positive integer. We shall show that *there exists no weak product of degree d whose weight is less than $f(p, d)$.*

Let Q be a weak product of degree d. If $d \leqq p - 1$, $f(p, d) = 0$, since $a = 0$ in (27). Thus the weight of Q is not less than $f(p, d)$. Assuming our statement to hold for $d < s$, where $s > p - 1$, we shall prove it for $d = s$. We can write Q, of degree s, in the form

$$Q = y_{i_1} y_{i_2} \cdots y_{i_{p-1}} Q',$$

with Q' a power product which involves no derivative which is lower than one or more of the y_j standing before Q'. If Q' involved y_0, Q would be divisible by y_0^p. If Q' involved y_1, the exponents of y_0 and y_1 in Q would add up to at least p. Thus Q' is free of y_0 and y_1.

Let each y_i in Q' be replaced by y_{i-2}. Then Q' goes over into a weak product Q'' whose weight is less than that of Q' by $2(s - p + 1)$. By (28), if the weight of Q were less than $f(p, s)$, that of Q'' would be less than $f(p, s - p + 1)$. This cannot be, since Q'' is a weak product of degree $s - p + 1$.

If now we refer to §24, the theorem of §21 is seen to be established.[24]

Levi showed that for every w not less than $f(p, d)$, there is a power product of degree d and weight w which is not in $[y^p]$. The proof is too long to be given here.

26. Let p be any positive integer and P any power product in the y_i, of degree d and weight w. We prove that if

$$d > \frac{p-1}{2} + \left[(p-1)\,w + \frac{(p-1)^2}{4}\right]^{1/2}, \tag{31}$$

then $P \equiv 0$, $[y^p]$.

We suppose, as we may, that $p > 1$. Let (31) be satisfied. Then

$$(p-1)\,w < d^2 - d(p-1). \tag{32}$$

Let d be expressed as in (27). As $b(p - 1 - b) \geqq 0$, (32) gives

$$(p-1)\,w < d^2 - d(p-1) + b\,(p-1-b). \tag{33}$$

We replace d in (33) by its expression in (27), finding that $w < f(p, d)$. This proves our statement.

Adjunction of Indeterminates

27. It is sometimes desirable to enlarge the system of indeterminates $y_1, \cdots, y_n$, introducing by their side a new indeterminate v.

We consider a prime ideal Σ in $\mathfrak{F}\{y_1, \cdots, y_n\}$. We can generate with Σ an ideal Σ_1 in $\mathfrak{F}\{y_1, \cdots, y_n; v\}$. If A is in Σ_1, A is linear in d.p. of Σ, with

[24] In dealing with partial d.p. in Chapter IX, we shall obtain a theorem similar to that of §21 by a simpler method, due to Kolchin. That method does not give the best bound, as the above method does.

d.p. in $\mathfrak{F}\{y_1, \cdots, y_n; v\}$ for coefficients; if A is arranged as a polynomial in the v_i, it will have d.p. in Σ for coefficients.

We are going to show that Σ_1 *is prime.*

Let A and B be absent from Σ_1, while AB is contained in it. Let A, B and AB be arranged as polynomials in the v_i. We suppose that no coefficient in A or B is in Σ, suppressing those which are.

We order power products as in §22. The coefficient of the first term in AB is the product of those in A and B. This, since Σ is prime and the coefficients in A and B are not in Σ, furnishes a contradiction which proves our statement.

Field extensions

28. Let Σ be an ideal in $\mathfrak{F}\{y_1, \cdots, y_n\}$. Let $\mathfrak{F}_1$ be an extension of $\mathfrak{F}$ (§1) with respect to which the y are indeterminates.[25] Σ generates an ideal Σ_1 in $\mathfrak{F}_1\{y_1, \cdots, y_n\}$. Each d.p. in Σ_1 is linear in d.p. of Σ with coefficients which are d.p. over $\mathfrak{F}_1$.

A set of elements $\gamma_1, \cdots, \gamma_r$ of $\mathfrak{F}_1$ will be said to be *linearly independent with respect to* $\mathfrak{F}$, or *independent*, if there exists no relation

$$c_1\gamma_1 + \cdots + c_r\gamma_r = 0$$

with the c in $\mathfrak{F}$ and not all zero.

It is easy to see that every nonzero d.p. over $\mathfrak{F}_1$ can be written in the form

$$\gamma_1 A_1 + \cdots + \gamma_r A_r \tag{34}$$

with A which are d.p. over $\mathfrak{F}$, and with independent γ. Of course, r is different for different d.p.

We shall prove that *if a nonzero d.p. G in Σ_1 is written in the form* (34) *with the A d.p. over $\mathfrak{F}$ and with the γ independent, each A is in Σ.*

G can be written as a linear combination, with coefficients in $\mathfrak{F}_1$, of d.p. in Σ. Let

$$\beta_1 B_1 + \cdots + \beta_s B_s \tag{35}$$

be such an expression for G, with s as small as possible.

We wish to show that each β is linear in the γ in (34), with coefficients in $\mathfrak{F}$. Given any power product in the y_{ij}, we find from (35) that its coefficient in G is linear in the β. We secure thus a system of linear equations for the β. We say that this system is of rank s; that is, it determines the β uniquely. The system is compatible. If it were of rank less than s, we would be able to replace some of the β by zero and determine the remaining β so as to satisfy the system. Then s in (35) would not be a minimum.

Thus the β are linear in the γ with coefficients in $\mathfrak{F}$. Then, by (35), G has an expression

$$\gamma_1 C_1 + \cdots + \gamma_r C_r$$

---

[25] Thus a d.p. in the y over $\mathfrak{F}_1$ (§3) is zero only when all its coefficients are zero.

with the C in Σ. As

$$\gamma_1(C_1 - A_1) + \cdots + \gamma_r(C_r - A_r) = 0,$$

it follows easily that $C_i = A_i$, $i = 1, \cdots, p$. This proves our statement.

Fields of constants

29. We shall at times wish to assume that $\mathfrak{F}$ contains at least one element which is not a constant (§1). We establish now a result which will permit us to make this assumption with no real loss of generality.

Suppose that $\mathfrak{F}$ consists purely of constants. We adjoin to $\mathfrak{F}$ a quantity x which we suppose to be *transcendental* with respect to $\mathfrak{F}$. By this, we mean that, considering x as a pure symbol, we form the totality $\mathfrak{F}_1$ of rational combinations of x with coefficients in $\mathfrak{F}$. Each element of $\mathfrak{F}_1$ is of the form P/Q with P and Q polynomials in x with coefficients in $\mathfrak{F}$. Two polynomials in x are considered equal only if coefficients of corresponding powers of x are equal.[26] Two expressions P_1/Q_1 and P_2/Q_2 are equal if $P_1Q_2 = P_2Q_1$. We attribute to x a derivative equal to unity and differentiate polynomials P, and quotients P/Q, using the familiar formulas of the calculus. On this basis, $\mathfrak{F}_1$ becomes a differential field and, indeed, an extension of $\mathfrak{F}$.

Suppose that we have a prime ideal Σ in $\mathfrak{F}\{y_1, \cdots, y_n\}$. Let Σ_1 be the ideal of d.p. over $\mathfrak{F}_1$ generated by Σ.

We shall show that Σ_1 *is prime.*

Let F be any d.p. in Σ_1 of the type

$$B_0 + B_1x + \cdots + B_rx^r$$

where the B are d.p. over $\mathfrak{F}$. As $1, x, \cdots, x^r$ are linearly independent with respect to $\mathfrak{F}$, each B is in Σ (§28).

Now let AB, but neither A nor B, be contained in Σ_1. Multiplying A, B, AB by elements of $\mathfrak{F}_1$, we may suppose them to be polynomials in x with d.p. over $\mathfrak{F}$ for coefficients. The coefficients in AB are in Σ. In A and B, we suppress all terms with coefficients in Σ. We may suppose A and B, when arranged in ascending powers of x, to start with terms free of x. Now Σ is prime, the first term of AB is in Σ, the first terms in A and B are not in Σ. This contradiction proves our statement.

[26] This is the basis for calling x transcendental with respect to $\mathfrak{F}$.

CHAPTER II

ALGEBRAIC DIFFERENTIAL MANIFOLDS

Manifolds and their decomposition

1. Let Σ be any finite or infinite system of d.p. in $\mathfrak{F}\{y_1, \cdots, y_n\}$. Let there be given an extension $\mathfrak{F}_1$ of $\mathfrak{F}$.[1] Suppose that there exists in $\mathfrak{F}_1$ a set of n elements $\eta_1, \cdots, \eta_n$ which are such that when each y_i is replaced by η_i in the d.p. of Σ, those d.p. all reduce to zero. We shall call the set $\eta_1, \cdots, \eta_n$ a *zero* of Σ. Thus a zero of Σ is a *solution* of the system of equations obtained by equating the d.p. in Σ to zero.

If Σ has zeros, the totality of its zeros, for all possible extensions $\mathfrak{F}_1$ of $\mathfrak{F}$, will be called the *manifold* of Σ, or of the system of equations obtained by equating the d.p. in Σ to zero.[2] A zero of Σ will at times be called a *point* of the manifold of Σ. The manifold of any system will be called an *algebraic differential manifold*, or, more briefly, a *manifold*.

Let $\mathfrak{M}_1$ and $\mathfrak{M}_2$ be respectively the manifolds of systems Σ_1 and Σ_2.[3] If $\mathfrak{M}_1$ is contained in $\mathfrak{M}_2$, we shall say that Σ_2 *holds* Σ_1. Also, we shall say that Σ_2 *vanishes over* or *holds* $\mathfrak{M}_1$. If Σ is a system with no zeros, every system will be said to hold Σ.

Let Σ be an infinite system, and Φ a basis of Σ (I, §12).[4] Because Σ contains Φ, Φ holds Σ. Because every d.p. in Σ has a power in $[\Phi]$, Σ holds Φ. Thus, if Σ has zeros, Σ has the same manifold as Φ. If Σ has no zeros, Φ has no zeros. Thus *the manifold of any infinite system of d.p. is the manifold of some finite subset of the system.*[5]

If $\mathfrak{M}_1$ and $\mathfrak{M}_2$ are manifolds of systems Σ_1 and Σ_2, the intersection $\mathfrak{M}_1 \cap \mathfrak{M}_2$, if not vacuous, is the manifold of $\Sigma_1 + \Sigma_2$. The union $\mathfrak{M}_1 + \mathfrak{M}_2$ is the manifold of the system of all products AB with A in Σ_1 and B in Σ_2.

2. A manifold $\mathfrak{M}$ will be said to be *reducible* if it is the union of two manifolds, not necessarily mutually exclusive, which are proper parts of $\mathfrak{M}$. If $\mathfrak{M}$ is not reducible, it will be called *irreducible*.

A manifold $\mathfrak{M}$ of a system Σ is irreducible if, and only if, whenever a product AB vanishes over $\mathfrak{M}$, at least one of A and B vanishes over $\mathfrak{M}$. Suppose first that AB holds $\mathfrak{M}$ while neither A nor B does. The manifolds of $\Sigma + A$ and

---

[1] The y need not be indeterminates with respect to $\mathfrak{F}_1$.

[2] Unfortunately, the totality of extensions of $\mathfrak{F}$ is an illegitimate totality. At the present time, there is no process of closure for differential fields analogous to the algebraic closure method. One knows, however, that troubles of this sort are not fatal to a theory.

[3] All d.p. have coefficients in $\mathfrak{F}$, even though extensions are used in connection with zeros.

[4] Chapter I, §12. When no chapter number is given, the chapter is that in which one is reading.

[5] We understand this statement to stand for the two sentences which precede it.

$\Sigma + B$, whose union is $\mathfrak{M}$, will be proper parts of $\mathfrak{M}$ and $\mathfrak{M}$ will be reducible. Again, let $\mathfrak{M}$ be the union of smaller manifolds $\mathfrak{M}_1$ and $\mathfrak{M}_2$, manifolds respectively of systems Σ_1 and Σ_2. Let A_i, $i = 1, 2$, be a d.p. of Σ_i which does not hold $\mathfrak{M}$. The product A_1A_2 holds $\mathfrak{M}$.

Let $\mathfrak{M}$ be the manifold of a system Σ. The totality Ω of those d.p. which vanish over $\mathfrak{M}$ is an ideal, and, indeed, a perfect ideal. We shall call Ω the perfect ideal *associated with* $\mathfrak{M}$. It will be seen in §7 that Ω is $\{ \Sigma \}$. $\mathfrak{M}$ is irreducible if, and only if, Ω is prime. When Ω is prime, we call it the prime ideal *associated with* $\mathfrak{M}$.

3. We prove the following fundamental theorem.

THEOREM: *Every manifold is the union of a finite number of irreducible manifolds.*

Let the theorem not hold for the manifold $\mathfrak{M}$ of some system Σ. Then $\mathfrak{M}$ is not irreducible. Let AB hold $\mathfrak{M}$, while neither A nor B does. Then $\mathfrak{M}$ is the union of the manifolds of $\Sigma + A$ and $\Sigma + B$. At least one of the latter manifolds must fail to be the union of a finite number of irreducible manifolds. Let such failure occur for the manifold of $\Sigma + A$, which system we represent by Σ_1. Continuing, we produce, with the help of the axiom of selection, an infinite sequence

$$\Sigma, \Sigma_1, \cdots, \Sigma_p, \cdots, \tag{1}$$

each Σ_p containing, while not holding, its predecessor. Let Ω be the union of the systems (1) and let Φ be a basis of Ω. Then Φ is contained in some system of (1), say in Σ_q. We see that Φ is a basis for Σ_q. By §1, Φ and Σ_q have the same manifold. But the same argument shows that Φ and Σ_{q+1} have the same manifold. This furnishes the contradiction that Σ_{q+1} holds Σ_q. The theorem is proved.

Let a manifold $\mathfrak{M}$ have a representation

$$\mathfrak{M} = \mathfrak{M}_1 + \cdots + \mathfrak{M}_p \tag{2}$$

as a union of irreducible manifolds $\mathfrak{M}_i$. If an $\mathfrak{M}_i$ contains an $\mathfrak{M}_j$ with $j \neq i$, then $\mathfrak{M}_j$ may be suppressed in (2). We thus suppose that no $\mathfrak{M}_i$ contains any $\mathfrak{M}_j$ with $j \neq i$.

Now let Σ be the perfect ideal associated with $\mathfrak{M}$ and let, for each i, Σ_i be the prime ideal associated with $\mathfrak{M}_i$. Each Σ_i is a divisor of Σ. If A is a d.p. common to all Σ_i, A holds $\mathfrak{M}$ and is thus in Σ. Then Σ is the intersection of the Σ_i. If $j \neq i$, Σ_j is not a divisor of Σ_i; otherwise $\mathfrak{M}_i$ would contain $\mathfrak{M}_j$. Then the Σ_i are the essential prime divisors of Σ.

If $\mathfrak{M}'$ is an irreducible manifold contained in $\mathfrak{M}$, the prime ideal associated with $\mathfrak{M}'$ is a divisor of some Σ_i (I, §17). Thus $\mathfrak{M}'$ is contained in some $\mathfrak{M}_i$.

An irreducible manifold contained in $\mathfrak{M}$ which is not part of a larger irreducible manifold contained in $\mathfrak{M}$ will be called an *essential irreducible component* of $\mathfrak{M}$

or a *component* of $\mathfrak{M}$.[6] The only components of $\mathfrak{M}$ are the $\mathfrak{M}_i$ in (2). Every irreducible manifold contained in $\mathfrak{M}$ is contained in some component of $\mathfrak{M}$. Our discussion shows that in every representation of $\mathfrak{M}$ as the union of a finite number of irreducible manifolds, every component of $\mathfrak{M}$ appears; all other irreducible manifolds in the union are redundant.

We partially summarize what precedes. *A manifold $\mathfrak{M}$ has a finite number of components, and is the union of them. The essential prime divisors of the perfect ideal associated with $\mathfrak{M}$ are the prime ideals associated with the components of $\mathfrak{M}$.*

A component of the manifold of a system Σ will at times be called a component of Σ.

ILLUSTRATIONS IN ANALYSIS

4. To illustrate the decomposition of manifolds, we shall employ differential equations of classical analysis.

We use an open region **A** in the plane of the complex variable x. Our field $\mathfrak{F}$ will be supposed to consist of functions meromorphic throughout **A**.[7]

Given a system Σ, we consider zeros of it obtained as follows. Let **B** be any open region contained in **A** and let $y_1(x), \cdots, y_n(x)$, analytic in **B**, annul every d.p. of Σ in **B**. We shall call the entity composed of the $y_i(x)$ and **B** an *analytic zero*,[8] or a zero, of Σ. Two sets $y_i(x)$ which are identical from the standpoint of analytic continuation will give different zeros if they are not associated with the same open region. For instance, if we use an open region $\mathbf{B}_1$ interior to **B**, and use, throughout $\mathbf{B}_1$, the $y_i(x)$ as defined for **B**, we get a different zero of Σ.[9]

The totality of analytic zeros of Σ will be called the *restricted manifold* of Σ. At this point in our work, we have no need to consider other types of zeros of Σ and it will turn out finally that the consideration of the restricted manifold produces a complete theory of the system Σ.

The case in which $\mathfrak{F}$ consists of meromorphic functions, and in which one uses restricted manifolds, will be called *the analytic case*. All definitions in §§1–3 following that of manifold retain their meaning and all proofs retain their validity, in the analytic case. Thus, in the analytic case, a system Σ_2 *holds* a system Σ_1 if every analytic zero of Σ_1 is a zero of Σ_2.[10] The theorem of §3

[6] No misunderstanding can arise, since the only subsets of manifolds which we employ are essential irreducible components.

[7] It is futile to seek greater generality through the use of functions analytic except for isolated singularities. If $f(x)$ has an isolated essential singularity for $x = a$ and if c is a rational value assumed by $f(x)$ in every neighborhood of a, the reciprocal of $f(x) - c$ has a pole in every neighborhood of a.

[8] No confusion with the term zero of the theory of functions will arise.

[9] Given an analytic zero, we have to go through the formality of constructing an extension of $\mathfrak{F}$ in which its $y(x)$ are contained. This is done by forming all rational combinations of the $y(x)$ and their derivatives, with coefficients in $\mathfrak{F}$. If such a combination coincides in **B** with a function $f(x)$ in $\mathfrak{F}$, we consider the combination to be identical with $f(x)$, and thus to be in $\mathfrak{F}$.

[10] In §11, it will be seen that, in this case, every zero of Σ_1 is a zero of Σ_2. Thus the word *hold* will be established as a word of a single meaning.

becomes: *Every restricted manifold is the union of a finite number of irreducible restricted manifolds.* By a component of the restricted manifold $\mathfrak{M}$ of a system Σ, we mean an irreducible restricted manifold $\mathfrak{M}'$ contained in $\mathfrak{M}$, which is not part of a larger irreducible restricted manifold contained in $\mathfrak{M}$. We may call $\mathfrak{M}'$ a *restricted* component, or an *analytic* component of Σ. It will be seen in §11 that the perfect ideal associated with the restricted manifold of Σ is identical with the perfect ideal associated with the complete abstract manifold. The essential prime divisors of this perfect ideal furnish both the analytic components of Σ and the full components discussed in §3.

In our present work under the analytic case, the term *manifold* will be understood to mean restricted manifold.

We consider some examples. $\mathfrak{F}$ will be any field of meromorphic functions.

Example 1. Let Σ consist of the single d.p. $A = y_1^2 - 4y$ in $\mathfrak{F}\{y\}$. We call attention to the fact that A, as a polynomial in y and y_1, cannot be factored in any field. The manifold of Σ consists of the functions $y = (x + c)^2$ with c constant, and of the function $y = 0$.[11] The derivative of A is $2y_1(y_2 - 2)$. Now $y_2 - 2$ vanishes for every $(x + c)^2$ but not for $y = 0$. Again, y_1 vanishes for $y = 0$, but for no $(x + c)^2$. Thus $\mathfrak{M}$ is reducible and is the union of $\mathfrak{M}_1$, composed of the functions $(x + c)^2$, and of $\mathfrak{M}_2$, composed of $y = 0$. $\mathfrak{M}_1$ is the manifold of the system $A, y_2 - 2$ and $\mathfrak{M}_2$ is the manifold of A, y_1. It is obvious that $\mathfrak{M}_2$ is irreducible. As to $\mathfrak{M}_1$, let it be held by BC. When y is replaced by $(x + c)^2$, B and C become polynomials in c with coefficients meromorphic in **A**. If the product of two such polynomials vanishes identically in x and c, one of the polynomials does. Thus one of B and C holds $\mathfrak{M}_1$ and $\mathfrak{M}_1$ is irreducible.

Example 2. Let Σ be the d.p. $A = y_2^2 - y$ in $\mathfrak{F}\{y\}$. Differentiating A successively, we have, over $\mathfrak{M}$,

$$2y_2y_3 - y_1 = 0,$$

$$2y_2y_4 + 2y_3^2 - y_2 = 0, \tag{3}$$

$$2y_2y_5 + 6y_3y_4 - y_3 = 0. \tag{4}$$

Multiplying (4) by $2y_3$ and substituting into the result the expression for y_3^2 found from (3), we have, over $\mathfrak{M}$,

$$y_2(4y_3y_5 - 12y_4^2 + 8y_4 - 1) = 0.$$

Thus $\mathfrak{M}$ is reducible. It is composed of $\mathfrak{M}_1$ and $\mathfrak{M}_2$, the respective manifolds of

$$A,\ y_2; \qquad A,\ 4y_3y_5 - 12y_4^2 + 8y_4 - 1.$$

As $\mathfrak{M}_1$ consists of $y = 0$, it is irreducible. We shall see later that $\mathfrak{M}_2$, which is the *general solution* of A, is irreducible.

Example 3. The manifold of $y_1(y_1 - y)$ decomposes into the two irreducible

---

[11] We shall not encumber our discussions with references to the areas in which the functions in a zero are analytic.

manifolds given by $y = c$ and $y = ce^x$. These two manifolds have $y = 0$ in common.

Example 4. Let Σ consist of $A = y_1^2y_2 - y$. We find with a single differentiation that $\mathfrak{M}$ is reducible and is made up of the manifolds of

$$A,\ y_1; \qquad A,\ y_1y_3 + 2y_2^2 - 1.$$

We call attention to the fact that A cannot be factored and is of the first degree in y_2.

Example 5. Let Σ be composed of $A = uy - u_1^2$ in $\mathfrak{F}\{u, y\}$. Differentiating, we find over $\mathfrak{M}$,

$$u_1y + uy_1 - 2u_1u_2 = 0.$$

Multiplying this equation by y and using $A = 0$, we find

$$u_1\,(y^2 + u_1y_1 - 2u_2y) = 0. \tag{5}$$

Neither factor in (5) holds $\mathfrak{M}$, so that $\mathfrak{M}$ is reducible. We call attention to the fact that A cannot be factored and is of zero order in y.

Example 6. In $\mathfrak{F}\{y, z\}$, let Σ be

$$y - xy_1 + \frac{y_1z_1}{4}, \qquad z - xz_1 + \frac{y_1z_1}{4}.$$

We are dealing with a pair of Clairaut equations. $\mathfrak{M}$ consists of two irreducible manifolds which are, to speak geometrically, the two-parameter family of lines

$$y = ax - \frac{ab}{4}, \qquad z = bx - \frac{ab}{4},$$

and their one-parameter family of envelopes

$$y = (x + c)^2, \qquad z = (x - c)^2.$$

The above examples might lead one to conjecture that the manifold of any finite system can be decomposed into irreducible manifolds by differentiations and eliminations. We shall see in Chapter V that this is actually so.

Prime ideals and regular zeros

5. We return to the use of an abstract field. We shall call $\mathfrak{F}\{y_1, \cdots, y_n\}$ the *unit ideal.* The prime ideal consisting of the d.p. 0 will be called the *zero ideal.* A prime ideal distinct from the unit ideal and the zero ideal will be said to be *nontrivial.*

Let Σ be a nontrivial prime ideal. Let

$$A_1, \cdots, A_r \tag{6}$$

be a characteristic set of Σ. The separant and initial of A_i will be denoted by S_i and I_i respectively. As the S and I are reduced with respect to (6), they are not in Σ (I, 5).

We prove that, *for a d.p. G to belong to Σ, it is necessary and sufficient that the remainder of G with respect to* (6) *be zero.* Let G be in Σ. As the remainder, R, is in Σ and is reduced with respect to (6), we have $R = 0$. Again, let $R = 0$. There is a relation

$$S_1^{s_1} \cdots I_r^{t_r} G \equiv 0, \quad (\Sigma). \tag{7}$$

As Σ is prime and the S and the I are not in Σ, it must be that G is in Σ.

A zero of the characteristic set (6) for which every S_i and every I_i is distinct from zero will be called a regular zero of (6).[12] We shall prove that *every regular zero of a characteristic set of Σ is a zero of Σ.* Let $\eta_1, \cdots, \eta_n$ be a regular zero of (6). Let G be any d.p. in Σ. In (7), the S and the I are not annulled by the η. Then G is annulled by the η. The η thus constitute a zero of Σ.

Generic zeros of a prime ideal

6. Let Σ be a prime ideal distinct from the unit ideal.

Let A be any d.p., not necessarily contained in Σ. We form a class α of d.p., putting into α every d.p. G such that $G \equiv A$, (Σ). We call α a *remainder class, modulo* Σ. Thus $\mathfrak{F}\{y_1, \cdots, y_n\}$ is composed of a set of remainder classes. As Σ contains no element of $\mathfrak{F}$ except zero, two distinct elements of $\mathfrak{F}$ belong to distinct remainder classes; there are thus an infinite number of remainder classes.

Let α and β be two remainder classes. All sums $A + B$ with A in α and B in β belong to the same remainder class. We call this class $\alpha + \beta$. Actually, every d.p. in $\alpha + \beta$ is the sum of a d.p. in α and a d.p. in β. We define $\alpha\beta$ as the remainder class which contains all products AB with A in α and B in β. Usually $\alpha\beta$ contains d.p. which are not products AB. The derivative α' of α is defined as the remainder class which contains the derivatives of the d.p. in α.

The remainder class which contains the d.p. 0 is Σ. We call Σ the *zero class.* As Σ is prime, a relation $AB \equiv 0$, (Σ), implies that either $A \equiv 0$, (Σ) or $B \equiv 0$, (Σ). Thus, if each of two remainder classes is distinct from the zero class, their product is distinct from the zero class.

We now consider pairs (α, β) of remainder classes in which β is not the zero class. Two pairs, (α, β) and (γ, δ), will be called equivalent if $\alpha\delta = \beta\gamma$. As the equivalence relation is transitive, the totality of pairs of classes separates into sets of equivalent pairs. If $\mathfrak{A}$ is the set containing (α, β) and $\mathfrak{B}$ that containing (γ, δ), we define $\mathfrak{A} + \mathfrak{B}$ as the set containing $(\alpha\delta + \beta\gamma, \beta\delta)$, and $\mathfrak{A}\mathfrak{B}$ as the set containing $(\alpha\gamma, \beta\delta)$. The operations of subtraction and division are then uniquely determined. In particular, $\mathfrak{A}/\mathfrak{B}$ can and must be taken as the set containing $(\alpha\delta, \beta\gamma)$.[13] The derivative of the set containing (α, β) is defined as the set containing $(\beta\alpha' - \alpha\beta', \beta^2)$. With these operations, the sets of pairs of remainder classes become a differential field, which we denote by $\mathfrak{F}_1$.

---

[12] It will be seen in §6 that regular zeros exist.

[13] We attempt division only when γ is not the zero class.

With an element a of $\mathfrak{F}$, we associate the set in $\mathfrak{F}_1$ containing the pair (α, β) in which α contains a and β contains 1. In this way we obtain a subset $\mathfrak{F}'$ of $\mathfrak{F}_1$ which is isomorphic with $\mathfrak{F}$. We replace each set of $\mathfrak{F}'$ by the corresponding element of $\mathfrak{F}$, and $\mathfrak{F}_1$ becomes an extension of $\mathfrak{F}$.

We are going to find a zero of Σ in $\mathfrak{F}_1$. Let ω be that one of the remainder classes above which contains unity, and for $i = 1, \cdots, n$, let α_i be the class which contains the d.p. y_i. Let η_i be the set in $\mathfrak{F}_1$ which contains (α_i, ω).

We shall show that $\eta_1, \cdots, \eta_n$ is a zero of Σ.

Let G be any d.p. in Σ. The derivative of η_i is the set containing (α_i', ω), and α_i' contains y_{i1}. It follows that when the η are substituted for the y in G, we obtain a set containing (β, ω), where β is the remainder class containing G, that is, the zero class. The set just described has 0 as its proxy in $\mathfrak{F}_1$. We see that $\eta_1, \cdots, \eta_n$ is a zero of Σ.

We see immediately, in a converse way, that if $\eta_1, \cdots, \eta_n$ annuls a d.p. G, G is contained in Σ.

A zero of Σ, naturally contained in some extension of $\mathfrak{F}$, which is such that every d.p. over $\mathfrak{F}$ which is annulled by the zero is contained in Σ, will be called a *generic zero*[14] of Σ, or a *generic point* of the manifold of Σ. We know that every prime ideal distinct from the unit ideal has a generic zero.

If we take Σ as in §5, we see that a generic zero of Σ is a regular zero of (6).

The theorem of zeros

7. We prove the following theorem:

Theorem: *If Σ is a perfect ideal distinct from the unit ideal, Σ has zeros and every differential polynomial which holds Σ is contained in Σ.*[15]

Let Σ be the intersection of essential prime divisors Σ_i, $i = 1, \cdots, p$. No Σ_i is the unit ideal. For each Σ_i, we form a generic zero. Each of these p zeros is a zero of Σ. Now let G be a d.p. which holds Σ. As G is annulled by each of the generic zeros, G is in each Σ_i and therefore in Σ.

We see, as was stated in §2, that, given a manifold $\mathfrak{M}$ of a system Σ, the perfect ideal associated with $\mathfrak{M}$ is $\{\Sigma\}$; it is the only perfect ideal whose manifold is $\mathfrak{M}$.

Modifying slightly the theorem just proved, we obtain the

Theorem of zeros: *Let*

$$F_1, \cdots, F_p$$

be any finite system of differential polynomials and let G be any differential polynomial which holds that system. Some power of G is a linear combination of the F and of their derivatives of various orders, with differential polynomials for coefficients. In particular, if $F_1, \cdots, F_p$ has no zeros, some linear combination of the F and of their derivatives of various orders equals unity.

[14] Raudenbush, 20.

[15] A.D.E., Chapter VII, and Raudenbush, 21.

Let Σ be the perfect ideal determined by the F. If Σ is the unit ideal, unity is a linear combination as described above. Let Σ be distinct from the unit ideal. Then G is in Σ.

8. Let us reexamine the decomposition theorem of I, §19. Let Σ be an ideal with a manifold $\mathfrak{M}$ which has a representation

$$\mathfrak{M} = \mathfrak{M}_1 + \cdots + \mathfrak{M}_p$$

where no two $\mathfrak{M}_i$ have a point in common. If Ω_i and Ω_j are the perfect ideals associated with $\mathfrak{M}_i$ and $\mathfrak{M}_j$, $i \neq j$, the system $\Omega_i + \Omega_j$ has no zeros. Then $\{ \Omega_i + \Omega_j \}$ is the unit ideal. This implies a relation $A + B = 1$ with A in Ω_i and B in Ω_j. Thus Ω_i and Ω_j are relatively prime. It follows that Σ has a unique representation as the product of ideals whose manifolds are the $\mathfrak{M}_i$.

Example: We consider, as in Example 1 of §4, the manifold $\mathfrak{M}$ of $A = y_1^2 - 4y$. At the present time, we use the full abstract manifold. $\mathfrak{M}$ is the union of $\mathfrak{M}_1$ and $\mathfrak{M}_2$, the respective manifolds of $A, y_2 - 2$ and A, y_1. As $y_2 - 2$ and y_1 have no zero in common, $\mathfrak{M}_1$ and $\mathfrak{M}_2$ have no point in common. As $y_1 (y_2 - 2)$ is in $[A]$, we have, by I, §11,

$$\{ A \} = \{ A, y_2 - 2 \} \cap \{ A, y_1 \}. \tag{8}$$

Of course, $\{ A, y_1 \} = \{ y \} = [y]$. As $[A]$ contains $y_1(y_2 - 2)$, it contains $y_2(y_2 - 2)^2$. Thus $[A]$ contains BC where

$$B = (y_2 - 2)^2, \qquad C = 4y_2 - y_2^2.$$

We have $B + C = 4$. It follows from (8) and I, §19, that

$$[A] = [A, B]\,[A, C].$$

Let $\Sigma_1 = [A, C]$. As Σ_1 contains y_2B, it contains $y_2\,(B + C)$ and therefore y_2. Then, as Σ_1 contains $y_1(y_2 - 2)$, it contains y_1 and hence y. Thus $\Sigma_1 = [y]$ and

$$[y_1^2 - 4y] = [y]\,[y_1^2 - 4y, (y_2 - 2)^2].$$

9. We shall now obtain a theorem of zeros for the analytic case.

With $\mathfrak{F}$ a field of meromorphic functions, we take Σ as in §5. Let G be any d.p. not in Σ. We are going to prove the existence of a regular zero of (6), composed of functions $y_1(x), \cdots, y_n(x)$, which is not a zero of G.

The remainder R of G with respect to (6) is not zero. Let

$$K = RS_1 \cdots S_rI_1 \cdots I_r$$

where the S and I are as in §5. We wish, for a short time, to consider K and the A_i not as d.p., but as ordinary polynomials in the y_{ij}. A letter y_{ij} enters into our present work only if it appears effectively in some of the $r + 1$ polynomials. Let σ be the system of polynomials A_i. By a zero of σ, we shall mean any set of functions $y_{ij}(x)$, analytic in some area contained in **A**, which annul every A_i. We do not ask that $y_{i,\,j+1}(x)$ be the derivative of $y_{ij}(x)$.

No power of K is linear in the A_i with coefficients which are polynomials in the y_{ij}.[16] Otherwise K, considered as a d.p., would be contained in the prime ideal Σ. We shall now invoke Hilbert's theorem of zeros for polynomials, which is proved in IV, §14. The system σ has at least one zero, composed of functions $\bar{y}_{ij}(x)$, which do not annul K. Let a be a value of x at which the $\bar{y}_{ij}(x)$ and all coefficients in the A_i and G are analytic, and at which K, when the $\bar{y}_{ij}(x)$ are substituted into it, has a value distinct from zero.

10. We return now to the consideration of K and the A_i as d.p. Let p_j be the class of A_j, $j = 1, \cdots, r$, and m_j the order of A_j in y_{p_j}. It may be that $r < n$ in (6), so that there are y_i which are not among the y_{p_j}. Every such y_i, we replace in the A by a function $y_i(x)$ analytic at a, which is chosen with the sole restriction that if some y_{ij} is a letter used in §9, the jth derivative of y_i has at a the value $\bar{y}_{ij}(a)$ as in §9. It is a matter of forming convergent series of powers of $x - a$, with a finite number of coefficients assigned in advance. For these replacements, each A_j goes over into an expression B_j in $y_{p_1}, \cdots, y_{p_j}$ and their derivatives.

We consider the equation $B_1 = 0$ as an equation determining $y_{p_1m_1}$ as a function of $x, y_{p_10}, \cdots, y_{p_1, m_1 - 1}$. We work at $x = a$. To every y_{p_1i} which is a letter of §9, we assign the value $\bar{y}_{p_1i}(a)$. There may be y_{p_1i} with $i < m_1$ which do not appear in §9. To them we assign arbitrary numerical values. For the values assigned to x and the y_{p_1i}, B_1 vanishes. Now $\partial B_1/\partial y_{p_1m_1}$ does not vanish for these values.[17] We can thus solve the equation $B_1 = 0$ for $y_{p_1m_1}$, finding

$$(9) \qquad y_{p_1m_1} = f_1(x, y_{p_10}, \cdots, y_{p_1, m_1 - 1})$$

with f analytic for the assigned values of its arguments and equal to $\bar{y}_{p_1m_1}(a)$ for those values.

We now regard (9) as a differential equation of order m_1 for y_{p_1}. For the initial conditions assigned as above at $x = a$, we obtain a solution $y_{p_1}(x)$ analytic at $x = a$. The functions $y_1(x), \cdots, y_{p_1}(x)$ annul A_1 but neither S_1 nor I_1.

We now substitute $y_{p_1}(x)$ for y_{p_1} in B_2 and treat the equation $B_2 = 0$ as above. Continuing, we construct a regular zero of (6). This zero does not annul K at $x = a$. Thus R, and also G, are not annulled by the zero at $x = a$.[18]

11. The theorems of §7 now go over to the analytic case. Thus, *if $\mathfrak{F}$ is a field of meromorphic functions, and if Σ is a perfect ideal distinct from the unit ideal, Σ has a nonvacuous restricted manifold. Every differential polynomial which vanishes over the restricted manifold of Σ is contained in Σ.*

In the theorem of zeros, if $F_1, \cdots, F_p$ has no analytic zeros, unity is contained in the ideal of the F, so that $F_1, \cdots, F_p$ has no zeros of any type. If there is a

[16] With coefficients in $\mathfrak{F}$.

[17] The partial derivative is what S_1 becomes for the replacements made above in the A. We note that K does not vanish for the $\bar{y}_{ij}(a)$.

[18] The work of §10 shows that a characteristic set of a prime ideal may be regarded as furnishing a system of differential equations, in a standard form, whose solutions more or less make up the manifold of the ideal.

restricted manifold, every d.p. which holds it is in the perfect ideal determined by the F and is thus annulled by all zeros of $F_1, \cdots, F_p$.

To sum up, given any system Σ with $\mathfrak{F}$ as above, and with $\{\Sigma\}$ distinct from the unit ideal, Σ has a restricted manifold $\mathfrak{M}$ and an abstract manifold $\mathfrak{M}'$ which contains $\mathfrak{M}$. Both $\mathfrak{M}$ and $\mathfrak{M}'$ have $\{\Sigma\}$ for associated perfect ideal. We shall find on this basis, in dealing with differential equations of analysis, that it suffices generally to work with restricted manifolds.

General solutions

12. We use $\mathfrak{F}\{y_1, \cdots, y_n\}$ with $\mathfrak{F}$ any field. A d.p. of positive class will be said to be *algebraically irreducible* if it is not the product of two d.p. of positive class.

Let F be of positive class p and algebraically irreducible. We are going to study the representation of $\{F\}$ as an intersection of prime ideals.[19]

Denoting the separant of F by S, we let Σ_1 be the totality of those d.p. A which are such that

$$SA \equiv 0, \qquad \{F\}. \tag{10}$$

By §7, A is in Σ_1 if A vanishes for every zero of F which does not annul S.

Clearly, the sum of two d.p. in Σ_1 is in Σ_1, as is also the product of a d.p. in Σ_1 by any d.p. From (10) it follows, by I, §10, that SA', with A' the derivative of A, is in $\{F\}$. Then A' is in Σ_1. Thus Σ_1 is an ideal.

We prove now that *the ideal Σ_1 is prime.* Let AB be in Σ_1. Let F be of order m in y_p. The process of reduction used for forming remainders shows the existence of relations

$$S^aA \equiv R, \qquad S^bB \equiv T, \qquad [F], \tag{11}$$

with R and T of order at most m in y_p. We shall prove that at least one of R and T is divisible by F. From (11) we have $SRT \equiv S^{a+b+1}AB$, $[F]$. As the second member of this congruence is in $\{F\}$, the first member is also. Let then

$$(SRT)^c = MF + M_1F' + \cdots + M_qF^{(q)},$$

superscripts indicating differentiation. We have

$$F^{(q)} = Sy_{p,\,m+q} + U$$

where U is of order less than $m + q$ in y_p. We replace $y_{p,\,m+q}$ in $F^{(q)}$ and in the M by $-U/S$. Clearing fractions, we find a relation

$$S^d(RT)^c = NF + N_1F' + \cdots + N_{q-1}F^{(q-1)}.$$

Continuing, we find that some $S^e(RT)^c$ is divisible by F. As F is algebraically irreducible, and not a factor of S, F must be a factor of at least one of R and T.

---

[19] Even if $p < n$, $\{\mathfrak{F}\}$ will contain d.p. of class as high as n.

Suppose that R is divisible by F. By (11), SA is in $\{F\}$ so that A is in Σ_1. Thus Σ_1 is prime.

13. We prove now that *for a d.p. A to belong to Σ_1, it is necessary and sufficient that the remainder of A with respect to F be zero. In particular, if A is in Σ_1 and if A has the same order in y_p as F, A is divisible by F.*

Let A belong to Σ_1. We have a relation

$$S^a A \equiv B, \qquad [F], \tag{12}$$

with B of order at most m in y_p. Now SB is in $\{F\}$ so that, as in §12, B is divisible by F. This means that the remainder of A is zero. Conversely, if the remainder is zero, we have (12) with B divisible by F so that A is in Σ_1.

We see, in particular, that Σ_1 does not contain S.

14. We prove that

$$\{F\} = \Sigma_1 \cap \{F, S\}.$$

$\{F\}$ is contained in each ideal in the second member, so that it will suffice to show that the second member is in $\{F\}$. Let A be in $\{F, S\}$. For some a,

$$A^a = B + C \tag{13}$$

with B in $[F]$ and C in $[S]$. Now, let A also belong to Σ_1. Then SA is in $\{F\}$ so that, by I, §10, the product of A by any derivative of S is in $\{F\}$. Then AC is in $\{F\}$ so that A^{a+1} is in $\{F\}$.

15. Let

$$\{F, S\} = \Lambda_1 \cap \cdots \cap \Lambda_q$$

where the Λ are the essential prime divisors of $\{F, S\}$. Certain Λ may be divisors of Σ_1. Suppressing these, and using symbols Σ_i with $i > 1$ for the remaining Λ, we have

$$\{F\} = \Sigma_1 \cap \Sigma_2 \cap \cdots \cap \Sigma_r. \tag{14}$$

Thus, *Σ_1 is an essential prime divisor of $\{F\}$ and, in the representation of $\{F\}$ as an intersection of essential prime divisors, there is precisely one prime ideal, namely Σ_1, which does not contain S.*

16. An interchange of the subscripts of the y may give F a new separant. Any such separant involves only derivatives present in F and is not divisible by F. Hence, for the original ordering of the y, such a separant has a remainder with respect to F which is not zero. Thus, in (14), *Σ_1 contains no separant of F, while $\Sigma_2, \cdots, \Sigma_r$ contain every separant.*[20]

We shall call the manifold of Σ_1 the *general solution* of F, or of the equation $F = 0$.

---

[20] It is only in our present work that we use several separants for a d.p., one for each indeterminate appearing effectively in the d.p. This matter will not cause confusion elsewhere.

Singular zeros and solutions

17. We take F as in §12. A zero of F will be called *nonsingular* if it fails to annul at least one separant of F, and *singular* if it annuls every separant. Correspondingly, we speak of nonsingular, and of singular, *solutions* of $F = 0$.

Every nonsingular zero of F is contained in the general solution of F. The other components of F are made up of singular zeros.

If a d.p. G vanishes for all nonsingular zeros of F, then G is in Σ_1. This is an immediate consequence of the fact that a generic zero of Σ_1 is a nonsingular zero of F. In the analytic case, we get a less trivial result. If G vanishes for all nonsingular analytic zeros of F, G is contained in Σ_1. This follows from the fact that the product of G and the separants holds the restricted manifold of F, therefore the restricted manifold of Σ_1. By the theorem of zeros, the product is in Σ_1, so that G is in Σ_1.

In the analytic case, we call the restricted manifold of Σ_1 the *restricted general solution* of F, and, as a rule, since misunderstandings do not occur, the *general solution* of F.

The general solution may contain singular solutions of $F = 0$, as well as the nonsingular ones. From what precedes, we see that *a singular solution belongs to the general solution if, and only if, every d.p. which vanishes for all nonsingular solutions vanishes also for the singular solution.* In the analytic case, one uses here only the analytic nonsingular solutions.

18. As Σ_1 contains no nonzero d.p. reduced with respect to F, F is a characteristic set for Σ_1. Let Σ be any nontrivial prime ideal (§5) which has a characteristic set consisting of a single d.p. G. We assume G to be algebraically irreducible since, if it is not, we can replace it by one of its factors. As Σ consists of those d.p. which have zero remainders with respect to G, the manifold of Σ is the general solution of G. The case in which the number n of indeterminates is unity is of special interest. *For a single indeterminate y, every irreducible manifold distinct from the manifold of the zero ideal is the general solution of a differential polynomial in y.*

For $n > 1$, this result does not hold. It will be seen, however, in Chapter III, that if G is any d.p. of positive class, every component of G is the general solution of some d.p.

19. We consider some examples in the analytic case. In Example 1 of §4, the component $y = (x + c)^2$ is composed of nonsingular zeros and is the general solution of $y_1^2 - 4y$. In Example 2, $y = 0$ is the only singular zero, so that $\mathfrak{M}_2$ is the general solution.

In Example 5, a consideration of the two separants shows that the singular zeros are those for which $u = 0$. We denote the general solution by $\mathfrak{M}_1$. The factor

$$B = y^2 + u_1y_1 - 2u_2y$$

in (5) vanishes, for $u = 0$, only if $y = 0$. As u_1 in (5) is not divisible by A, u_1 does not hold $\mathfrak{M}_1$. Thus B holds $\mathfrak{M}_1$, so that the only zero with $u = 0$ which can belong to $\mathfrak{M}_1$ is $u = 0, y = 0$. The zeros of A with $u = 0$ constitute an irreducible manifold, the manifold $\mathfrak{M}_2$ of the d.p. u. Thus $\mathfrak{M} = \mathfrak{M}_1 + \mathfrak{M}_2$. We can now see that $\mathfrak{M}_1$ contains the singular zero $u = 0, y = 0$. Let G be any d.p. in Σ_1 and $\bar{u}, \bar{y}$, with $\bar{u} \neq 0$, a zero of A. For every constant $c \neq 0$, $c\bar{u}, c\bar{y}$ annuls A and is thus in $\mathfrak{M}_1$. Thus G vanishes for $c\bar{u}, c\bar{y}$ and hence for $u = 0$, $y = 0$. This puts $u = 0, y = 0$ in $\mathfrak{M}_1$.

For another example of a general solution which contains a singular zero, we consider $A = y_1^2 - 4y^3$, whose manifold is $y = (x + c)^{-2}$ and $y = 0$. The only singular zero is $y = 0$. We see, letting $| c |$ increase, that a d.p. which vanishes for every $(x + c)^{-2}$ vanishes for $y = 0$. Thus $y = 0$ is in the general solution.

20. The above formulation of the concept of the general solution of an algebraic differential equation appears to be the first fully precise one which has ever been given. In the literature in general, the term "general solution" is used in a loose sense. For a differential equation of order n, an n-parameter family of solutions is called the "general solution." Some authors are aware that singular solutions should sometimes be considered as belonging to the general solution, but no sharp criterion is given.

It is interesting, however, that a paper on singular solutions published by Lagrange[21] in 1774 shows him to have possessed a really good idea of the nature of a general solution. Dealing with an equation

$$V\left(x, y, \frac{dy}{dx}\right) = 0, \tag{15}$$

he supposes determined for it a one-parameter family of solutions $y = f(x, a)$, which he calls the *complete integral*. He seeks conditions for a *particular* (in modern parlance, singular) solution $y(x)$ to be considered as belonging to the complete integral. He furnishes conditions under which $y(x)$ satisfies not only (15), but also "all equations of higher orders which can be derived from it." The satisfaction of all such higher equations is given as the condition for $y(x)$ to belong to the complete integral. How the higher equations are to be determined is left to be guessed. One is apparently supposed to perform differentiations and eliminations, as in the examples treated by Lagrange. It is proper, however, to credit Lagrange with the possession of a heuristic version of the criterion for membership in the general solution given in §17 above, and to regard his work on singular solutions, like that of Laplace and of Poisson which will be considered in Chapter III, as precursive to the present theory.

Parametric indeterminates

21. Let Σ be a nontrivial prime ideal in $\mathfrak{F}\{y_1, \cdots, y_n\}$.

There may be some y, say y_j, such that no nonzero d.p. in Σ involves only y_j; that is, every d.p. in which y_j appears effectively also involves some y_i with $i \neq j$. If there exist such y_j, let us pick one of them, arbitrarily, and call it u_1.

There may be a y distinct from u_1 such that no nonzero d.p. in Σ involves only u_1 and the new y. If there exist such y, we pick one of them and call it u_2.

[21] Lagrange, 15.

Continuing, we find a set $u_1, \cdots, u_q$ $(q < n)$, such that no nonzero d.p. of Σ involves the u alone and such that, given any y_j not among the u, there is a nonzero d.p. of Σ in y_j and the u alone.[22]

Let the indeterminates distinct from the u, taken in any order, be represented now by $y_1, \cdots, y_p$ $(p + q = n)$.

We now list the indeterminates in the order

$$u_1, \cdots, u_q; \qquad y_1, \cdots, y_p. \tag{16}$$

We shall speak generally as if u exist. It will be easy to see, in every case, what slight changes of language are necessary when they do not.

Of the nonzero d.p. in Σ involving only y_1 and the u, let A_1 be one of least rank. There certainly exist d.p. of Σ of class $q + 2$ which are reduced with respect to A_1; for instance, any nonzero d.p. in y_2 and the u is of this type. Of such d.p., let A_2 be one of least rank.

Continuing, we build a characteristic set of Σ,

$$A_1, A_2, \cdots, A_p. \tag{17}$$

We shall say that A_i *introduces* y_i.

We shall call $u_1, \cdots, u_q$ a *parametric set of indeterminates* for Σ, or for the manifold of Σ.

The resolvent

22. The investigation which we now undertake will show that every irreducible manifold except that of [0] may be regarded as a birational[23] transform of the general solution of some d.p.[24]

Through §23, we shall work with a field $\mathfrak{F}$ which contains at least one nonconstant element.

We present first two lemmas of a special character.

A set of elements $\eta_1, \cdots, \eta_s$ of $\mathfrak{F}$ will be called *linearly dependent* if there exists a relation

$$c_1\eta_1 + \cdots + c_s\eta_s = 0 \tag{18}$$

where the c are constant elements of $\mathfrak{F}$, not all zero.

We prove that *for* $\eta_1, \cdots, \eta_s$ *to be linearly dependent, it is necessary and sufficient that*

$$\begin{vmatrix} \eta_1 & \cdot & \cdot & \cdot & \eta_s \\ \eta_1' & \cdot & \cdot & \cdot & \eta_s' \\ \cdot & \cdot & \cdot & \cdot & \cdot \\ \eta_1^{(s-1)} & \cdot & \cdot & \cdot & \eta_s^{(s-1)} \end{vmatrix} = 0, \tag{19}$$

where superscripts indicate differentiation.

---

[22] It will be seen in §32 that q does not depend on the particular manner in which the u are selected.

[23] The birational transformations which we use will involve derivatives.

[24] A.D.E., Chapter II, and Kolchin, 10. The treatment given here is taken over from Kolchin's paper.

The proof is conducted as in analysis. For the necessity, we differentiate (18) $s - 1$ times. We secure a set of s homogeneous equations for the c. The determinant must vanish, since there is a solution with some c distinct from zero. For the sufficiency proof, we proceed by induction. For $s = 1$, (19) is evidently sufficient. We treat the case of $s = r$, supposing earlier cases to have been examined. By (19) the equations

$$c_1\eta_1^{(j)} + \cdots + c_r\eta_r^{(j)}, \qquad j = 0, \cdots, r-1, \tag{20}$$

are satisfied by elements $c_1, \cdots, c_r$ of $\mathfrak{F}$, not all zero. We may evidently suppose that when the last row and last column are suppressed in (19), the resulting determinant is not zero. Then, in (20), $c_r \neq 0$. We may thus take c_r equal to unity. For $j \leqq r - 2$, we differentiate (20) and then subtract the equation (20) corresponding to $j + 1$.

We find that

$$c_1'\eta_1^{(j)} + \cdots + c_{r-1}'\eta_{r-1}^{(j)} = 0, \qquad j = 0, \cdots, r-2, \tag{21}$$

where accents indicate differentiation. As the determinant of (21) is not zero, the c_i with $i < r$ are constants. This completes the proof.

We prove now that *if G is a nonzero d.p. in $\mathfrak{F}\{u_1, \cdots, u_q\}$, there exist elements $\mu_1, \cdots, \mu_q$ in $\mathfrak{F}$ such that G is not zero for $u_i = \mu_i$, $i = 1, \cdots, q$.*

It suffices to treat a d.p. G in a single indeterminate u. Let ξ be a nonconstant element in $\mathfrak{F}$. Let r be any nonnegative integer. We shall prove that if G is a nonzero d.p. of order not exceeding r, there is an element

$$c_0 + c_1\xi + c_2\xi^2 + \cdots + c_r\xi^r, \tag{22}$$

where the c are constants in $\mathfrak{F}$, which does not annul G. Let this be false, and let H be a nonzero d.p. of lowest rank which vanishes for every element (22). Let the order of H be s. We know that $s \leqq r$. It is easy to see that $s > 0$.

When u is replaced in H by (22) and each u_i with $1 \leqq i \leqq s$ by

$$c_1\xi^{(i)} + c_2(\xi^2)^{(i)} + \cdots + c_r(\xi^r)^{(i)}, \tag{23}$$

the superscript (i) denoting i differentiations, H, considered as a polynomial in the indeterminates c, must vanish identically. Its partial derivatives with respect to the c are thus all zero. We have thus, from $c_0, \cdots, c_s$,

$$\begin{aligned}
&\frac{\partial H}{\partial u} &&= 0,\\
&\frac{\partial H}{\partial u}\xi + \frac{\partial H}{\partial u_1}\xi' + \cdots + \frac{\partial H}{\partial u_s}\xi^{(s)} &&= 0,\\
&\frac{\partial H}{\partial u}\xi^2 + \frac{\partial H}{\partial u_1}(\xi^2)' + \cdots + \frac{\partial H}{\partial u_s}(\xi^2)^{(s)} &&= 0,\\
&\cdots\cdots\cdots\cdots\cdots\cdots\cdots\cdots\cdots\cdots &&,\\
&\frac{\partial H}{\partial u}\xi^s + \frac{\partial H}{\partial u_1}(\xi^s)' + \cdots + \frac{\partial H}{\partial u_s}(\xi^s)^{(s)} &&= 0.
\end{aligned} \tag{24}$$

In each $\partial H/\partial u_i$, $i = 0, \cdots, s$, the substitutions (22), (23) are supposed to be made.

We regard equations (24) as equations for the $\partial H/\partial u_i$. As $\partial H/\partial u_s$ is of lower rank than H, it does not vanish identically in the c. The determinant of (24) is therefore zero. This means, by the preceding lemma, that there is a relation

$$a_1\xi' + a_2(\xi^2)' + \cdots + a_s(\xi^s)' = 0$$

where the a are constants in $\mathfrak{F}$, not all zero. Then

$$a_1\xi + a_2\xi^2 + \cdots + a_s\xi^s = a_0$$

with a_0 a constant. Thus ξ satisfies an algebraic equation whose coefficients are in $\mathfrak{F}$ and are not all zero. Let an equation of this type of least degree be

$$f(\xi) = 0.$$

Then $f'(\xi)\xi' = 0$. As $f'(\xi) \neq 0$, we have $\xi' = 0$. We reach the contradiction that ξ is a constant and the lemma is proved.

23. Working in $\mathfrak{F}\{u_1, \cdots, u_q; y_1, \cdots, y_p\}$,[25] we consider a nontrivial prime ideal Σ for which the u are a parametric set (§21). We are going to show *the existence in* $\mathfrak{F}$ *of elements*

$$\mu_1, \cdots, \mu_p \tag{25}$$

and the existence of a nonzero d.p. G, free of the y, such that either

(a) *there exist no two distinct zeros of* Σ, *contained in a single extension of* $\mathfrak{F}$,

$$\begin{matrix} \bar{u}_1, \cdots, \bar{u}_q; & y'_1, \cdots, y'_p, \\ \bar{u}_1, \cdots, \bar{u}_q; & y''_1, \cdots, y''_p, \end{matrix} \tag{26}$$

with the same u, which u do not annul G, or

(b) *such pairs of zeros exist and, for each pair,*

$$\mu_1(y'_1 - y''_1) + \cdots + \mu_p(y'_p - y''_p) \tag{27}$$

is not zero.[26]

We consider the system Σ' obtained from Σ by replacing each y_i by a new indeterminate z_i. Introducing p more indeterminates $\lambda_1, \cdots, \lambda_p$, we consider the perfect ideal Ω determined by Σ, Σ' and

$$\lambda_1(y_1 - z_1) + \cdots + \lambda_p(y_p - z_p).$$

We have thus $3p + q$ indeterminates, the u, y, z, λ, and we operate in $\mathfrak{F}\{u; y; z; \lambda\}$.

Let Λ be any essential prime divisor of Ω. Suppose that not every $y_i - z_i$,

---

[25] We recall that $\mathfrak{F}$ is supposed to contain nonconstant elements.

[26] If no u exist, this is to mean that, if Σ has a pair of distinct zeros in a single extension of $\mathfrak{F}$, (27) does not vanish for the pair. We take $G = 1$ in this case.

$i = 1, \cdots, p$, is in Λ. We shall prove that Λ contains a nonzero d.p. which involves no indeterminates other than the u and λ.

If Λ contains a d.p. in the u alone,[27] we have our result. Suppose that Λ contains no such d.p.

Since Λ has all d.p. in Σ, Λ has, for $j = 1, \cdots, p$, a d.p. B_j in y_j and the u alone. Let B_j be taken so as to be of as low a rank as possible in y_j. Then S_j, the separant of B_j, is not in Λ.

Similarly let C_j, $j = 1, \cdots, p$, be a d.p. of Λ in z_j and the u, of as low a rank as possible in z_j. Letting z_j follow the u in C_j, we see that the separant S_j' of C_j is not in Λ.

To fix our ideas, suppose that $y_1 - z_1$ is not in Λ. Consider any generic zero of Λ. For it, we have

$$\lambda_1 = -\frac{\lambda_2 (y_2 - z_2) + \cdots + \lambda_p (y_p - z_p)}{y_1 - z_1}. \tag{28}$$

From (28) we find, for the jth derivative of λ_1 in the generic zero, an expression

$$\lambda_{1j} = \rho_j (\lambda_2, \cdots, \lambda_p; y_1, \cdots, y_p; z_1, \cdots, z_p), \tag{29}$$

in which ρ_j is rational in the λ, y, z and their derivatives, with coefficients in $\mathfrak{F}$. The denominator in each ρ_j is a power of $y_1 - z_1$.

Let B_i be of order r_i in y_i and C_i be of order s_i in z_i, $i = 1, \cdots, p$.

If a ρ_j involves derivatives of y_i of order higher than r_i, we can get rid of those derivatives by using their expressions in the derivatives of y_i of order r_i or less, found from $B_i = 0$. Similarly, we transform each ρ_j so as to be of order not exceeding s_i in z_i, $i = 1, \cdots, p$.

The new expression for each ρ_j, which will involve the u, will have a denominator which is a product of powers of $y_1 - z_1$, S_i, S_i', $i = 1, \cdots, p$. Let g be the maximum of the integers r_i, s_i. Let

$$h = 2p(g + 1) + 1.$$

Let k be the total number of letters y_{ij}, z_{ij} which appear in the relations (29), transformed as indicated. Then $h > k$.

We consider the first h of the relations (29).[28] (That is, we let $j = 0, 1, \cdots, h - 1$.) Let D, an appropriate product of powers of $y_1 - z_1$, the S_i, S_i', be a common denominator for the second members of these relations. We write

$$\lambda_{1j} = \frac{E_j}{D}, \qquad j = 0, \cdots, h - 1. \tag{30}$$

Let D and the E_j be written as polynomials in the k letters y_{ij}, z_{ij} present in them, with coefficients which are d.p. in $\lambda_2, \cdots, \lambda_p$ and the u. Let m be the maximum of the degrees of these polynomials (total degrees in the y_{ij}, z_{ij}).

[27] At times the term *nonzero* will be omitted. One will always know when it is being tacitly employed.

[28] When $j = 0$, (29) is (28).

Let α represent a positive integer to be fixed later. The total number of distinct power products of degree $m\alpha$ or less, in k letters, is[29]

(31)
$$\frac{(m\alpha + k) \cdots (m\alpha + 1)}{k!}.$$

Using (30), let us form expressions for all power products of the λ_{1j} in (30) of degree α or less. Let each expression be written in the form

(32)
$$\frac{F}{D^\alpha}.$$

Then F, as a polynomial in the y_{ij}, z_{ij}, will be of degree at most $m\alpha$.

The number of power products of the h letters λ_{1j} of degree α or less is

(33)
$$\frac{(\alpha + h) \cdots (\alpha + 1)}{h!}.$$

Now (31) is a polynomial of degree k in α, whereas (33) is of degree h in α. As $h > k$ and as m, h, k are fixed, (33) will exceed (31) if α is large. Let α be taken large enough for this to be realized.

If now the F in (32) are considered as linear expressions in the power products in the y_{ij}, z_{ij}, we shall have more linear expressions than power products. Hence the linear expressions F are linearly dependent. That is, some linear combination of the F, with coefficients which are d.p. in $\lambda_2, \cdots, \lambda_p$ and the u, not all zero, vanishes identically.

The same linear combination of the power products of the λ_{1j} will vanish for the generic zero of Λ for which (28) was written. Now this last linear combination is a d.p. H in the u and λ. H is not identically zero, since the power products in the λ_{1j} in H are all distinct.

As H vanishes for a generic zero of Λ, H is in Λ.

Let $\Lambda_1, \cdots, \Lambda_r$ be the essential prime divisors of Ω. Let $\Lambda_1, \cdots, \Lambda_s$ each not contain some $y_i - z_i$ and let $\Lambda_{s+1}, \cdots, \Lambda_r$ each contain every $y_i - z_i$. Let H_i be a nonzero d.p. in Λ_i, $i = 1, \cdots, s$, involving only the u and λ. Let $K = H_1 \cdots H_s$.

Using the second lemma of §22, we replace each λ_i in K by an element μ_i of $\mathfrak{F}$, in such a way that K reduces to a nonzero d.p. G in the u. We shall show that G and the μ serve as in the statement at the head of this section.

The zeros of Ω with $\lambda_j = \mu_j$, $j = 1, \cdots, p$, will be the zeros of the Λ_i with $\lambda_j = \mu_j$. Now the zeros with $\lambda_j = \mu_j$ of $\Lambda_1, \cdots, \Lambda_s$ have u which annul G. The zeros of $\Lambda_{s+1}, \cdots, \Lambda_r$, even with $\lambda_j = \mu_j$, have $y_i = z_i$, $i = 1, \cdots, p$.

Suppose now that $\Lambda_1, \cdots, \Lambda_s$ actually exist. Then there exist distinct pairs (26); the y' can be taken as the y in a zero of some Λ_i, $i \leqq s$, and the y'' as the z.[30] For any such pair (26), (27) is zero only if the u, y', y'' are in a zero, with

[29] Perron, *Lehrbuch der Algebra*, vol. 1, p. 46.

[30] We are not supposing here that the λ are replaced by the μ.

$\lambda_j = \mu_j$, $j = 1, \cdots, p$, of some Λ_i with $i \leqq s$. In that case, G vanishes for the u.

When every Λ_j contains every $y_i - z_i$, we take $G = 1$, $\mu_1 = \cdots = \mu_p = 0$. We have thus produced the required G and μ.[31]

24. We shall now relinquish the condition that $\mathfrak{F}$ contain a nonconstant element. Let us assume that parametric indeterminates u exist. We are going to prove *the existence of d.p. G, $M_1, \cdots, M_p$, in the u alone, with $G \neq 0$, such that, for two distinct zeros* (26) *for which G does not vanish,*

$$(34) \qquad M_1(y_1' - y_1'') + \cdots + M_p(y_p' - y_p'')$$

is not zero.

The discussion of §23 holds through the construction of K. We are going to prove the existence of d.p. $M_1, \cdots, M_p$ in the u alone, such that when λ_i is replaced by M_i in K, the resulting d.p. G is not identically zero.

Let K be arranged as a polynomial in the λ_{1j}, with d.p. in $\lambda_2, \cdots, \lambda_p$ and the u for coefficients. Let u_{1k} be a derivative of u_1 of order greater than that of any derivative of u_1 which may appear in the coefficients. If λ_1 is replaced by u_{1k}, K becomes a d.p. K_1 in $\lambda_2, \cdots, \lambda_p$ and the u which is not identically zero. Similarly, if we replace λ_2 by a sufficiently high derivative of u_1 in K_1, we obtain a nonzero d.p. K_2 in $\lambda_3, \cdots, \lambda_p$ and the u. Continuing these replacements, we obtain a nonzero d.p. G in the u alone.

Continuing as in §23, we see that the zeros of Ω with $\lambda_j = M_j$, $j = 1, \cdots, p$, are the zeros of the Λ_i with $\lambda_j = M_j$. Now the zeros with $\lambda_j = M_j$ of $\Lambda_1, \cdots, \Lambda_s$ have u which annul G. The zeros of $\Lambda_{s+1}, \cdots, \Lambda_r$, even with $\lambda_j = M_j$, have $y_i = z_i$ for $i = 1, \cdots, p$. This proves our statement.

25. The results of §§23, 24 permit us to state that if either

(a) $\mathfrak{F}$ does not consist purely of constants, or

(b) there exist u,

triads of d.p. G, P, Q exist in $\mathfrak{F}\{u_1, \cdots, u_q; y_1, \cdots, y_p\}$, with G and P not in Σ and G free of the y, such that, for two distinct zeros of Σ in a single extension of $\mathfrak{F}$, with the same u, the zeros annulling neither G nor P, the expression Q/P has two distinct values. For instance, if (a) holds, we can take $P = 1$ and $Q = \mu_1 y_1 + \cdots + \mu_p y_p$.

The ideas will be more complete, and even simpler, if we use general d.p. P. The following is a nontrivial case in which P is of positive class. Let $\mathfrak{F}$ be the totality of rational functions of x. We take Σ as $\{y_{11}, y_{21}\}$ in $\mathfrak{F}\{y_1, y_2\}$. The zeros are $y_1 = c$, $y_2 = d$ with c and d constant, but otherwise unrestricted. We take $G = 1$. If

$$P = y_1 + xy_2, \qquad Q = y_1^2 + x^2,$$

---

[31] The following example shows that Σ may have many zeros with given u and that a G may exist such that, for $G \neq 0$, there is only one zero for given u. Let Σ be the perfect ideal generated by $u_1y_1 - u_2$ in $\mathfrak{F}\{u_1, u_2, y_1\}$. Σ is prime, since the separant for u_2 is unity. The set u_1, u_2 is parametric. Let $G = u_1$. If $u_1 = u_2 = 0$, y_1 may be taken arbitrarily, but, for given u_1, u_2 with $G \neq 0$, there is only one y_1.

the expression Q/P assumes distinct values for distinct zeros of Σ with $P \neq 0$.[32]

In certain cases in which $\mathfrak{F}$ consists purely of constants and in which no u exist, there may exist no pair P, Q as described above. For instance, let $\mathfrak{F}$ be the totality of complex numbers. Let Σ be as in the preceding example. For every zero, the y_{ij} are zero for $j > 0$. We therefore lose no generality in seeking a P and Q of order zero in y_1 and y_2. For any such P and Q, Q/P will yield the same result for infinitely many distinct pairs of constants y_1, y_2.

In developing the theory of a prime ideal Σ for the case in which $\mathfrak{F}$ has only constants and in which there are no u, two courses are open to us. If we adjoin an element x to $\mathfrak{F}$, as in I, §29, Σ will generate, for the enlarged field, a prime ideal whose theory may be expected to be equivalent to that of Σ; in the analytic case, the ideals have the same restricted manifold. Again, by I, §27, we can introduce a new indeterminate u_1 and Σ will generate a prime ideal in $\mathfrak{F}\{u_1; y_1, \cdots, y_n\}$. After either type of adjunction, the theory which follows will apply.

26. From this point on, through §30, we work with a nontrivial prime ideal Σ. We assume that either

(a) $\mathfrak{F}$ does not consist purely of constants, or

(b) parametric indeterminates exist.

We take a triad G, P, Q as in §25. Introducing a new indeterminate, w, we let Λ represent the ideal $\{\Sigma, Pw - Q\}$ in $\mathfrak{F}\{u; y; w\}$. Let Ω be the totality of those d.p. G in $\mathfrak{F}\{u; y; w\}$ which have the property that

$$PG \equiv 0, \qquad (\Lambda).$$

We see immediately that Ω is an ideal. We shall prove that Ω is prime.

Let B and C be such that BC is in Ω. For s appropriate, P^sB minus a linear combination of $Pw - Q$ and its derivatives is a d.p. R free of w. We obtain similarly, from a P^tC, a d.p. S free of w. As RS is in Ω, PRS is in Λ. A generic zero of Σ does not annul P, and thus furnishes a zero of Λ. Thus a generic zero of Σ annuls RS, so that one of R and S is in Σ. If R is in Σ, P^sB is in Λ. Then B is in Ω, so that Ω is prime.

We notice that those d.p. of Ω which are free of w are precisely the d.p. of Σ. In particular, Ω contains no d.p. in the u alone.

We are going to show that Ω contains a d.p. in w and the u alone.

Let B_i, $i = 1, \cdots, p$, be a d.p. of Σ involving only y_i; $u_1, \cdots, u_q$, of minimum rank in y_i. Let S_i be the separant of B_i. Consider any generic zero of Ω. For it, we have

$$w = \frac{Q}{P}.$$

For the jth derivative of w, we have an expression

$$w_j = \frac{Q_j}{P^{j+1}}. \qquad (35)$$

[32] As usual, we compare only zeros contained in the same extension.

Using the relations $B_i = 0$, we free each Q_j from those derivatives of each y_i which are of order higher than the maximum of the orders of Q, P and B_i in y_i. Each w_j will then be expressed as a quotient of two d.p., the denominator being a product of powers of $P, S_1, \cdots, S_p$. If we use a sufficient number of the relations (35), as just transformed, we will have more w_i than there are y_{ij} in the second members. Using the process of elimination employed in §23, we obtain a d.p. K in $w; u_1, \cdots, u_q$ which vanishes for a generic zero of Ω and is therefore in Ω.

27. We now list the indeterminates in the order

$$u_1, \cdots, u_q; w; y_1, \cdots, y_p$$

and take a characteristic set of Ω,

$$A, A_1, \cdots, A_p. \tag{36}$$

Here $w, y_1, \cdots, y_p$ are introduced in succession (§21). The separants for (36) will be represented by $S, S_1, \cdots, S_p$ and the initials by $I, I_1, \cdots, I_p$.

If A is not algebraically irreducible, we can replace it by one of its irreducible factors. We assume therefore that *A is algebraically irreducible.*

We are going to prove that $A_1, \cdots, A_p$ are of order 0 in $y_1, \cdots, y_p$ respectively and, indeed, that A_i is of the first degree in y_i. Thus, since, for $i > j$, A_i is of lower degree in y_j than A_j, each equation $A_i = 0$ expresses y_i rationally in terms of $w; u_1, \cdots, u_q$ and their derivatives.

The determination of the manifold of Σ will in this way be made to depend on the determination of the general solution of $A = 0$ (§16), which equation will be called a *resolvent* of the prime ideal Σ, or of the system of equations obtained by equating the d.p. in Σ to zero.

28. Let us suppose that our claim with respect to the A_i is false and let A_k be the A_i of highest subscript for which it breaks down. Thus the A_i with $i > k$, if they exist, are of zero order in $y_{k+1}, \cdots, y_p$ respectively and are linear in those letters. On the other hand, either A_k is of positive order in y_k, or A_k is of zero order in y_k and is not linear in y_k. We shall force a contradiction.

Let P_1 be the remainder with respect to (36) of P of §26 and let U be the remainder with respect to (36) of

$$P_1 S_k I_k I_{k+1} \cdots I_p.$$

In $\mathfrak{F}\{u_1, \cdots, u_q; w; y_1, \cdots, y_k\}$, let

$$\Xi = (A, A_1, \cdots, A_k, U).$$

U is not zero and is reduced with respect to (36).[33] Of all nonzero d.p. in Ξ which are reduced with respect to (36), let B be one of a least degree in y_{kr}, where r is the order of A_k in y_k. We say that B is free of y_{kr}.

---

[33] The fact that $A_{k+1}, \cdots, A_p$ involve $y_{k+1}, \cdots, y_p$, which do not figure in Ξ, need give no concern. Note that U is free of those indeterminates.

Suppose that this is not so. Let C be the initial of B, that is, the coefficient of the highest power of y_{kr} in B. For m appropriate,

$$C^m A_k = DB + E$$

with D of lower degree than A_k in y_{kr}, and E, if not zero, of lower degree than B in y_{kr}. E is in Ξ.

We shall prove that E is in Ω. This is certainly true if $E = 0$. Suppose that E is not zero. Let F be the remainder of E with respect to $A, A_1, \cdots, A_{k-1}$.[34] Then F is in Ξ and is reduced with respect to (36). If F were not zero, it would be, like E, of lower degree than B in y_{kr}. Thus $F = 0$ and E is in Ω.

Thus DB is in Ω. B is not, since it is reduced with respect to (36). Then D is in Ω. With t the degree of D in y_{kr}, let

$$D = G_0 + G_1 y_{kr} + \cdots + G_t y_{kr}^t.$$

As E, if not zero, is of lower degree than A_k in y_{kr}, the initial of DB is identical with that of $C^m A_k$. Now C, reduced with respect to (36), is not in Ω. Thus G_t is not in Ω. It is easy to see that there exist integers $a, a_1, \cdots, a_{k-1}$ such that

$$I^a I_1^{a_1} \cdots I_{k-1}^{a_{k-1}} G_i \equiv G_i', \qquad (\Omega), \qquad i = 1, \cdots, t,$$

where each G_i' is reduced with respect to $A, A_1, \cdots, A_{k-1}$. We see that $G_t' \neq 0$. Then

$$G_0' + \cdots + G_t' y_{kr}^t$$

is a nonzero d.p. in Ω which is reduced with respect to (36). This contradiction proves that B is free of y_{kr}.

29. Now let Ω' be the totality of those d.p. in Ω which are free of $y_k, \cdots, y_p$. We see immediately that Ω' is a prime ideal with $A, \cdots, A_{k-1}$ as a characteristic set.

Let

$$(37) \qquad u_i = \tau_i, i = 1, \cdots, q; w = \xi; y_i = \eta_i, i = 1, \cdots, p,$$

be a generic zero of Ω, contained in an extension $\mathfrak{F}_1$ of $\mathfrak{F}$. Then

$$(38) \qquad \tau_1, \cdots, \tau_q; \xi; \eta_1, \cdots, \eta_{k-1}$$

is a generic zero of Ω'. We replace $u_1, \cdots, u_q; w; y_1, \cdots, y_{k-1}$ in A_k by the quantities (38). We secure a d.p. H_k in $\mathfrak{F}_1 \{ y_k \}$.

We examine H_k. Let A_k be arranged as a polynomial in the y_{ki}, $i = 0, \cdots, r$, with nonzero coefficients. The coefficients are not in Ω and hence do not vanish for (38). Thus H_k has the same degree in y_{kr} that A_k has.

Let H_k be expressed as a product of irreducible factors over $\mathfrak{F}_1$ and let K be an irreducible factor which is of order r in y_k. Let ζ_k be a generic point (§6) in the general solution of K.

[34] For $k = 1$, we take the remainder of E with respect to A.

For (38), B becomes a d.p. L in $\mathfrak{F}_1\{y_k\}$. As B is not in Ω, L is not identically zero. L is of order less than r in y_k if $r > 0$ and is an element of $\mathfrak{F}_1$ if $r = 0$. Thus L cannot vanish for $y_k = \zeta_k$ (§13). Then B does not vanish for

(39) $$\tau_1, \cdots, \tau_p; \xi; \eta_1, \cdots, \eta_{k-1}; \zeta_k.$$

As $A, A_1, \cdots, A_k$ vanish for (39), U does not. Then (39) annuls none of

$$P_1, S_k, I_k, \cdots, I_p.$$

The failure of $I_{k+1}, \cdots, I_p$ to vanish for (39) shows that, when (39) is substituted into an A_j with $j > k$, the equation $A_j = 0$ determines y_j as a quantity ζ_j in the extension of $\mathfrak{F}_1$ which contains ζ_k. The quantities

(40) $$\tau_1, \cdots, \tau_q; \xi; \eta_1, \cdots, \eta_{k-1}; \zeta_k, \cdots, \zeta_p$$

are seen to constitute a regular zero of (36) which does not annul[35] PG. Thus (40) is a zero of Ω and

(41) $$\tau_1, \cdots, \tau_q; \eta_1, \cdots, \eta_{k-1}; \zeta_k, \cdots, \zeta_p$$

is a zero of Σ which does not annul PG.

Suppose now that $r > 0$. We cannot have $\eta_k = \zeta_k$. Otherwise $y_k - \eta_k$ would be a d.p. in $\mathfrak{F}_1\{y_k\}$ of lower rank than K which is annulled by ζ_k. In (41) and in the generic zero of Σ

$$\tau_1, \cdots, \tau_q; \eta_1, \cdots, \eta_p,$$

we have two zeros of Σ which do not annul PG and which yield the same value ξ for w. This contradicts the nature of G, P, Q.

We have thus proved that A_k is of order zero in y_k.

30. The denial made at the beginning of §28 now becomes a claim that A_k is not linear in y_k. We use the material of §29. As ζ_k must equal[36] η_k, $y_k - \eta_k$ must be divisible by K. This means, if H_k is of degree t in y_k, that

(42) $$H_k = \alpha(y_k - \eta_k)^t$$

where α is the coefficient of y_k^t in H_k. Let β be the coefficient of y_k^{t-1} in H_k. By (42),

(43) $$t\alpha\eta_k + \beta = 0.$$

In α and β, we reverse the substitution made to convert A_k into H_k. Also, in the first member of (43), we replace η_k by y_k. We obtain a d.p.

$$My_k + N$$

which is in Ω, since, by (43), it is annulled by (37). As $\alpha \neq 0$, M is not zero.

[35] G, which is not in Ω, cannot vanish for the τ.

[36] Note that the theory of the general solution applies to d.p. which do not involve proper derivatives.

Furthermore, M, which is the product by t of a coefficient of A_k, is reduced with respect to $A, \cdots, A_{k-1}$; so is N.

We have a final contradiction of the assumption of falsity made in §28.

Thus, *every A_i is linear in y_i and, in the manifold of Σ, each y_i has an expression rational in w; $u_1, \cdots, u_q$ and their derivatives, with coefficients in $\mathfrak{F}$.*

31. We say that *if*

$$\bar{u}_1, \cdots, \bar{u}_q; \bar{w}; \bar{y}_1, \cdots, \bar{y}_p \tag{44}$$

is a zero of Ω, then $\bar{u}_1, \cdots, \bar{u}_q$; $\bar{w}$ belongs to the general solution of A.[37] Let K be any d.p. in w and the u belonging to the prime ideal whose manifold is the general solution of A. As the remainder of K with respect to A is zero, K is in Ω and therefore vanishes for $\bar{u}_1, \cdots, \bar{u}_q; \bar{w}$.

32. The introduction of the resolvent accomplishes the following:

(a) It reduces the study of an irreducible manifold $\mathfrak{M}$ to the study of the general solution $\mathfrak{M}'$ of some d.p. The correspondence between $\mathfrak{M}$ and $\mathfrak{M}'$ may be described as *birational.* Of course, in the expression for w in terms of the y, and in those of the y in terms of w, derivatives may appear. For zeros in $\mathfrak{M}$ with $P = 0$, there may be no corresponding w, and for other zeros in $\mathfrak{M}$ the initial of some A_i may vanish. For restricted manifolds, we shall gain information on these special zeros in Chapter VI.

(b) It extends into the theory of differential equations a property of systems of algebraic functions of several variables. It is well known that, given a finite system of algebraic functions, we can find a single algebraic function in terms of which, and of the variables, the functions in the system can be expressed rationally.

(c) It furnishes an instrument useful in the treatment of various problems.

Dimension of an irreducible manifold

33. Let Σ be a nontrivial prime ideal in $\mathfrak{F}\{y_1, \cdots, y_n\}$ with $\mathfrak{F}$ any field.

We propose to show that, if parametric indeterminates exist, their number, q, does not depend on the manner in which they are selected; in other words, two sets of parametric indeterminates contain the same number of indeterminates.

Let us suppose that a set $u_1, \cdots, u_q$ has been selected, and that one has, in addition, $y_1, \cdots, y_p$. It will suffice to show that, given any $q + 1$ indeterminates among the u and y

$$z_1, \cdots, z_{q+1},$$

there exists a d.p. in Σ which involves only the z.

We form a resolvent for Σ. As u exist, this is possible. Let us consider a generic zero of Ω. The z in that zero have expressions rational in w, the u and their derivatives. If a z_i happens to be a u, say u_j, the expression for z_i is simply u_j. We write

[37] Here we consider A as a d.p. in w and the u alone.

(45) $$z_i = \rho_i(w; u_1, \cdots, u_q), \qquad i = 1, \cdots, q+1.$$

On differentiating (45) repeatedly, we get expressions for the z_{ij} which are rational in the w_j and u_{ij}. Making use of the relation $A = 0$, we transform these expressions so as not to contain derivatives of w of order higher than r, where r is the order of A in w.

Since there are $q + 1$ of the z and only q of the u, it follows that if we differentiate (45) often enough (and then transform), the z_{ij} will become more numerous than the u_{ij} and $w, w_1, \cdots, w_r$.

It follows as in §23 that there exists a nonzero d.p. in the z which vanishes for a generic zero of Σ. Such a d.p. is in Σ.

We shall call the number q the *dimension* of Σ, or of the manifold of Σ. To a nontrivial prime ideal without parametric indeterminates, we attribute the dimension 0. The dimension of [0] will be defined as n.

From §18, it follows that, for $\mathfrak{F}\{y_1, \cdots, y_n\}$, *every manifold of dimension* $n - 1$ *is the general solution of a differential polynomial.*

Order of the resolvent

34. We work with a nontrivial prime ideal Σ of dimension q in $\mathfrak{F}\{u_1, \cdots, u_q; y_1, \cdots, y_p\}$, the u being parametric for Σ.[38] We suppose that triads G, P, Q, and therefore resolvents, exist. Let

(46) $$A_1, \cdots, A_p$$

be a characteristic set for Σ, the separant and initial of A_i being S_i and I_i respectively. We denote the order of A_i in y_i by r_i. Let

$$h = r_1 + \cdots + r_p.$$

We shall prove that *every resolvent of* Σ *is of order* h *in* w.[39]

We begin by proving that Ω contains a d.p. in $w; u_1, \cdots, u_q$ whose order in w does not exceed h.

Consider a generic zero of Ω,

(47) $$\bar{u}_1, \cdots, \bar{u}_q; \bar{w}; \bar{y}_1, \cdots, \bar{y}_p.$$

For it, we have

(48) $$w = \frac{Q}{P}.$$

We shall show the existence of d.p. R and T, each of order not exceeding r_i in y_i, $i = 1, \cdots, p$, such that, for (47), T is not zero and

(49) $$w = \frac{R}{T}.$$

---

[38] When $q = 0$, there are no u.

[39] For a brief proof, based on the theory of algebraic fields, see Kolchin, 13.

Let Q_1 and P_1 be the remainders of Q and P respectively relative to (46). Let Q_1 be obtained by subtracting a linear combination of the A_i and their derivatives from

$$S_1^{s_1} \cdots I_p^{t_p} Q$$

and let P_1 be obtained similarly from

$$S_1^{\sigma_1} \cdots I_p^{\tau_p} P.$$

Then, for (47), we have

$$w = \frac{Q_1 S_1^{\sigma_1} \cdots I_p^{\tau_p}}{P_1 S_1^{s_1} \cdots I_p^{t_p}}. \tag{50}$$

For R and T in (49), we take the numerator and denominator in (50).

We find from (49), for the jth derivative of w, an expression

$$w_j = \frac{B_j}{T^{j+1}}. \tag{51}$$

If U_j is the remainder of B_j with respect to (46), we can write (51)

$$w_j = \frac{U_j}{W_j} \tag{52}$$

where W_j is a product of powers of $T, S_1, \cdots, I_p$.

Consider (49) and the first h of the relations (52). Let D be a common denominator for the second members in these $h + 1$ relations. We write

$$w_j = \frac{E_j}{D}, \tag{53}$$

$j = 0, \cdots, h$.

Let D, the E, and the A in (46) be written as polynomials in the y_{ij} with coefficients which are d.p. in the u. Let m be the maximum of the degrees of these polynomials.

For convenience, we represent the r_ith derivative of y_i by z_i. Let A_i be of degree v_i in z_i.

Let α be a positive integer, to be fixed later. In (53), let us form all power products in the w_j of degree α or less. Let the expression for each power product be written in the form

$$\frac{F}{D^\alpha}. \tag{54}$$

Then each F is a polynomial in the y_{ij}, of degree not exceeding $m\alpha$.

Let each expression (54) be written

$$\frac{F I_p^{m\alpha}}{D^\alpha I_p^{m\alpha}}. \tag{55}$$

Consider a particular F, and let it be written as a polynomial in z_p. Suppose that its degree d in z_p is not less than m. Then, as $A_p = 0$ for (47), we have, letting

$$M = A_p - I_p z_p^{v_p},$$

the relation

(56) $$I_p z_p^d = -Mz_p^{d-v_p}.$$

If

$$F = J_0 + J_1 z_p + \cdots + J_d z_p^d,$$

with the J free of z_p, we may write the numerator in (55) in the form

(57) $$(J_0 I_p + \cdots + J_d I_p z_p^d) I_p^{m\alpha - 1}.$$

Since I_p is of degree less than m in the y_{ij}, each term in the parentheses in (57) is of degree less than $m(\alpha + 1)$

We replace $J_d I_p z_p^d$ by $-J_d M z_p^{d-v_p}$ in (57). As J_d is of degree not exceeding $m\alpha - d$ in the y_{ij} and as M is of degree at most m, then $J_d M z_p^{d-v_p}$ is of degree less than $m(\alpha + 1)$ in the y_{ij}. Thus (55) goes over into

$$\frac{F_1 I_p^{m\alpha-1}}{D^\alpha I_p^{m\alpha}},$$

where F_1 is of degree less than $m(\alpha + 1)$ in the y_{ij} and of degree less than d in z_p. If the degree of F_1 in z_p is not less than m, we repeat the above operation. After $t \leqq m\alpha$ operations, we get an expression

(58) $$\frac{HI_p^{m\alpha-t}}{D^\alpha I_p^{m\alpha}}$$

with H of degree less than m in z_p and of degree less than $m(\alpha + t)$ in the y_{ij}. The numerator in (58) is of degree in the y_{ij} less than

$$m(\alpha + t) + m(m\alpha - t) \leqq 2m^2\alpha.$$

Thus, if we let $D_1 = DI_p^m$, we can write each power product in the w_j of degree α or less in the form

(59) $$\frac{K}{D_1^\alpha}$$

where K is of degree less than $2m^2\alpha$ in the y_{ij} and of degree less than m in z_p.

We now write each expression (59) in the form

(60) $$\frac{KI_{p-1}^{2m^2\alpha}}{D_1^\alpha I_{p-1}^{2m^2\alpha}}$$

and employ, with respect to z_{p-1}, the procedure used above. We find for each expression (60) an equivalent expression

(61) $$\frac{L}{D_2^\alpha}$$

with $D_2 = D_1 I_{p-1}^{2m^2}$ and with L of degree less than $4m^3\alpha$ in the y_{ij} and of degree less than m in z_p and z_{p-1}. Continuing, we find, for each power product of the w_j, an expression

$$\frac{W}{D_p^\alpha} \tag{62}$$

where W is of degree less than $2^p m^{p+1}\alpha$ in the y_{ij} and of degree less than m in z_i, $i = 1, \cdots, p$. Let c represent $2^p m^{p+1}$.

The number of power products in $z_1, \cdots, z_p$ of degree less than m in each letter is m^p. Thus, as the y_{ij} with $j < r_i$ are h in number, the number of power products of the y_{ij} of degree $c\alpha$ or less, and of degree less than m in each z_i, is not more than

$$m^p \frac{(c\alpha + h) \cdots (c\alpha + 1)}{h!}. \tag{63}$$

The number of power products of degree α or less in the $h + 1$ letters w_j is

$$\frac{(\alpha + h + 1) \cdots (\alpha + 1)}{(h + 1)!}. \tag{64}$$

As (64) is of degree $h + 1$ in α and (63) is only of degree h, (64) will exceed (63) for α large. This, we know from §23, implies the existence of a nonzero d.p. of Ω in w and the u alone, of order not exceeding h in w.

This shows that the order in w of the resolvent does not exceed h. Suppose that the order of A in w is $k < h$. For (47), we have relations

$$y_i = \frac{C_i}{D_i} \tag{65}$$

where the C and D are d.p. in w and the u, of order not exceeding k in w. We obtain from (65) expressions for the y_{ij}, $j = 0, \cdots, r_i - 1$, which are rational in the w_j and u_{ij} with powers of the D for denominators. Using the relation $A = 0$, we depress the orders in w of the numerators until they do not exceed k. The transformed expressions will have denominators which are power products of S and the D.

By an elimination, we obtain a nonzero d.p. W in the u and y which belongs to Ω, hence to Σ. This W, which is of order less than r_i in each y_i, is reduced with respect to (46). This is impossible.

We have thus proved that the order in w of every resolvent is h.

35. Let Σ be as in §34, except that we waive the condition that resolvents exist.

If we consider any $h + 1$ of the y_{ij}, the elimination process of §34 shows that Σ contains a nonzero d.p. which, in addition to those y_{ij}, involves only the u and their derivatives.[40] Thus, *if $\mathfrak{M}$ is the manifold of Σ, there exist h of the y_{ij} such that no algebraic relation among those y_{ij} and any set of u_{ij} holds throughout*

[40] The statement which follows is an informal one, whose meaning is clear.

$\mathfrak{M}$, whereas, given any $h + 1$ of the y_{ij}, an algebraic relation holds throughout $\mathfrak{M}$ for those y_{ij} and certain u_{ij}.

The quantity h will be called the *order* of Σ (or of $\mathfrak{M}$) *relative to* $u_1, \cdots, u_q$. When $q = 0$, we call h the *order* of Σ.

The two numbers q and h measure the extensiveness of $\mathfrak{M}$. In the analytic case, we may think of q as the number of arbitrary functions which figure in $\mathfrak{M}$, and of h as the number of arbitrary constants at one's disposal when the arbitrary functions are selected. This can be seen from §10.

The relative order depends, as one would expect, on the choice of the u. For instance, the manifold of $y_{11} - y_2$ is irreducible. If we let $u_1 = y_2$ we have $h = 1$. If $u_1 = y_1$, $h = 0$.

If $\mathfrak{F}$ consists purely of constants and if $\mathfrak{F}_1$ is secured from $\mathfrak{F}$ by the adjunction of an element x of derivative unity, the prime ideal Σ_1 of d.p. over $\mathfrak{F}_1$ which Σ generates has the same parametric sets and the same relative orders as Σ. This is because a characteristic set of Σ is also one of Σ_1.[41]

Embedded manifolds[42]

36. Theorem: *Let Σ and Σ' be nontrivial prime ideals, with Σ' a proper divisor of Σ, of the respective dimensions q and q'. Then $q \geqq q'$. If $q = q'$, every parametric set $u_1, \cdots, u_q$ for Σ' is such a set for Σ and the order of Σ' relative to $u_1, \cdots, u_q$ is less than that of Σ.*[43]

To show that $q \geqq q'$, we observe that Σ, which is contained in Σ', can have no d.p. in the $u_1, \cdots, u_{q'}$ of a parametric set for Σ'. Thus we can build a parametric set for Σ starting with $u_1, \cdots, u_{q'}$.

Suppose now that $q = q'$. By the final remark of §35, we may suppose, even if $q = 0$, that resolvents exist for Σ and Σ'.

We can build resolvents simultaneously for Σ and Σ', using a single relation

$$w = \mu_1 y_1 + \cdots + \mu_p y_p.$$

The μ and G which serve for Σ will serve also for Σ', because the manifold of Σ' is part of that of Σ. For Σ we obtain an Ω, and for Σ' an Ω' which is a proper divisor of Ω. Let

$$A, A_1, \cdots, A_p; A', A_1', \cdots, A_p'$$

be characteristic sets of Ω and Ω' respectively. As A is in Ω', A' is not of higher order in w than A. Suppose that A' is of the same order in w as A. By §13, A is divisible by A'. The algebraic irreducibility of A and A' implies that $A = cA'$ with c in $\mathfrak{F}$. This implies that $A, A_1, \cdots, A_p$ is a characteristic set for Ω' as well as for Ω. Now a prime ideal is the totality of those d.p. which have zero remainders with respect to one of its characteristic sets. Thus Ω'

---

[41] A d.p. in Σ_1 which is a polynomial in x has coefficients in Σ. (I, §29).

[42] Gourin, 5.

[43] If $q = 0$, Σ' is of lower order than Σ.

and Ω are identical. This contradiction shows that A' is of lower order in w than A. The theorem is proved.

When $q = q'$, not every parametric set for Σ need be such a set for Σ'. Let $\Sigma = \{ y_{10}y_{20} + y_{11} \}$. Either y_1 or y_2 is a parametric set. If $\Sigma' = \{ y_1 \}$, y_2 is parametric and y_1 is not.

Prime ideals and field extensions

37. Let Σ be a nontrivial prime ideal. Let $\mathfrak{F}_1$ be an extension of $\mathfrak{F}$ and Σ' the ideal of d.p. over $\mathfrak{F}_1$ which Σ generates. We are going to show that Σ' is perfect and we shall discuss the essential prime divisors of Σ'.

Let us suppose first that Σ is of dimension $q > 0$, with a parametric set $u_1, \cdots, u_q$. We build a resolvent for Σ, using a d.p.

$$w - \mu_1 y_1 - \cdots - \mu_p y_p. \tag{66}$$

Let

$$A, A_1, \cdots, A_p \tag{67}$$

be a characteristic set of Ω, with $A = 0$, of order r in w, a resolvent for Σ.

Suppose now that the irreducible factors of A over $\mathfrak{F}_1$ are $B_1, \cdots, B_s$. Then each B_i is of order r in w. Otherwise, the coefficients of the powers of w_r in A, having a common factor over $\mathfrak{F}_1$, would have one over $\mathfrak{F}$ and A would not be algebraically irreducible.

We consider some B_j. Let its general solution have a generic point

$$\tau_1, \cdots, \tau_q; \xi. \tag{68}$$

We now examine any A_i in (67), denoting its initial by I_i. It cannot be that I_i vanishes for (68). Otherwise I_i, being of order not greater than r in w, would be divisible by B_j. Thus A and I_i would have a common factor over $\mathfrak{F}_1$, hence one over $\mathfrak{F}$. This is impossible because I_i is of lower rank than A. Thus the equation $A_i = 0$, when w and the u are as in (68), determines y_i as a quantity η_i in the extension of $\mathfrak{F}_1$ which contains (68).

We consider the quantities

$$\tau_1, \cdots, \tau_q; \xi; \eta_1, \cdots, \eta_p. \tag{69}$$

The totality Ω_j of d.p. over $\mathfrak{F}_1$ which vanish for (69) is easily seen to be a prime ideal. We shall prove that Ω_j contains Ω.

To take care of a point which arises later, let us start with any d.p. G over $\mathfrak{F}_1$. Let H be the remainder of G with respect to

$$A_1, \cdots, A_p.$$

For some a, if S is the separant of A,

$$S^a H \equiv K, \qquad [A],$$

where K is of order not higher than r in w.

Suppose now that G is in Ω. Then K is divisible by A and hence by B_j. Thus K vanishes for (68). Now S does not vanish for (68); if it did, S would be divisible by B_j and would have a factor over $\mathfrak{F}$ in common with A. Then G vanishes for (69) and is in Ω_j. Thus Ω_j contains Ω.

Let Ω' be the ideal of d.p. over $\mathfrak{F}_1$ which Ω generates. Because a d.p. in Ω goes over into one in Σ when w is replaced by $\mu_1 y_1 + \cdots + \mu_p y_p$, those d.p. of Ω' which are free of w constitute Σ'. Each Ω_j contains Ω'. Let G be any nonzero d.p. which is contained in each Ω_j. Let K be found from G as above. Then K is divisible by each B_j, and hence by A. Thus $S^a H$ is in Ω'. Then some JG, with $J = S^a I_1^{a_1} \cdots I_p^{a_p}$, is in Ω'. Let G be written, as in I, §28, in the form

$$\gamma_1 C_1 + \cdots + \gamma_m C_m \tag{70}$$

with the C d.p. over $\mathfrak{F}$ and the γ linearly independent with respect to $\mathfrak{F}$. When we multiply by J in (70), we get a d.p. in Ω'. Hence each JC_i is in Ω. Then each C_i is in Ω and G is in Ω'. Thus Ω' is the intersection of the Ω_j.

On this basis, if Σ_j is the prime ideal consisting of those d.p. in Ω_j which are free of w, Σ' is the intersection of $\Sigma_1, \cdots, \Sigma_s$. Thus Σ' is perfect.

No Ω_j contains any Ω_i with $i \neq j$; if it did, B_i would be divisible by B_j. Now Ω_j is the ideal of d.p. over $\mathfrak{F}_1$ generated by Σ_j and the d.p. in (66). Thus none of the Σ_i contains any other, and the Σ_i are the essential prime divisors of Σ'.

Consider some Σ_j. If it contained a d.p. G in the u alone, G would vanish for the τ in (68). Thus each Σ_j is of dimension q, with the same parametric sets as Σ. One can see now that $B_j = 0$ is a resolvent for Σ_j. Thus the order of Σ_j relative to any parametric set equals that of Σ.

Suppose now that $q = 0$. We adjoin a new indeterminate u. Σ generates a prime ideal Λ of d.p. in u and the y (I, §27). Λ is of dimension unity, with u as a parametric set and with an order relative to u equal to the order of Σ.[44] Let Λ' be the ideal of d.p. over $\mathfrak{F}_1$ generated by Λ. Then Σ' consists of those d.p. in Λ' which are free of u. Let the essential prime divisors of Λ' be $\Lambda_1, \cdots, \Lambda_s$. If Σ_j is the prime ideal composed of those d.p. in Λ_j which are free of u, Λ_j contains the prime ideal Ξ_j in $\mathfrak{F}_1\{u; y_1, \cdots, y_n\}$ generated by Σ_j. As Σ_j is a divisor of Σ', Ξ_j is a divisor of Λ'. This means that $\Lambda_j = \Xi_j$. Then no Σ_j contains any Σ_i with $i \neq j$, and the Σ_j are the essential prime divisors of Σ'. As the order of any Σ_j equals that of Λ_j relative to u, each Σ_j has the same order as Σ.

We summarize. *Let Σ be a nontrivial prime ideal of dimension q, and Σ' the ideal of d.p. over $\mathfrak{F}_1$, an extension of $\mathfrak{F}$, generated by Σ. Then Σ' is perfect and each of its essential prime divisors Σ_j, $j = 1, \cdots, s$, is of dimension q. If $q > 0$, every parametric set for Σ is such a set for every Σ_j and the orders of the Σ_j relative to such a set all equal that of Σ. If $q = 0$, every Σ_j has the same order as Σ.*[45]

---

[44] A characteristic set of Σ is one for Λ.

[45] A.D.E., Chapter VI, and Kolchin, 13.

Adjunctions to fields[46]

38. Let $\mathfrak{F}$ be a field and $\mathfrak{F}_1$ an extension of $\mathfrak{F}$. Let σ be any set of elements of $\mathfrak{F}_1$. There exist fields which are contained in $\mathfrak{F}_1$ and contain $\mathfrak{F}$ and σ. The intersection of all such fields is a field which will be denoted by $\mathfrak{F}<\sigma>$ and will be called the *field obtained by the adjunction of σ to $\mathfrak{F}$*. $\mathfrak{F}<\sigma>$ consists of all rational combinations of elements of σ, and of derivatives of such elements, with coefficients in $\mathfrak{F}$.

A quantity η lying in an extension of $\mathfrak{F}$ will be said to be *differential with respect to* $\mathfrak{F}$ if η annuls a nonzero d.p. in one indeterminate over $\mathfrak{F}$.

Theorem: *Let $\mathfrak{F}$ contain a nonconstant element. Let $\eta_1, \cdots, \eta_n$ be elements lying in an extension of $\mathfrak{F}$, each differential with respect to $\mathfrak{F}$. The field $\mathfrak{F}<\eta_1, \cdots, \eta_n>$ contains an element ξ such that*

$$\mathfrak{F}<\eta_1, \cdots, \eta_n> = \mathfrak{F}<\xi>.$$

Let Σ be the set of those d.p. in $\mathfrak{F}\{y_1, \cdots, y_n\}$ which vanish for $y_i = \eta_i$, $i = 1, \cdots, n$. Then Σ is a prime ideal of dimension zero. We form a resolvent for Σ, using a d.p. as in (66) with $p = n$. Let $\xi = \Sigma\, \mu_i\eta_i$. Consider the initial I_i of some A_i in (67). If I_i vanished for ξ and the η, I_i would go over into a d.p. in Σ when w is replaced by the sum of the $\mu_i y_i$; thus I_i would be in Ω. It follows that each η_i is contained in $\mathfrak{F}<\xi>$. This proves the theorem.

Analogue of Lüroth's theorem

39. Let $\mathfrak{F}$ be any field and u an indeterminate. The totality of rational combinations of the u_i, with coefficients in $\mathfrak{F}$, is a field which, by §38, it is proper to call $\mathfrak{F}<u>$.

We prove the following theorem.

Theorem: *Let $\mathfrak{F}'$ be any extension of $\mathfrak{F}$ which is contained in $\mathfrak{F}<u>$. Then $\mathfrak{F}'$ contains an element v such that $\mathfrak{F}<v> = \mathfrak{F}'$.*[47]

This theorem is analogous to a well known theorem on algebraic fields which is equivalent to Lüroth's theorem on the parametrization of unicursal curves.[48]

40. Every element of $\mathfrak{F}<u>$ can be written in various ways in the form P/R with P and R in $\mathfrak{F}\{u\}$. We shall write $F(u)$ for a d.p. F in u, irrespective of the number of derivatives of u which appear in F.

Lemma: *Let P, Q, R be in $\mathfrak{F}\{u\}$, with R not zero. Let the relation*

$$\frac{P(\eta)}{R(\eta)} = \frac{P(\tau)}{R(\tau)}, \tag{71}$$

where η and τ lie in the same extension of $\mathfrak{F}$ and do not annul R, imply the relation

---

[46] Kolchin, 12.

[47] A.D.E., Chapter VIII, and Kolchin, 12.

[48] van der Waerden, *Moderne Algebra*, vol. 1, p. 126.

$$\frac{Q(\eta)}{R(\eta)} = \frac{Q(\tau)}{R(\tau)}. \tag{72}$$

Then $Q(u)/R(u)$ is contained in the field obtained by adjoining $P(u)/R(u)$ to $\mathfrak{F}$.

If $Q(u)/R(u)$ is an element of $\mathfrak{F}$, the conclusion holds in a trivial way. If $P(u)/R(u)$ is an element of $\mathfrak{F}$, (71) holds when η and τ are indeterminates. Then (72) holds when η and τ are indeterminates and Q/R is in $\mathfrak{F}$. In what follows, we assume that neither P/R nor Q/R is in $\mathfrak{F}$.

Let F be a d.p. in $\mathfrak{F}\{u, y, z\}$. For the substitution $y = P(u)/R(u)$, $z = Q(u)/R(u)$, F becomes an element of $\mathfrak{F}<u>$. There exist d.p. in $\mathfrak{F}\{u, y, z\}$, for instance, 0, which vanish for the indicated substitution. The totality Σ of such d.p. is a prime ideal.

We show first that Σ contains no d.p. in y alone. Let such a d.p. G exist. Let P/R be written P_1/R_1 with P_1 and R_1 relatively prime as polynomials in the u_i. We consider the algebraically irreducible d.p. $K = P_1(u) - yR_1(u)$. Let $u = \tau$, $y = \eta$ be a generic point in the general solution of K. R is not annulled by τ. Hence $G(\eta) = 0$. This contradicts the fact that no nonzero d.p. in y alone holds the general solution of K, and our statement is proved. Similarly, Σ contains no nonzero d.p. in z alone.

A generic zero of Σ satisfies the relations $y = P(u)/R(u)$, $z = Q(u)/R(u)$. With an elimination, we find that Σ contains a d.p. in y and z alone.

For the order y, z, u, let Z, U be a characteristic set of Σ with Z algebraically irreducible. Here y is parametric, Z introduces z and U introduces u. We claim that Z is of order zero in z and linear in z. The justification of this claim will amount to the proof of our lemma.

We denote the order of Z in z by r. Let $y = \eta$, $z = \zeta$, $u = \tau$ be a generic zero of Σ. In Z, we replace y by η, securing a d.p. Z_1 in $\mathfrak{F}<\eta>\{z\}$, of order r in z. Let Z_1 be factored in $\mathfrak{F}<\eta, \zeta, \tau>$, and let Z_2 be one of those irreducible factors of Z_1 which are of order r in z. Let ζ' be a generic point in the general solution of Z_2.

We shall show that η, ζ', which annuls Z, is a generic point in the general solution of Z. It will suffice to show that η, ζ' annuls no d.p. B which is reduced with respect to Z. On the one hand, this will show that η, ζ' does not annul the separant of Z, and is therefore in the general solution. On the other hand, it will prove that a d.p. whose remainder with respect to Z is not zero cannot vanish for η, ζ'. We shall know thus that the only d.p. which vanish for η, ζ' are those which hold the general solution of Z.

Let η, ζ' annul a B as above. By §28, some linear combination C of B and Z is reduced with respect to Z and free of z_r. As η, ζ' cannot annul C, it cannot annul B.

Thus, if we substitute η, ζ' into U, we obtain a d.p. U_1 in u whose order in u is the same as that of U. Let s be that common order. We factor U_1 in $\mathfrak{F}<\eta, \zeta, \tau, \zeta'>$. Let U_2 be one of those irreducible factors of U_1 which are of order s in u and let τ' be a generic point in the general solution of U_2.

We say that η, ζ', τ' is a generic zero of Σ. For this, it suffices to show that η, ζ', τ' annuls no C which is reduced with respect to Z, U. Given such a C, some linear combination of Z, U, and C is, by §28, reduced with respect to Z, U and free of u_s. The proof is now easily completed.

We see now that $\zeta' = \zeta$. Otherwise τ and τ', which do not annul R, would produce the same P/R and two distinct Q/R.

We find as in §§29, 30 that $r = 0$ and that Z is linear in z.

41. There exist d.p. in $\mathfrak{F}'\{ y \}$ which vanish for $y = u$. For instance, if $P(u)/R(u)$ is an element of $\mathfrak{F}'$, we can use

$$P(y) - \frac{P(u)}{R(u)} R(y). \tag{73}$$

The totality Σ of such d.p. is a prime ideal. Clearly $y = u$ is a generic zero of Σ. We shall prove that the manifold of Σ is the general solution of a d.p. of the type (73).

We know that the manifold of Σ is the general solution of some d.p. B (§18). We suppose each coefficient in B to be written as the ratio of two d.p. in $\mathfrak{F}\{ u \}$. Multiplying B by a suitable element of $\mathfrak{F}\{ u \}$, we obtain a d.p. C in $\mathfrak{F}\{u, y\}$ which is not divisible by any d.p. in $\mathfrak{F}\{ u \}$ actually involving one or more u_i. If C is arranged as a polynomial in the y_i, the ratio of any two of its coefficients will be in $\mathfrak{F}'$.

42. There must be a pair of coefficients, $P(u)$ and $R(u)$, in C, whose ratio is not an element of $\mathfrak{F}$. Otherwise, we could secure from C a d.p. in $\mathfrak{F}\{ y \}$ vanishing for $y = u$. Let

$$D = R(u)P(y) - P(u)R(y). \tag{74}$$

We are going to show that D is the product of C by an element of $\mathfrak{F}$.

Let $E = D/R(u)$. We consider E as a d.p. in $\mathfrak{F}'\{ y \}$. Then E vanishes for $y = u$ and so is in Σ. Hence, if S_1 is the separant of B, there is a relation

$$S_1^a E \equiv 0, \qquad [B]. \tag{75}$$

From (75), if we represent the separant of C for the order u, y by S, we secure a relation

$$FS^a D \equiv 0, \qquad [C], \tag{76}$$

with F in $\mathfrak{F}\{ u \}$. Let

$$C = G_1 \cdots G_p \tag{77}$$

be a resolution of C into factors which are algebraically irreducible in $\mathfrak{F}$. Each G involves y. Let r be the order of C in y. We say that each G is of order r in y. Suppose that G_1 is of order $s < r$ in y. Then, when C is arranged as a polynomial in y_r, each coefficient is divisible by G_1. Let B above be arranged as a polynomial in y_r. Let $H_1, \cdots, H_t$ be the coefficients in B. The H, considered as polynomials in $y_1, \cdots, y_{r-1}$, are relatively prime. Hence, there is a relation[49]

$$(78) \qquad M_1H_1 + \cdots + M_tH_t = N$$

where N and the M are polynomials in $y_1, \cdots, y_{r-1}$ and where N is distinct from zero and free of y_s. We can obtain from (78) a relation which shows that the coefficients of the powers of y_r in C are not divisible by a d.p. of order s in y.

No two of the G in (77) have a ratio which is an element of $\mathfrak{F}$. Otherwise S would have a factor in common with C. As above, we see that this is impossible for the reason that S_1 has no factor in common with B. By §13, no G_i holds the general solution of a G_j with $j \neq i$.

We wish to show that D holds the general solution of each G. This will follow from (76) if we can show that S holds no such general solution. For this, we observe first that S is of order not more than r in y. As S has no factor in common with C, S is not divisible by any G.

Let s be the order of C in u. By (74) the order s' of D in u does not exceed s. Let $G_1, \cdots, G_m$ be those G which are of order s in u. As $s' \leqq s$ and as D holds the general solutions of $G_1, \cdots, G_m$, it must be that $s' = s$ and that D is divisible by each G_i with $i \leqq m$.[50] Then let

$$(79) \qquad D = KG_1 \cdots G_m.$$

The degree of $G_1 \cdots G_m$ in u_s is that of C. As, by (74), D has a degree in u_s which does not exceed that of C, K is of order less than s in u.

Let $G_{m+1}, \cdots, G_{m'}$ be those G which are of order $s - 1$ in u. Their general solutions are held by D but by no G_i with $i \leqq m$. Thus K holds the general solutions and is divisible by $G_{m+1} \cdots G_{m'}$.

If C and D are arranged as power products in the u_i and if such power products are ordered as in I, §22, the highest product in D will not be higher than that in C. It follows from (77) and (79) that

$$K = LG_{m+1} \cdots G_{m'}$$

with L of order less than $s - 1$ in u. Continuing, we find D to be the product of C by a d.p. $M(y)$ in $\mathfrak{F}\{ y \}$. M has to be an element of $\mathfrak{F}$. Otherwise, D, by its symmetry, would be divisible by $M(u)$ and $M(u)$ would be a factor of C.[51]

43. Let T be the d.p. in $\mathfrak{F}'\{ y \}$ obtained by dividing D by $R(u)$. Then T is of type (73) and is the product of B by an element of $\mathfrak{F}'$.

Let $v = P(u)/R(u)$. We are going to prove that $\mathfrak{F}' = \mathfrak{F}\langle v \rangle$.

Let $U(u)/V(u)$ be any element of $\mathfrak{F}'$. We shall show that $U(u)/V(u)$ is in $\mathfrak{F}\langle v \rangle$. Let

---

[49] Perron, *Lehrbuch der Algebra*, vol. 1, p. 204.

[50] The remainder of D with respect to G_i for the order y, u is zero.

[51] It is easy now to prove that the G are all of order r in u.

$$W = U(y) - \frac{U(u)}{V(u)} V(y).$$

Then W is in Σ. If S_1 is the separant of T, there is a relation

$$S_1^a W \equiv 0, \qquad [T].$$

This gives

$$XS^a[V(u)U(y) - U(u)V(y)] \equiv 0, \qquad [D],$$

with X in $\mathfrak{F}\{ u \}$ and S the separant of D. Let $u = \tau$, $y = \eta$ be a zero of D. We suppose that $X(\tau)R(\tau) \neq 0$. Let τ, η annul S. Then, if

$$Y = P'(y)R(y) - R'(y)P(y),$$

where $P' = \partial P/\partial y_r$ and $R' = \partial R/\partial y_r$, η annuls Y. We shall show that $Y(y)$ is not zero. As C is not divisible by a d.p. in u alone, D is not. Hence P and R are relatively prime. If, for instance, R' is not zero, R' is not divisible by R. Thus $Y(y)$ is not zero. If $Y(\eta) \neq 0$, τ, η annuls $V(u)U(y) - U(u)V(y)$.

We now write $P(u)/R(u)$ and $U(u)/V(u)$ with a common denominator $RVXY$. Applying the lemma of §40, we find that U/V is rational in P/R and its derivatives. This proves the theorem of §39.

44. Let w be any element of $\mathfrak{F}'$ such that $\mathfrak{F}\langle w\rangle = \mathfrak{F}'$. We seek a relation between w and the v found above. The totality of those d.p. in $\mathfrak{F}\{ y, z \}$ which vanish for $y = v$, $z = w$ is a prime ideal Σ whose manifold is the general solution of a d.p. F (§33). As w has an expression rational in v and its derivatives, Σ contains a d.p. which is of order zero in z and linear in z. F must be such a d.p. Similarly, F is of zero order in y and linear in y. This means that $w = (\alpha v + \beta)/(\gamma v + \delta)$ where α, β, γ, δ are elements of $\mathfrak{F}$.

45. From the theorem of §39, it follows that if v and w are elements of $\mathfrak{F}\langle u\rangle$, that is, quotients of two d.p. in u, there exists a quotient t of two d.p. in u such that v and w are rational in t and its derivatives while t is rational in v, w and their derivatives. This result parallels Lüroth's theorem on unicursal curves.

CHAPTER III

STRUCTURE OF DIFFERENTIAL POLYNOMIALS

I. Manifold of a Differential Polynomial

Theorem on dimension of components

1. If F is an algebraically irreducible d.p. in $\mathfrak{F}\{y_1, \cdots, y_n\}$, the dimension of the general solution of F is $n - 1$. One might inquire as to the dimensions of the other components of F (II, §3). This question is answered by the following theorem:

THEOREM: *Let F be a differential polynomial*[1] *of positive class in $\mathfrak{F}\{y_1, \cdots, y_n\}$. Every component of F is of dimension $n - 1$.*

From II, §33, it follows that *every component of F is the general solution of a differential polynomial.*

2. Let the essential prime divisors of $\{F\}$ be $\Sigma_1, \cdots, \Sigma_s$. We have to show that every Σ_i is of dimension $n - 1$. Consider some Σ_j and let $\eta_1, \cdots, \eta_n$ be a generic zero of Σ_j. We shall show that $\eta_1, \cdots, \eta_n$ is a zero of some Σ_i of dimension $n - 1$. Any such Σ_i must be contained in Σ_j and must therefore be identical with Σ_j. This will prove that Σ_j is of dimension $n - 1$.

3. We use new indeterminates $z_1, \cdots, z_n$. In F, we replace each y_i by $z_i + \eta_i$. Then F goes over into a d.p. K in $\mathfrak{F}_0\{z_1, \cdots, z_n\}$ where $\mathfrak{F}_0$ is $\mathfrak{F}\langle\eta_1, \cdots, \eta_n\rangle$. K vanishes when each z_i is replaced by 0.

4. Now let W be the sum of the terms of lowest degree in K considered as a polynomial in the z_{ij}. Let V be a factor of W, algebraically irreducible in $\mathfrak{F}_0$. Changing subscripts if necessary, we shall assume that V involves z_1 effectively. Let $\zeta_1, \cdots, \zeta_n$ be a generic point in the general solution of V and let $\mathfrak{F}_1$ represent $\mathfrak{F}_0\langle\zeta_1, \cdots, \zeta_n\rangle$.

Arbitrary constants

5. We shall explain now what is to be meant by the term *arbitrary constant.* At each stage of our work we operate in a definite field; thus far we have met $\mathfrak{F}$, $\mathfrak{F}_0$, $\mathfrak{F}_1$. A field having been given, we understand by an arbitrary constant with respect to the field, a quantity c which can be adjoined to the field,[2] which is transcendental with respect to the field (I, §29), and whose derivative is zero.

The polygon process

6. We are going to show that K has a zero

---

[1] Algebraic irreducibility is not necessary.

[2] That is, c lies in an extension of the field.

$$z_i = \zeta_i c, \qquad i = 2, \cdots, n, \tag{1}$$
$$z_1 = \zeta_1 c + \varphi_2 c^{\rho_2} + \cdots + \varphi_k c^{\rho_k} + \cdots.$$

Here the φ are elements of a field $\mathfrak{F}'$ which contains $\mathfrak{F}_1$ while c is an arbitrary constant with respect to $\mathfrak{F}'$. The ρ are rational numbers with a common denominator; they exceed unity and increase with their subscripts.[3]

7. It may be that K vanishes for $z_i = \zeta_i c$, $i = 1, \cdots, n$, where c is an arbitrary constant with respect to $\mathfrak{F}_1$. In that case, the $\zeta_i c$ are suitable expressions (1) with $\mathfrak{F}' = \mathfrak{F}_1$.[4] In what follows, we assume that such vanishing does not occur.

We put in K

$$z_i = \zeta_i c, \qquad i = 2, \cdots, n; \qquad z_1 = \zeta_1 c + u_1. \tag{2}$$

Then K goes over into an expression K' which is a polynomial in c and the u_{1i}. We may write

$$K' = a'(c) + \sum_{i=1}^{p} b_i'(c)\, U_i'. \tag{3}$$

Here $a'(c)$ and the $b'(c)$ are polynomials in c with coefficients in $\mathfrak{F}_1$, p is a positive integer and the U' are power products, of positive degree, in the u_{1i}. We know that $a'(c)$ is not zero. We understand that no $b'(c)$ is zero.

8. Let σ' be the least exponent of c in a' and σ_i' the least exponent of c in b_i'. Let d_i be the total degree of U_i'. Finally, let

$$\rho_2 = \operatorname{Max} \frac{\sigma' - \sigma_i'}{d_i}. \tag{4}$$

We shall prove that $\rho_2 > 1$.

To begin with, if d is the degree of W of §4, $\sigma' > d$ since W is annulled by the ζ. Under (2), the constituent W of K contributes to K' terms which effectively involve one or more u_{1i}.[5] The total degree of any such term in c and the u_{1i} is d. Thus, for at least one i in (3), we have $\sigma_i' + d_i = d$. As $\sigma' > d$, we have then $\sigma' - \sigma_i' > d_i$. Thus $\rho_2 > 1$.

9. Let g' be the coefficient of $c^{\sigma'}$ in a'. Let h'_i denote the coefficient of $c^{\sigma_i'}$, or denote zero, according as $(\sigma' - \sigma_i')/d_i$ equals ρ_2 or is less than ρ_2. Let

$$L'(u_1) = g' + \sum_{=1}^{p} h_i' U_i'. \tag{5}$$

---

[3] The zero (1) will lie in an extension of $\mathfrak{F}'$. How to use formal infinite series, and how the fractional powers of c are to be regarded, will be obvious.

[4] One sees how to go through the formality of building an extension of $\mathfrak{F}'$ which contains the z_i presented.

[5] To see this, it suffices to show that W does not vanish identically for $z_2 = \zeta_2, \cdots, z_n = \zeta_n$. Let W be arranged as a polynomial in the z_{1i}. The coefficients are d.p. in $z_2, \cdots, z_n$ and thus cannot hold the general solution of V, which d.p. involves z_1.

We consider L' as a d.p. in $\mathfrak{F}_1\{ u_1 \}$. Let $\{ L' \}$ have $\Omega_1, \cdots, \Omega_q$ for essential prime divisors. Each Ω_i has a generic zero ψ_i in an extension (depending on i) of $\mathfrak{F}_1$. We select one of the ψ_i in the following manner.

Let L' be of effective degree f in the u_{1i}. Then certain partia derivatives of L', of order f, with respect to the u_{1i}, are elements of $\mathfrak{F}_1$ distinct from zero. Of all positive integers r for which there is a ψ_i which does not annul every partial derivative of L' of order r, let f_1 be the least. We choose a ψ_i which does not annul every partial derivative of order f_1 and designate it by φ_2. Let $\mathfrak{F}_2 = \mathfrak{F}_1 < \varphi_2 >$.

10. From now on we understand that c, used above, is an arbitrary constant with respect to $\mathfrak{F}_2$. It may be that $\varphi_2 c^{\rho_2}$ causes K' to vanish when substituted for u_1. In that case we have suitable expressions (1) with

$$z_1 = \zeta_1 c + \varphi_2 c^{\rho_2}.$$

Let us suppose that the vanishing does not occur.

We make in K' the substitution

(6) $$u_1 = \varphi_2 c^{\rho_2} + u_2.$$

Then K' goes over into an expression K'' in c and u_2 which may be written

(7) $$K'' = a''(c) + \sum b_i''(c)\, U_i''.$$

Here a'' and the b'' are sums in which each term is the product of a rational power of c and an element of $\mathfrak{F}_2$. We know that $a'' \neq 0$, and we assume that no b'' vanishes. The sums $\sum$ in (3) and in (7) do not necessarily involve the same power products.

Let σ'' be the least exponent of c in a''; σ_i'' the least exponent in b_i''; d_i the degree of U_i''. Let

(8) $$\rho_3 = \operatorname{Max} \frac{\sigma'' - \sigma_i''}{d_i}.$$

We are going to prove that $\rho_3 > \rho_2$.

Using an indeterminate v, we replace u_1 in K' by $c^{\rho_2} v$. The ith term of $\sum$ in (3) will produce a set of terms, each of the type $\beta c^q T$, where T is a power product in the v_i,[6] β an element of $\mathfrak{F}_1$, and where

(9) $$q \geqq \sigma_i' + \rho_2 d_i.$$

By (4), $q \geqq \sigma'$. We will have $q = \sigma'$ only if β is an h' in (5). On this basis, we may write

(10) $$K'(c^{\rho_2} v) = c^{\sigma'} L'(v) + c^{\tau'} M'(c, v),$$

where, in regard to L', M', τ', the following statements apply.

L' is as in (5) with u_1 replaced by v. M' is a polynomial in the v_i with co-

---

[6] T is the same in all terms and is merely U_i' with u_1 replaced by v.

efficients which are sums of terms, each the product of a nonnegative rational power of c by an element of $\mathfrak{F}_1$. As to τ', which we understand to be taken as large as possible, it is a rational number greater than σ'.

We now put $v = \varphi_2 + c^{-\rho_2} u_2$. Then (10) gives, by (6),

$$K''(u_2) = c^{\sigma'}L'(\varphi_2 + c^{-\rho_2}u_2) + c^{\tau'}M'(c, \varphi_2 + c^{-\rho_2}u_2). \tag{11}$$

Let K' be of order r in u_1. Suppose that, for some set of nonnegative integers $l_0, \cdots, l_r$,

$$\frac{\partial^{l_0 + \cdots + l_r} L'(u_1)}{\partial^{l_0} u_{10} \cdots \partial^{l_r} u_{1r}} \tag{12}$$

does not vanish for $u_1 = \varphi_2$. This implies that at least one l is positive. Let $Z = u_{20}^{l_0} \cdots u_{2r}^{l_r}$. We shall prove that Z is present in $\sum$ in (7) and we shall determine the σ_i'' associated with that power product.

The coefficient of any $u_{20}^{l_0} \cdots u_{2r}^{l_r}$ in the second member of (11), whether (12) vanishes for it or not, is the quotient by $l_0! \cdots l_r!$ of

$$c^{\sigma' - \rho_2\lambda}L'_{l_0 \cdots l_r}(\varphi_2) + c^{\tau' - \rho_2\lambda}M'_{l_0 \cdots l_r}(c, \varphi_2) \tag{13}$$

where $\lambda = l_0 + \cdots + l_r$; $L'_{l_0 \cdots l_r}$ is (12) with u_1 replaced by φ_2; $M'_{l_0 \cdots l_r}$ is obtained by the same differentiation and substitution from $M'(c, u_1)$.

The assumption that (12) does not vanish for $u_1 = \varphi_2$ implies that Z is present in (7). The associated σ_i'' is given by

$$\sigma_i'' = \sigma' - \rho_2\lambda = \sigma' - \rho_2 d_i. \tag{14}$$

On the other hand, if φ_2 annuls (12) and if Z is present in (7), we have

$$\sigma_i'' > \sigma' - \rho_2 d_i. \tag{15}$$

We can now study ρ_3 in (8). We have, for every i,

$$\frac{\sigma'' - \sigma_i''}{d_i} = \frac{\sigma'' - \sigma'}{d_i} + \frac{\sigma' - \sigma_i''}{d_i}. \tag{16}$$

By (14) and (15) we have

$$\frac{\sigma' - \sigma_i''}{d_i} = \rho_2 \tag{17}$$

or

$$\frac{\sigma' - \sigma_i''}{d_i} < \rho_2, \tag{18}$$

according as (12) with suitable l does not vanish or does vanish. From (17) and (18) we see that $(\sigma' - \sigma_i'')/d_i$ is a maximum, namely ρ_2, for those i for which (12) does not vanish. Such i exist, as was seen in connection with the stipulation made in regard to φ_2 in §9.

From (13) with every l zero, we see now that $\sigma'' > \sigma'$. Turning now to (16), we see that there are i for which the first member of (16) exceeds ρ_2.

This proves that $\rho_3 > \rho_2$.

11. We now form for K'' a d.p. L'' analogous to (5) and obtain a zero φ_3 of L'' in the manner followed for φ_2. In this, we consider L'' as a d.p. in $\mathfrak{F}_2\{u_2\}$.

We continue this procedure. It may be that at some stage we reach a $K^{(k-1)}$ which is annulled by $\varphi_k c^{\rho_k}$. In that case

$$z_1 = \zeta_1 c + \varphi_2 c^{\rho_2} + \cdots + \varphi_k c^{\rho_k} \tag{19}$$

is suitable for (1). We suppose in what follows that our procedure does not terminate in a finite number of steps, so that we are led to form an infinite series

$$z_1 = \zeta_1 c + \varphi_2 c^{\rho_2} + \cdots. \tag{20}$$

We shall then be working in a field $\mathfrak{F}'$ which is the union of all $\mathfrak{F}_i$ and we understand c to be an arbitrary constant with respect to $\mathfrak{F}'$.

We shall prove that the ρ_k have a common denominator. This will imply that the ρ_k become infinite with k. It will be seen also that the z_i of (1) annul K.

12. We begin by showing that the degrees of the $L^{(k)}$ as polynomials in the u_{ki} do not increase with k. Let us compare the degree of L' with that of L''. Let f, and $f_1 \leqq f$, be as in the stipulation of §9 relative to φ_2, with f the degree of L'.

In (16), $(\sigma'' - \sigma')/d_i$ is less for $d_i > f_1$ than for $d_i \leqq f_1$. On the other hand, $(\sigma' - \sigma_i'')/d_i$ obtains its maximum value ρ_2 for some d_i equal to f_1. This shows that the first member of (16) cannot be as great as ρ_3 for $d_i > f_1$. Referring now to the description of the coefficients in (5), which description is similar to that of the coefficients in L'', we see that the degree of L'' does not exceed f_1.

Thus there is a positive integer e such that, for $k \geqq e$, the $L^{(k)}$ are all of the same degree, say m. Consider any $k \geqq e$, the corresponding $L^{(k)}$, and the partial derivatives of all orders of $L^{(k)}$ with respect to the u_{ki}. We shall prove that if R is any such derivative of order less than m, R is in $\{L^{(k)}(u_k)\}$.[7] Let $\{L^{(k)}\}$ have the essential prime divisors $\Omega_1, \cdots, \Omega_q$. If one refers to the stipulation made in regard to the various φ_i (§9), and considers that the degree of $L^{(k+1)}$ equals that of $L^{(k)}$, one sees that R is annulled by a generic zero of every Ω_i. Thus R is in every Ω_i and so in $\{L^{(k)}\}$.

Let, now, R be a partial derivative of $L^{(k)}$ of order $m - 1$, distinct from zero. Then R is linear in the u_{ki}. Let $L^{(k)}$ be decomposed into factors over $\mathfrak{F}_k$ which are algebraically irreducible. Let Z be an irreducible factor of the same order in u_k as $L^{(k)}$. Then R is in $\{Z\}$ so that the remainder of R with respect to Z is zero. As the order of R in u_k does not exceed that of Z, R is divisible by Z. As R is linear, Z is the product of R by an element of $\mathfrak{F}_k$. We have thus, for some g,

$$L^{(k)} = QR^g \tag{21}$$

where Q, except perhaps in the case in which it is an element of $\mathfrak{F}_k$, has an order which is less than the common order, call it h, of $L^{(k)}$ and R in u_k. We have

[7] We work in $\mathfrak{F}_k\{u_k\}$.

$$\frac{\partial^g L^{(k)}}{\partial u_{kh}^g} = \mu Q$$

with μ in $\mathfrak{F}_k$. As μQ is reduced with respect to R, it is not in $\{ R \}$ and thus not in $\{ L^{(k)} \}$. It follows that g in (21) equals m, so that

$$L^{(k)} = \lambda R^m \tag{22}$$

with λ in $\mathfrak{F}_k$.

In the expression for $L^{(k)}$ analogous to (5), there is a term like g' in (5), free of the u_{ki}. This means that R has such a term, so that, by (22), $L^{(k)}$ has terms of the first degree. Thus, in the equation of definition of ρ_{k+1} analogous to (4), there will be, among those i which give a maximum, certain i for which $d_i = 1$. In other words, the denominator of ρ_{k+1} can be taken as the common denominator of $\sigma^{(k)}$ and the $\sigma_i^{(k)}$. For that common denominator, we can use that of $\rho_2, \cdots, \rho_k$.

This shows that the ρ_k have a common denominator, so that they approach ∞ with k.

13. We have to show now that the expressions in (1), obtained as above, annul K. Because $a^{(k)}$, for any $k > 1$, is the result of performing in K the substitutions

$$(23) \qquad z_i = \zeta_i c, \qquad i = 2, \cdots, n,$$
$$z_1 = \zeta_1 c + \cdots + \varphi_k c^{\rho_k},$$

it suffices to show that $\sigma^{(k)}$ approaches ∞ with k. This is so because the $\sigma^{(k)}$ increase with k and have a common denominator.

Dimensions of components

14. We see now that F of our theorem has a zero

$$(24) \qquad y_i = \eta_i + \zeta_i c, \qquad i = 2, \cdots, n,$$
$$y_1 = \eta_1 + \zeta_1 c + \varphi_2 c^{\rho_2} + \cdots.$$

Then (24) is a zero of some Σ_i of §2, say of Σ_k. We shall prove that Σ_k is of dimension $n - 1$. It will suffice to prove that Σ_k contains no d.p. in $y_2, \cdots, y_n$. Let M be such a d.p. in Σ_k. We replace each y_i in M by $z_i + \eta_i$ Then M goes over into a d.p. N in $\mathfrak{F}_0\{ z_2, \cdots, z_n \}$ which vanishes for $z_i = \zeta_i c$, $i = 2, \cdots, n$. Let P be the sum of the terms of lowest degree in N. Then P vanishes for $z_i = \zeta_i$, $i = 2, \cdots, n$. We have here the contradiction that P, which is free of z_1, holds the general solution of V of §4.

Then Σ_k is of dimension $n - 1$. If, in any d.p. M of Σ_k, we replace each y_i by its expression in (24), the term free of c which is obtained is the result of replacing each y_i in M by η_i. Thus $\eta_1, \cdots, \eta_n$ is a zero of Σ_k. This, as was seen in §2, implies the truth of our theorem.

Degrees of Generality

15. Suppose that F is algebraically irreducible, and let Σ_1, in §2, be the prime ideal associated with the general solution of F. Consider any Σ_i with $i > 1$. The manifold of Σ_i is the general solution of a d.p. A. We say that if y_k *is an indeterminate effectively present in* A, *the order of* F *in* y_k *exceeds that of* A. This follows from the fact that F is in Σ_i, so that, if F were not of higher order in y_k than A, F would be divisible by A and Σ_i would be identical with Σ_1.

II. Low Powers and Singular Solutions

Components

16. Let F be as in §15. We know that the components which F may have in addition to its general solution are general solutions of d.p. $A_1, \cdots, A_p$. There arises the problem of determining the A. More than this, one will desire to know whether the A are visible in some way in the structure of F.

There will be developed, in Chapter V, a method for determining a finite set of algebraically irreducible d.p. whose general solutions make up the manifold of F. However, not all of the general solutions there found need be components of F; it may be that some of them are contained in others of them. The problem of selecting the components is identical with that of determining the influence of the components on the structure of F. It is best formulated as follows, without requiring the algebraic irreducibility of F. *Let* F *and* A *be d.p. in* $\mathfrak{F}\{y_1, \cdots, y_n\}$ *with* A *algebraically irreducible. Let* F *hold the general solution of* A, *that is, let the remainder of* F *with respect to* A *be zero. It is required to determine whether the general solution of* A *is a component of* F. The solution of this problem is contained in the low power theorem presented below.

Preparation Process

17. Let F and A be any two d.p. of class n.[8] Let the orders of F and A in y_n be m and l respectively. Let A_j represent the jth derivative of A, and S the separant of A. We shall show *the existence of a nonnegative integer* t *and of a positive integer* r *such that* S^tF *has a representation*

$$\sum_{j=1}^{r} C_j A^{p_j} A_1^{i_{1j}} A_2^{i_{2j}} \cdots A_{m-l}^{i_{m-l,\,j}} \tag{25}$$

with nonnegative p_j *and* i_{kj}, *where no two of the* r *sets* $i_{1j}, \cdots, i_{m-l,\,j}$ *are identical, the* C_j *being of orders not exceeding* l *in* y_n, *and not divisible by* A.

If $m \leqq l$, we express F in the form CA^p with C not divisible by A and we understand this expression of F to be that which is indicated in (25). In what follows, we assume that $m > l$.

We let z represent y_n and we start with the case of $m = l + 1$. Let F be of degree a in z_{l+1}. Then S^aF can be written as a polynomial in Sz_{l+1} with coefficients whose orders in z do not exceed l. Now

[8] We are not assuming algebraic irreducibility for A.

$$A_1 = Sz_{l+1} + T$$

with the order of T in z at most l. Thus S^aF can be written as a polynomial in $A_1 - T$, and hence as a polynomial in A_1, with coefficients whose orders in z are at most l. If we write each coefficient in the form CA^p, $p \geqq 0$, with C not divisible by A, we have a representation (25) for S^aF.

Suppose now that (25) can be produced for $m < s$ where $s > l + 1$. We make an induction to $m = s$. Let F, of order s in z, be of degree a in z_s. We see as above that S^aF can be written as a polynomial in A_{s-l} with coefficients whose orders in z are less than s. For a sufficiently large positive integer b, the product of any of these coefficients by S^b will have a representation (25). Thus $S^{b+a}F$ has a representation (25).

18. We shall show now that, for any admissible t, (25) is unique. Let S^tF have two distinct representations (25). By a subtraction, we get a relation

$$0 = \sum_{j=1}^{v} D_j A_1^{i_{1j}} \cdots A_{m-l}^{i_{m-l,j}} \tag{26}$$

where the v sets of exponents are distinct and where the D, distinct from zero and of order no more than l in z, may be divisible by A.

We have

$$A_{m-l} = Sz_m + T$$

with T of order less than m in z. In (26), let us replace z_m by $(u - T)/S$ where u is an indeterminate in the customary sense of algebra. Then A_{m-l} is replaced by u in (26). Continuing, we see that (26) holds if the A_j are considered as algebraic indeterminates. This contradicts the fact that the D are not zero.

19. Suppose now that A is algebraically irreducible. We see, because S is not divisible by A, that for two distinct values t_1 and t_2 of t, with $t_2 > t_1$, (25) is the same except that the C for t_2 are those for t_1 multiplied by $S^{t_2 - t_1}$.

By taking t as small as possible, we are led to a unique expression (25). In all that follows, it will be understood that the smallest admissible t is used.

When A and F are both algebraically irreducible, the smallest t can be found as follows. If S is an element of $\mathfrak{F}$, we take $t = 0$. Otherwise, we first secure (25) with any admissible t and then determine the highest power S^q of S which is a factor of every C. As F is algebraically irreducible, S^t must be divisible by S^q. A division by S^q will thus give the unique representation sought.

The low power theorem[9]

20. Let F and A be of class n, of the respective orders m and l in y_n, with A algebraically irreducible. Let F hold the general solution of A. Then there is no term in (25) which is free of A and the A_i. Otherwise some C would hold

---

[9] First proved by the author in paper 31. The analytic sufficiency proof there given is reproduced in Chapter VI. The algebraic sufficiency proof, to be given now, is due to Levi, 17.

the general solution of A. This is impossible since the C are of order at most l in y_n, and not divisible by A. We can now state the

LOW POWER THEOREM: *For the general solution of A to be a component of F, it is necessary and sufficient that* (25) *contain a term $C_k A^{p_k}$, free of proper derivatives of A, which, if* (25) *is considered as a polynomial in $A, A_1, \cdots, A_{m-l}$, is of lower degree than every other term of* (25).[10]

The assumption that F and A are of class n is made only for convenience. Any indeterminate present in A is present in F and may be used as y_n.

The low power theorem is very easily remembered for the case of a single indeterminate y, with $A = y$. It then becomes: *Let F, in $\mathfrak{F}\{y\}$, vanish for $y = 0$. For $y = 0$ to be a component of F, it is necessary and sufficient that F, considered as a polynomial in y and its derivatives, contain a term in y alone, that is, a term free of derivatives of y, which is of lower degree than every other term of F.*

Thus $y = 0$ is a component of $y_1 y_2 - y$, but not of $y y_3 - y_2$ or of $y_2 y_3 - y^2$.

One of the ideas in the sufficiency proof can be seen in a simple example. In $\mathfrak{F}\{y\}$, let $F = y + y_1 y_2$, $A = y$. We have

$$y + y_1 y_2 \equiv 0, \qquad [F].$$

Differentiating, we find

$$y_1 + y_1 y_3 + y_2^2 \equiv 0, \qquad [F],$$

$$y_2 + y_1 y_4 + 3 y_2 y_3 \equiv 0, \qquad [F].$$

The three congruences may be written

$$\begin{aligned} (1 + B_{10})\, y + B_{11}\, & y_1 + B_{12}\, y_2 \equiv 0, \qquad [F], \\ B_{20}\, y + (1 + B_{21})\, & y_1 + B_{22}\, y_2 \equiv 0, \qquad [F], \\ B_{30}\, y + B_{31}\, & y_1 + (1 + B_{32})\, y_2 \equiv 0, \qquad [F], \end{aligned}$$

where the B vanish for $y = 0$. The determinant D of the coefficients of y, y_1, y_2, in the congruences just written, contains unity as a term and is thus not zero. If we solve for y, we find that

$$y D \equiv 0, \qquad [F].$$

Then yD holds F. Thus D holds every component of F which y does not. As D does not vanish for $y = 0$, the manifold of y is not part of any larger irreducible manifold held by F. This makes $y = 0$ a component of F.

The above method can be applied to any d.p. F of the type $y + C$ where the terms of C are of degree at least 2. The pth derivative of F contains y_p. Now, as is easy to see from a consideration of weights, when p is large each term in the pth derivative of C involves a y_i with $i < p$. This leads to a system of congruences of the type met above.

[10] That is, for $j \neq k$, $p_k < p_j + i_{1j} + \cdots + i_{m-l,j}$. If $m = l$, so that (25) has just one term, and that of the type $C_k A^{p_k}$, the condition will be regarded as fulfilled.

For F of the type $y^p + C$ with $p > 1$, further elements of proof are necessary. These are provided by Levi's theory of power products, considered in Chapter I.

We shall now treat the general case.

SUFFICIENCY PROOF

21. Using indeterminates $w, z, u_1, \cdots, u_g$ and the field of rational numbers, we prove the following lemma.

LEMMA: *Let*

$$C = wz^p - \sum_{j=1}^{g} u_j B_j \tag{27}$$

where p is a positive integer and the B are power products, of degree p + 1, in z and its derivatives. There exists a relation

$$z^d(w^s + D) \equiv 0, \qquad [C], \tag{28}$$

with d and s positive integers and with each power product in D of positive degree in the z_j and of degree s in the w_j, u_{ij}.

Let r be the maximum of the weights of the B. If $r = 0$, each B is z^{p+1} and we have immediately a relation (28) with $d = p$ and $s = 1$.[11]

We suppose now that $r > 0$ and refer to I, §21. Let

$$d = r(p - 1) + 1, \qquad t = d(r - 1).$$

We say that every power product in the z_j of degree d and weight not more than t is contained in $[z^p]$. If $p = 1$, this is a trivial statement. Let $p > 1$. In (27) of I, §21, we have, for d as above, $a = r$, $b = 1$. Then

$$f(p, d) = t + r + 1$$

and the truth of our statement follows.

Let $E_1, \cdots, E_\mu$ be the power products of degree d and of weight not more than t. Let p_j be the weight of E_j. Let G represent z^p. Consider the representation of an E_j as a linear combination of the derivatives G_i of G. Each G_i is homogeneous, of degree p, and isobaric, of weight i. On this basis, we cast out, from the representation of E_j, all G_i with $i > p_j$; from the coefficient of a G_i with $i \leq p_j$, we cast out all terms which are not of degree $d - p$ and of weight $p_j - i$. Thus we write, for $j = 1, \cdots, \mu$,

$$E_j = \sum_{k=0}^{p_j} H_{jk} G_k \tag{29}$$

where H_{jk} is either zero or else homogeneous, of degree $d - p$, and isobaric, of weight $p_j - k$.

By (27),

---

[11] The case of $r = 1$ is also trivial.

(30) $$wG \equiv \sum_{j=1}^{g} u_j B_j, \qquad [C].$$

Representing by $(wG)_k$ the kth derivative of wG, we have by (30), for $k = 0, 1, \cdots, t$,

(31) $$(wG)_k \equiv K_k, \qquad [C],$$

where each term in K_k is of the first degree in the u_{ij} and of degree $p + 1$ in the z_j; the $p + 1$ letters z_j in each term have a total weight no more than $r + k$.

By I, §10, we have, for any k,

(32) $$w^{k+1}G_k = \sum_{i=0}^{k} L_{ki}(wG)_i.$$

We may suppose each L_{ki} to be a d.p. in w alone, which is homogeneous, of degree k, and isobaric, of weight $k - i$. By (29) and (32), we have for $j = 1, \cdots, \mu$,

(33) $$w^{t+1}E_j = \sum_{=0}^{p_j} M_{ji}(wG)_i.$$

An M_{ji} which is not zero is homogeneous, of degree t, in the w_k and homogeneous, of degree $d - p$, in the z_k; it is isobaric, of weight $p_j - i$, in all of its letters. By (31) and (33),

(34) $$w^{t+1}E_j \equiv \sum_{i=0}^{p_j} M_{ji}K_i, \qquad [C].$$

If N is a term of some K_i, the total weight of the $p + 1$ letters z_k in N is, as has been noted, no more than $r + i$.

We shall now write (34), with prompt explanations, in the form

(35) $$w^{t+1}E_j \equiv \sum c_\nu P_\nu, \qquad [C].$$

The sum in (35) depends on j. Each c_ν is a rational number. Each P_ν is a power product, which is of the first degree in the u_{lk}, of degree t in the w_k and of degree $d + 1$ in the z_k. The total weight of P_ν in the w_k and z_k is, for some $i \leqq p_j$, not more than

$$(p_j - i) + (r + i) = p_j + r \leqq t + r.$$

Certainly then, the total weight of the $d + 1$ letters z_k in P_ν is no more than $t + r$.

Working with some P_ν, let Q be the product of the $d + 1$ letters z_k in P_ν. Let z_q be the highest derivative of z in Q and let $Q = z_qR$. The weight of R cannot exceed t. Otherwise, as $t = d(r - 1)$, some derivative in R would be of order at least r. We would have $q \geqq r$ and the weight of Q would exceed $t + r$. Then R is one of the E_i.

We may now write (35)

$$w^{t+1}E_j \equiv \sum_{i=1}^{\mu} T_{ji}E_i, \qquad [C], \tag{36}$$

with each nonzero T homogeneous, of the first degree, in the u_{ik}; homogeneous, of degree t, in the w_k; homogeneous, of the first degree, in the z_k. We write (36)

$$\begin{aligned} &(T_{11} - w^{t+1})\,E_1 + T_{12}E_2 + \cdots + T_{1\mu}E_\mu \equiv 0, \qquad [C], \\ &\cdots\cdots\cdots\cdots\cdots\cdots\cdots\cdots\cdots\cdots \\ &T_{\mu1}E_1 + T_{\mu2}E_2 + \cdots + (T_{\mu\mu} - w^{t+1})\,E_\mu \equiv 0, \qquad [C]. \end{aligned} \tag{37}$$

If U is the determinant of the system (37),

$$UE_j \equiv 0, \qquad [C], \qquad\qquad j = 1, \cdots, \mu.$$

We have

$$U = (-1)^\mu w^{\mu(t+1)} + V$$

where each power product in V is of positive degree in the z_j and of degree $\mu(t+1)$ in the w_j and u_{ij}. Observing that z^d is an E_j, we have (28) with $s = \mu(t+1)$ and $D = (-1)^\mu V$.

22. We now prove a theorem which gives a result somewhat stronger than the sufficiency of the condition in the low power theorem.

THEOREM: *If* (25) *contains a term* $C_kA^{p_k}$ *which is the only term in* (25) *of degree as low as* p_k, *every component of* A *which is held by* F, *but not by* C_k, *is a component of* F.

Let $\mathfrak{M}$ be a component of A. If $m = l$, (25) becomes $F = C_kA^{p_k}$ and the theorem holds. Let $m > l$. We compare (25) and (27). We let A in (25) correspond to z in (27), C_k to w and p_k to p. In a term of (25) other than $C_kA^{p_k}$, we take a power product of degree $p + 1$ in A and the A_i and make it a B as in (27). Corresponding to (28), there is a relation

$$A^d(C_k^s + E) \equiv 0, \qquad [S^tF], \tag{38}$$

where E holds A.

Suppose now that $\mathfrak{M}$ is not a component of F but rather a proper part of a component $\mathfrak{M}'$ of F. Then A does not hold $\mathfrak{M}'$ so that, by (38), $C_k^s + E$ holds $\mathfrak{M}'$. As E holds A, C_k holds $\mathfrak{M}$ and the theorem is proved.

We note that C_k does not hold the general solution of A. The question of sufficiency, in the low power theorem, is settled.

23. THEOREM: *If* (25) *contains a term* $C_kA^{p_k}$ *which is the only term in* (25) *of degree as low as* p_k, *every zero of* A *which is contained in a component of* F *which is not held by* A *is a zero of* C_k.

Let the zero $\eta_1, \cdots, \eta_n$ of A be contained in a component $\mathfrak{M}$ of F which is not held by A. By (38), $C_k^s + E$ holds $\mathfrak{M}$. As E holds A, C_k is annulled by $\eta_1, \cdots, \eta_n$.

Necessity proof

24. Let $\mathfrak{M}$ be the general solution of A. The set $y_1, \cdots, y_{n-1}$ is parametric for $\mathfrak{M}$ and the order of $\mathfrak{M}$ with respect to $y_1, \cdots, y_{n-1}$ is l. We shall prove the following theorem, which will settle the question of necessity in the low power theorem.

THEOREM: *Let the terms of lowest degree in* (25) *involve proper derivatives of A and let A_h be the highest derivative of A which appears in the terms of lowest degree. Then $\mathfrak{M}$ is not a component of F and $\mathfrak{M}$ is contained in a component $\mathfrak{M}_1$ of F whose order with respect to $y_1, \cdots, y_{n-1}$ is at least $l + h$.*[12]

We shall replace y_n in (25) by $y_n + u_0$, where u_0 is an indeterminate, and examine the resulting d.p. in u_0 and the y. Such a replacement, made in any d.p. B in the y, of order s in y_n will convert B into

(39) $$B + B_0 u_{00} + \cdots + B_s u_{0s} + \text{terms of higher degree in the } u_{0i},$$

where B_i is the partial derivative of B with respect to y_{ni}.

For $B = A$, (39) will contain the term $S u_{0l}$ and for $B = A_i$, (39) will contain $S u_{0,\, l+i}$.

Let $\eta_1, \cdots, \eta_n$ be a generic point of $\mathfrak{M}$. In (25), we make the substitution

(40) $$y_i = \eta_i, \qquad i = 1, \cdots, n-1; \qquad y_n = \eta_n + u_0.$$

Then $S^t F$, as in (25), goes over into a d.p. K in $\mathfrak{F}_0\{u_0\}$, where $\mathfrak{F}_0 = \mathfrak{F}\langle \eta_1, \cdots, \eta_n \rangle$.

Each C in (25) will produce, under (40), a nonzero term free of the u_{0j}. As each A_i, $i = 0, \cdots, m - l$, vanishes for the η, while S does not, the terms of lowest degree in the u_{0j} produced by A_i will be of the first degree and will involve $u_{0,\, l+i}$.

From the terms of lowest degree in (25), we select those which are of a highest degree in A_h. From the terms just taken, we select those which are of a highest degree in A_{h-1}. We continue through A_1. Our process isolates a single term of (25)

$$T = C_j A^{p_j} A_1^{i_{1j}} \cdots A_h^{i_{hj}}.$$

Under (40), T produces a term in $u_{0l}^{p_j} \cdots u_{0,\, l+h}^{i_{hj}}$ which is not cancelled. Thus the sum W of the terms of lowest degree in K, which sum is of positive degree, will be of order $l + h$ in u_0.

We are going to find for K a zero

(41) $$u_0 = \zeta c + \varphi_2 c^{\rho_2} + \cdots + \varphi_k c^{\rho_k} + \cdots$$

of the type exhibited in (1).

Let V be a factor of W, irreducible in $\mathfrak{F}_0$, which is of order $l + h$ in u_0. Let ζ be a generic point in the general solution of V. It may be that K vanishes for

[12] Note that $y_1, \cdots, y_{n-1}$ is parametric for $\mathfrak{M}_1$ if $\mathfrak{M}_1$ contains $\mathfrak{M}$.

$u_0 = \zeta c$. If so, ζc is a suitable series (41). In what follows, we assume that the vanishing does not occur.

We make, in K, the substitution $u_0 = c\zeta + u_1$. Then K goes over into an expression K', a polynomial in c and the u_{1i}, which may be written as in (3). The lowest exponent of c in a' exceeds the degree of W. W contributes, to the sum in (3), terms, free of c, whose degree in the u_{1j} is the degree of W. This justifies us in imagining that it is the present K' which is being used in §§7–13. We secure thus the zero (41) of K.

25. We have thus a zero of $S^t F$

$$y_i = \eta_i, \qquad i = 1, \cdots, n-1,$$
(42)
$$y_n = \eta_n + \zeta c + \varphi_2 c^{\rho_2} + \cdots.$$

As the η do not annul S, (42) gives a zero of F.

Let the components of F be general solutions of d.p. $B_1, \cdots, B_s$. Then (42) is in the general solution of some B_i. To fix our ideas, we suppose that the general solution $\mathfrak{M}_1$ of B_1 contains (42). Let D be any d.p. which holds $\mathfrak{M}_1$. Then D must vanish for the η, else it could not vanish for (42). Then D holds $\mathfrak{M}$. Thus $\mathfrak{M}_1$ contains $\mathfrak{M}$.

Under (40), let B_1 go over into a d.p. E in u_0. Let U be the sum of the terms of lowest degree in E. Then U is annulled by ζ. Hence the order of U in u_0 is at least that of V, namely $l + h$. Thus B_1 is of order at least $l + h$ in y_n so that the order of $\mathfrak{M}_1$ with respect to $y_1, \cdots, y_{n-1}$ is at least $l + h$. This proves our theorem, and, with it, the necessity of the condition in the low power theorem.

An example

26. We consider, in $\mathfrak{F}\{y\}$, the d.p.

$$F = B^2 + \prod_{j=1}^{m} (y_1 - y + jy^2)$$

where $B = yy_2 + yy_1 - 2y_1^2$ and m is any positive integer.

We show first that F is algebraically irreducible. Suppose that F has a factor G free of y_2. Then G is a factor of y^2, the coefficient of y_2. As F is not divisible by y, there is no factor free of y_2. As the equation $F = 0$ defines y_2 as a function of two branches of y and y_1, there are no factors of the first degree in y_2.

Thus the manifold of F consists of the general solution, $\mathfrak{M}$, and perhaps, of components held by S, the separant of F. As $S = 2yB$, and as B holds y, B holds the components other than $\mathfrak{M}$. Thus every zero of F not in $\mathfrak{M}$ must annul one of the d.p.

$$A_j = y_1 - y + jy^2, \qquad j = 1, \cdots, m.$$

We have, for each j, with A_j' the derivative of A,

$$B = yA_j' - 2y_1A_j.$$

The low power theorem shows us immediately that the manifold of each A_j is a component of F.

FURTHER THEOREMS ON LOW POWERS

27. Levi obtained a very broad theorem, dealing with systems of d.p., which is essentially a generalization of the low power theorem, at least as far as the question of sufficiency in that theorem is concerned. We consider a special case, which involves a single d.p.

Let

$$F = y_1^{p_1} y_2^{p_2} \cdots y_n^{p_n} + D$$

where the p are nonnegative integers whose sum is positive and where D is a d.p. of the following description:

(a) Each of its terms has a degree in the y_{ik} which exceeds $p_1 + \cdots + p_n$.

(b) Given any of its terms, E, and any y_j, E is either divisible by $y_j^{p_j}$ or else of degree higher than p_j in the y_{jk}.

It is easy to see, and, in fact, it will be explicitly shown in the course of our work, that, if $p_i > 0$, the manifold of y_i is a component of F.

We shall prove that *the zero* $y_i = 0$, $i = 1, \cdots, n$, *of* F *is not contained in any component of* F *which is not the manifold of some* y_i *with* $p_i > 0$.

We treat first the case in which only one of the p, say p_n, is positive. We collect those terms of F which are not of degree higher than p_n in the y_{nk}; they are all divisible by $y_n^{p_n}$. We write

$$F = G y_n^{p_n} + H \tag{43}$$

where each term of H is of degree greater than p_n in the y_{nk}. We have $G = 1 + K$ where K is free of y_n and vanishes for $y_i = 0$, $i = 1, \cdots, n$.

We can now apply the low power theorem, taking A as y_n. The manifold of y_n is a component of F. The zero $y_i = 0$, $i = 1, \cdots, n$, of y_n does not annul G. By §23, it cannot lie in any component of F other than the manifold of y_n.

Suppose now that the proof has been carried through for the case in which no more than r of the p are positive, where $r < n$. We make an induction to the case in which $r + 1$ of the p are positive.

Let p_n be positive. We use (43). H satisfies (a) and (b) and each of its terms is of degree greater than p_n in the y_{nk}. We have

$$G = y_1^{p_1} \cdots y_{n-1}^{p_{n-1}} + K$$

where K satisfies the following two conditions:

(c) Each of its terms is of degree higher than $p_1 + \cdots + p_{n-1}$ in the y_{ik}, $i = 1, \cdots, n$.

(d) Given any of its terms, E, and any y_j with $j < n$, E is either divisible by $y_j^{p_j}$ or else of higher degree than p_j in the y_{jk}.

We write (43)

$$F = Gy_n^{p_n} + L_1M_1 + \cdots + L_gM_g$$

where the M are power products of degree $p + 1$ in the y_{nk} and where the L, like K, satisfy (d) above.

By §21, there exists a relation

$$y_n^d(G^s + N) \equiv 0, \qquad [F],$$

where N is a homogeneous polynomial, of degree s, in derivatives, proper or improper, of G and the L, with coefficients which vanish when $y_n = 0$.

Suppose now that the zero $y_i = 0$, $i = 1, \cdots, n$, lies in a component $\mathfrak{M}$ of F other than the manifold of y_n. Then $G^s + N$ holds $\mathfrak{M}$. Now $G^s + N$ is of the form

$$y_1^{sp_1} \cdots y_{n-1}^{sp_{n-1}} + P,$$

where P satisfies (a) and (b) above if, in those statements, p_n is taken as zero and each p_i with $i < n$ is replaced by sp_i. By the earlier cases, $\mathfrak{M}$ is held by some y_i with $i < n$ and is thus the manifold of such a y_i. The result is established.

28. In $\mathfrak{F}\{ y \}$, let

$$F = y^p y_1^q + D,$$

where $p > 0$, $q > 0$, and each term of D is of degree greater than q in proper derivatives. The manifold of y_1 is a component of F. The only point which this manifold can have in common with other components is $y = 0$.

Suppose now that *each term of D is of degree greater than $p + q$ in y and proper derivatives.* We shall show that *the only component of F which contains $y = 0$ is the manifold of y_1.*[13]

We find readily that

$$y_1^d(y^{ps} + N) \equiv 0, \qquad [F],$$

where each term of N is of degree greater than ps.

If $y = 0$ were in a second component, $\mathfrak{M}$, of F, $\mathfrak{M}$ would be held by $y^{ps} + N$. That d.p. has $y = 0$ as a component.

29. In $\mathfrak{F}\{ y \}$, let

$$F = y^p + D \tag{44}$$

with p positive and less than the degree of any term of D. There exists a relation

$$y^d(1 + N) \equiv 0, \qquad [F], \tag{45}$$

where N vanishes for $y = 0$. We are interested in the least value of d for which it is possible to have a relation (45).

It is easy to see that d cannot be less than p. If F is of positive order, the

[13] Levi, 17, where a more general result is secured.

work of §21 gives $r(p-1)+1$, with r the greatest of the weights of the terms of D, as an employable value of d. If $p=1$, we can thus take d as unity. It is not possible to take d as p for every p. For instance, let $F = y^3 + y_1^4$. Suppose that we have a relation

$$y^3(1+N) = MF + M_1F' + \cdots + M_sF^{(s)}. \tag{46}$$

For the second member of (46) to have y^3 as one of its terms, it is necessary for M to have unity as a term. Then MF has y_1^4 as a term. Equating terms of degree 4 and weight 4 for both sides of (46), we find $y_1^4 \equiv 0$, $[y^3]$, which is easily shown to be false.

We now let A represent y^p and A_j the jth derivative of A. Suppose that, for some $m > 0$,

$$F = A + \sum_{i=0}^{m} M_iA_i, \tag{47}$$

where each M vanishes for $y = 0$. We are going to show that d may be taken as p.[14]

We assume, as we may, that no M is zero. We may write, on the basis of (47) with a suitable range for i and j,

$$A \equiv \sum_{i,j} C_{ij}y_iA_j, \qquad [F], \tag{48}$$

in which we understand that no C is zero. If, in the second member of (48), each A_j is replaced by the jth derivative of the second member, there results a congruence

$$A \equiv \sum_{i,j,k} C_{ijk}y_iy_jA_k, \qquad [F]. \tag{49}$$

For each C_{ij} in (48), we consider $i+j$. Let r be the maximum of these sums. Then, in (49), no $i+j+k$ can exceed $2r$. If the substitution just made is carried out $s-1$ times, we find a congruence

$$A \equiv \sum Cy_{i_1}y_{i_2}\cdots y_{i_s}A_{i_{s+1}}, \qquad [F],$$

C depending on the i. No sum $i_1 + \cdots + i_{s+1}$ can exceed sr. By §21, if $s = (r+1)(p-1)+1$, every $y_{i_1}\cdots y_{i_s}$ will be in $[A]$. We have thus a congruence

$$A - \sum D_{ij}A_iA_j \equiv 0, \qquad [F]. \tag{50}$$

Let L represent the first member of (50). We know from what precedes that there is a relation

$$A(1+N) \equiv 0, \qquad [L],$$

with $N \equiv 0$, $[A]$. Q.E.D.

---

[14] Levi, 17.

Terms of lowest degree

30. We prove the following theorem.

THEOREM: *Let A and B be nonzero d.p. in $y_1, \cdots, y_n$. Let B hold A. Let A_1 be the sum of the terms of lowest degree in A considered as a polynomial in the y_{ij} and let B_1 be the corresponding sum for B. Then B_1 holds A_1.*

A similar result holds for the terms of highest degree.

31. **Remark.** The simplest case is that in which $B \equiv 0, [A]$. One might expect to have then $B_1 \equiv 0, [A_1]$. We shall show by means of an example that this need not be so. Let, in $\mathfrak{F}\{y\}$,

$$A = y_1^2 + y^3; \qquad B = 2y_2A - y_1A' = 2y^3y_2 - 3y^2y_1^2.$$

Then $A_1 = y_1^2$, $B_1 = B$. If we had $B_1 \equiv 0$, $[A_1]$, it would follow that $y^3y_2 \equiv 0, [A_1]$. The derivatives of y_1^2 have weights which exceed 2. Thus y^3y_2 would have to be a multiple of y_1^2. This proves our statement. From the expression of B in terms of A, one might now conjecture that *some power* of B_1 is linear in A_1 and the *first* derivative of A_1. In that case, some power of y^3y_2 would be such a linear combination. This is impossible since y^3y_2 is not divisible by y_1. Actually, the cube of B_1 is linear in A_1 and its first two derivatives.

32. We enter into the proof. If A_1 is free of the y, B_1 certainly holds A_1. In what follows, we assume that the terms of A_1 are of positive degree. Then A_1 vanishes for $y_i = 0$, $i = 1, \cdots, n$.

We shall prove the permissibility of assuming that A_1 contains a term involving only the y_{1j}. Let $z_2, \cdots, z_n$ and $w_2, \cdots, w_n$ be indeterminates. Let y_i, for $i > 1$, be replaced in A_1 by $z_i + w_i$. Then A_1 goes over into a d.p. C in y_1, the z and w. C contains terms free of the z_{ij}; the sum D of such terms is found by substituting w_i for y_i in A_1 for $i > 1$. Let t_2 be an integer which exceeds the order of D in y_1. On putting $w_2 = y_{1t_2}$ in D, we convert D into a nonzero d.p. D_1 in $y_1, w_3, \cdots, w_n$. We now replace w_3 in D_1 by y_{1t_3}, where t_3 exceeds the order of D_1 in y_1. Continuing, we find a substitution

$$y_i = z_i + y_{1t_i}, \qquad i = 2, \cdots, n, \tag{51}$$

which converts A_1 into a d.p. E in y_1 and the z_i, E possessing terms free of the z_{ij}. The terms of E will have the same degree as those of A_1.

The substitution (51) may be applied to A and B and will give a situation in which E takes the place of A_1. This proves the legitimacy of the assumption described above, and, in what follows, A_1 will be understood to have terms involving only the y_{1j}.

Now let $\zeta_1, \cdots, \zeta_n$ be any zero of A_1. We wish to show that A has a zero

$$\begin{aligned} y_i &= \zeta_i c, \qquad i = 2, \cdots, n, \\ y_1 &= \zeta_1 c + \varphi_2 c^{\rho_2} + \cdots, \end{aligned} \tag{52}$$

of the familiar type. If A vanishes for $y_i = \zeta_i c$, $i = 1, \cdots, n$, we have (52).

Otherwise, we replace each y_i with $i > 1$ in A by $\zeta_i c$ and y_1 by $\zeta_1 c + u_1$. Then A goes over into an expression K' in c and u_1 which may be written as in (3). The lowest exponent of c in a' exceeds the degree of A_1. Also, because A_1 has terms in y_1 alone, A_1 contributes to the sum in (3) terms, free of c, whose degree in the u_{1j} equals the degree of A_1. The discussion of §§7–13 thus holds for the present K', and we have the zero (52) of A.

As (52) annuls B, the ζ annul B_1. The theorem is proved.

33. The case of the terms of highest degree, mentioned in §30, is perhaps most conveniently treated as follows. Let A_1 and B_1 be the sums of the terms of highest degree in A and B respectively. Using indeterminates $u; z_1, \cdots, z_n$, we put in A and B

$$y_i = z_i/u^2, \qquad i = 1, \cdots, n. \tag{53}$$

We have then

$$A = C/u^m, \qquad A_1 = C_1/u^m,$$
$$B = D/u^m, \qquad B_1 = D_1/u^m,$$

with m a positive integer and C, C_1, D, D_1 d.p. in u and the z. C_1 and D_1 will be the sums of terms of *least* degree in C and D. Because B holds A, uD holds C. By what precedes, uD_1 holds C_1. Because every zero of A_1 yields zeros of C_1 with $u \neq 0$, B_1 holds A_1.

Singular solutions

34. In studying the components of a d.p. F, and in examining the manner in which they make themselves visible in the structure of F, we have thus far had no need to assume F algebraically irreducible. For a closer examination of the components, algebraic irreducibility is important for F, and accordingly we assume it.

As we saw in Chapter II, the discussion of the manifold of F is allied to the study of the singular solutions of $F = 0$. The general solution of F contains all nonsingular solutions and sometimes, in addition, some or all singular solutions. If there are other components, they are made up of singular solutions.

The problem of singular solutions has two aspects. On the one hand, one will wish to know how the singular solutions are distributed among the components of F. On the other, one will, in the analytic case, desire to know how the singular solutions are related analytically to the nonsingular ones. For instance, singular solutions may be envelopes of nonsingular solutions, or may be embedded among them in an interesting way.

35. Let us examine the first question. With what we already know of the components and with what will be developed in Chapter V, we shall be able to produce a set of d.p.

$$F, A_1, \cdots, A_p \tag{54}$$

whose general solutions are the components of F. The general solution of a d.p.

in (54) contains all nonsingular zeros of the d.p. One will wish to determine the singular zeros which are contained in the general solution. If one has done this, and thus knows the nature of each component of F, one may be interested in determining the intersection of two or more components; this is a matter of finding the intersection of the general solutions of two or more d.p.

If it were possible effectively to construct bases for the various essential prime divisors of the perfect ideal determined by a given finite system of d.p., the above questions would be answered. For instance, we could get a finite system of d.p. whose manifold is the general solution of F and, after that, a finite system whose manifold consists of the singular zeros in the general solution.

The problem of determining bases for the prime divisors is at present far from being solved.[15] It is thus a matter, at this time, of treating special differential equations with such methods as one can devise.

For the case of a single indeterminate, the problem of the singular zeros in a general solution, and that of the intersection of components, reduce to the following problem: *Given two algebraically irreducible d.p. in y, F and A, with F holding the general solution of A, to determine whether the general solution of A is contained in the general solution of F.*

If F is of order n in y, and A of order $n - 1$, this is merely a matter of deciding whether the general solution of A is a component of F. The low power theorem gives the decision. If the order of A is less than $n - 1$, the question becomes complicated. For instance, suppose that A is of order $n - 2$. It may be that F has certain components $\mathfrak{M}_1, \cdots, \mathfrak{M}_q$ of order $n - 1$. The general solution $\mathfrak{M}$ of A may be found, when the low power theorem is used, to be contained in some of the $\mathfrak{M}_i$. In that case, the question of testing for the presence of $\mathfrak{M}$ in the general solution of F is an intricate one, which thus far has been solved only for the case of $n = 2$.[16]

For the case of $n = 2$, our problem can be reduced to the following: *Let F, of order 2, vanish for $y = 0$. It is required to determine whether $y = 0$ is contained in the general solution of F.* This question can always be answered after there are performed a finite number of operations in which one examines polygons, of the Newton type, associated with F. The discussion is too lengthy to be presented here.

For instance, let F be the d.p. of §26. F is annulled by $y = 0$. For $m > 3$, it follows from §24 that $y = 0$ is in the general solution of F. For $m = 3$, the methods of the paper cited above show that $y = 0$ is in the general solution.

We wish, in conclusion, to compare two very simple d.p. According to §28, $y = 0$ is not in the general solution of $yy_1 + y_2^3$. Consider, again, $yy_1 + y_2^2$. By §24, its general solution contains $y = 0$.

36. The second problem on singular solutions mentioned in §34 belongs to

[15] A theoretical solution of the problem is presented in Chapter V. This solution is incomplete in that one does not know how far the process used in the solution must be carried to be effective.

[16] Ritt, 31.

classical analysis rather than to differential algebra. For instance, Hamburger's work on differential equations of the first order[17] shows that if a singular solution of such an equation is not contained in the general solution, the singular solution is an envelope of nonsingular ones. If the singular solution is contained in the general solution, it is analytically embedded among nonsingular solutions. Another paper of Hamburger's deals with algebraic differential equations of any order n, supposed to have a component of order $n - 1$. Of course, the notions of component, and of general solution, as we have them, did not exist when Hamburger wrote. The component of order $n - 1$ is shown, speaking geometrically, to consist of envelopes of curves in the general solution. The theory of algebraic differential manifolds throws new light on the analytic theory of singular solutions, and, as one sees in connection with partial differential equations,[18] points the way in analytical investigations.

37. Just as Lagrange dealt, to an extent, with the general solution of a differential equation, so Laplace,[19] in a paper published in 1772, treated questions resembling those of the present chapter. Dealing with a differential equation $F = 0$ of order n, in an unknown y, Laplace uses the term *general integral* to designate a family of solutions depending on n arbitrary constants. By a *solution* of the given equation, he understands an equation $A = 0$ of order lower than n which "satisfies" the given equation. What seems to be meant, in a vague way, is that F holds the general solution of A. A *particular integral* is a solution "contained in" the general integral and a *particular solution* is one which is not so contained. Laplace sets the following two problems:

Being given a differential equation of any order,

(1) *to determine whether an equation of lower order which satisfies it is contained in the general integral;*

(2) *to determine all of the particular solutions of the given equation.*

The second problem corresponds to that of the determination of the components of a d.p., the problem which is solved by the low power theorem. The first problem corresponds to that of determining whether the general solution of A is contained in that of F.

As one would expect, Laplace's treatment of his problems is of a heuristic nature. It does not contain the elements of a sound theory, or even serviceable conjectures. One can have only admiration, however, for his ability to imagine problems which, with the mathematics of his day, could not be soundly formulated, much less solved.

38. A paper published by Poisson in 1806 treats,[20] in a manner somewhat different from that of Laplace, the questions raised by the latter. Poisson's method is most easily understood from his discussion of "algebraic particular solutions." These, which had been considered by Laplace, have for counter-

---

[17] Hamburger, 6.

[18] Ritt, 41.

[19] Laplace, 16.

[20] Poisson, 19.

parts, in the theory of manifolds, components composed of one point, for instance, the manifold of y when

$$F = y + \left(\frac{d^2y}{dx^2}\right)^2.$$

Poisson considers that it is proper to call a solution $y(x)$ of a differential equation an algebraic particular solution if and only if the equation does not have a one-parameter family of solutions $y(x) + cz$ with c an arbitrary constant and z a function of x and c. More or less, an algebraic particular solution is, for Poisson, one which cannot be analytically embedded in a one-parameter family of solutions. With this definition, Poisson is able to state, for certain classes of equations, necessary and sufficient conditions for a given solution to be an algebraic particular solution. The results of Poisson may be regarded, as may also those of Laplace, as heuristic equivalents of portions of the low power theorem. For instance, Poisson concludes that $y = 0$ is a particular solution of

$$\left(\frac{dy}{dx}\right)^m \frac{d^2y}{dx^2} = y^n$$

if and only if $m \geqq n$. Poisson's treatment of his problem vaguely resembles the necessity proof for the low power theorem.

39. There is an aspect of the theory of singular solutions which is not revealed by our algebraic considerations. The equation

$$y^2 - y\frac{dy}{dx} + \left(\frac{dy}{dx}\right)^3 = 0 \tag{55}$$

has $y = 0$ in its general solution. If we solve for y in (55) in terms of dy/dx, we secure two expansions proceeding according to increasing integral powers of dy/dx. They are

$$y = \frac{dy}{dx} - \left(\frac{dy}{dx}\right)^2 + \cdots, \tag{56}$$

$$y = \left(\frac{dy}{dx}\right)^2 + \cdots. \tag{57}$$

Now the solution $y = 0$ of (57) can be shown to be an envelope of solutions of (57). Furthermore, the low power theorem can be extended to cover equations like (57), in which infinite series appear. This suggests extending the theory of differential polynomials into one of *differential power series*.[21]

III. Exponents of Ideals

40. In $\mathfrak{F}\{y_1, \cdots, y_n\}$, we consider an ideal Σ and, with it, $\{\Sigma\}$. Every d.p. in $\{\Sigma\}$ has a power in Σ. By I, §15, if, for some p, and for every A in $\{\Sigma\}$, $A^p \equiv 0$, (Σ), the pth power of $\{\Sigma\}$ will be contained in Σ. If there is a positive integer p such that Σ contains $\{\Sigma\}^p$, the least such integer is called

[21] Ritt, 33.

the *exponent* of $\{\Sigma\}$ *relative to* Σ. When no such integer exists, the relative exponent is taken as ∞.

Relative exponents were investigated by Kolchin.[22] He studied, in particular, for an algebraically irreducible d.p. A in y, of the first order, the exponent of $\{A\}$ relative to $[A]$. The exponent depends on the nature of the singular zeros of A. We shall content ourselves with the presentation of an example.

41. Let $A = y_1^2 - 4y$. (See Example 1 of II, §4.) We shall prove that the exponent of $\{A\}$ relative to $[A]$ is 2. We have, subscripts of A indicating differentiation,

$$\begin{aligned} A_1 &= 2y_1y_2 - 4y_1, \\ A_2 &= 2y_1y_3 + 2y_2^2 - 4y_2, \\ A_3 &= 2y_1y_4 + 6y_2y_3 - 4y_3, \\ &\cdots\cdots\cdots\cdots\cdots\cdots, \\ A_r &= 2y_1y_{r+1} + \cdots + 2ry_2y_r - 4y_r \qquad (r > 2). \end{aligned} \tag{58}$$

The unwritten terms in A_r with $r > 2$ are of the form cy_py_q with $p + q = r + 2$ and with p and q greater than 2 and less than r. As $y_1(y_2 - 2)$ is in $[A]$, $y_2(y_2 - 2)^2$ is in $[A]$. If $r > 2$,

$$y_2(y_2 - 2)^2 = P_r(2ry_2 - 4) + c_r$$

with c_r a constant distinct from zero. We find then, from the last equation of (58),

$$c_ry_r \equiv P_r(2y_1y_{r+1} + \cdots), \qquad [A], \tag{59}$$

the unwritten terms being as in A_r.

We shall now prove that, for $r > 2$,

$$y_r(y_2 - 2) \equiv 0, \qquad [A]. \tag{60}$$

By (59) with $r = 3$, we have

$$c_3y_3 \equiv 2y_1y_4P_3, \qquad [A]. \tag{61}$$

We multiply by $y_2 - 2$ in (61), noting that $A_1 = 2y_1(y_2 - 2)$. We obtain (60) with $r = 3$. If we observe that the subscripts in the unwritten terms of (59) exceed 2 and are less than r, the induction necessary to establish (60) for all r is accomplished.

Then, for $r > 2$,

$$y_{r+1}(y_2 - 2) + y_ry_3 \equiv 0, \qquad [A]. \tag{62}$$

As the first term in (62) is in $[A]$, we have, for $r > 2$, $y_ry_3 \equiv 0$, $[A]$. Then

$$y_{r+1}y_3 + y_ry_4 \equiv 0, \qquad [A],$$

---

[22] Kolchin, 10.

so that $y_r y_4$ is in $[A]$ for $r > 2$. In this way, we see that

(63) $$y_p y_q \equiv 0, \qquad [A],$$

for $p > 2$, $q > 2$.

Let P, any d.p. in $\{A\}$, be written

$$P = Q + R,$$

where Q consists of those terms of P which involve only y, y_1, y_2. The y_i with $i > 2$ are in $\{A\}$. Thus Q is in $\{A\}$. We write

$$Q = M(y_2 - 2) + N$$

with N free of y_2. Then $y_1 N$ is in $\{A\}$ so that N is divisible by A. Thus

$$P \equiv M(y_2 - 2) + R, \qquad [A].$$

Then

$$P^2 \equiv M^2(y_2 - 2)^2 + 2MR(y_2 - 2) + R^2, \qquad [A].$$

Now R^2 is in $[A]$ by (63) and $R(y_2 - 2)$ is in $[A]$ by (60). Hence

$$P^2 \equiv M^2(y_2 - 2)^2, \qquad [A].$$

Each term in M involves at least one of y, y_1, y_2. We know that $y_1(y_2 - 2)$ and $y_2(y_2 - 2)^2$ are in $[A]$. Also, because $y_1^2 \equiv 4y$, (A), we see that $y(y_2 - 2)$ is in $[A]$. Hence $P^2 \equiv 0$, $[A]$.

Thus $\{A\}^2$ is contained in $[A]$.

42. It remains to be proved that $\{A\}$ is not identical with $[A]$. This we show by proving that y_3 is not in $[A]$. Suppose that

(64) $$y_3 = CA + C_1A_1 + \cdots + C_rA_r.$$

In the second member of (64), we put $y = y_1^2/4$, $y_2 = 2$. We find, writing

$$B_2 = y_1y_3, \qquad B_3 = y_1y_4 + 4y_3,$$

$$B_r = y_1y_{r+1} + \cdots + (2r - 2)y_r \qquad (r > 2),$$

that

(65) $$y_3 = D_2B_2 + \cdots + D_rB_r.$$

We see immediately that $r > 2$. The only term in the second member of (65) which can yield a constant times y_3 is D_3B_3. Thus $1/4$ must be a term in D_3 so that D_3B_3 must contain $(y_1y_4)/4$. The term just mentioned must cancel out in (65). The only B other than B_3 which contains a term of which y_1y_4 is a multiple is B_4, which contains $6y_4$. Thus D_4 must contain $-y_1/24$ so that $-(y_1^2y_5)/24$ appears in D_4B_4. The only term other than B_4 which contains a factor of $y_1^2y_5$ is B_5, in which y_5 appears. It follows that D_5B_5 contains a term in $y_1^3y_6$. Continuing, we produce the contradiction that r in (64) is not exceeded by any integer. This completes the proof.

CHAPTER IV

SYSTEMS OF ALGEBRAIC EQUATIONS

1. The preceding chapters contain, of course, a theory of systems of algebraic equations. One has only to suppose oneself working with a system of d.p. which are of order zero in each indeterminate. It is, however, desirable to make a separate examination of algebraic equations.

For instance, the theory of algebraic equations can be developed from the algorithmic standpoint, so that every entity whose existence is established is constructed with a finite number of operations. The results of the algebraic theory will permit us, in Chapter V, to give an algorithmic treatment of various questions connected with finite systems of d.p.

Again, we shall obtain an approximation theorem for systems of algebraic equations (§39) which will be found useful in the study of algebraic differential manifolds in the analytic case.

Our account of algebraic equations differs in certain respects from the classical treatments. On the one hand, it is convenient for us to use the methods of the preceding chapters; on the other, it is necessary for us to develop formal procedures which can be applied later to differential equations.

Polynomials and their ideals

2. In the present chapter, we use an *algebraic* field $\mathfrak{F}$ of characteristic zero (I, §1), without requiring that an operation of differentiation exist in $\mathfrak{F}$. We study polynomials in algebraic indeterminates $y_1, \cdots, y_n$, with coefficients in $\mathfrak{F}$. The totality of such polynomials is represented by $\mathfrak{F}[y_1, \cdots, y_n]$. Polynomials will be represented by capital italics and systems of polynomials by large Greek letters.

We carry over definitions from Chapter I as follows. Let $\mathfrak{F}$ be regarded momentarily as a differential field in which all derivatives are zero, and the y as differential indeterminates. We then define, as in Chapter I, the terms *class, separant, initial, chain, characteristic set* and *remainder*.

3. Let Σ be a system of polynomials in $\mathfrak{F}[y_1, \cdots, y_n]$. We shall call Σ a *polynomial ideal* (p.i.) if, for every finite subset $A_1, \cdots, A_r$ of Σ and for all $C_1, \cdots, C_r$ in $\mathfrak{F}[y_1, \cdots, y_n]$, the polynomial $C_1A_1 + \cdots + C_rA_r$ is contained in Σ.

If Σ_1 and Σ_2 are p.i., and if Σ_2 contains Σ_1, Σ_2 is called a *divisor* of Σ_1.

Let Λ be any system of polynomials. Let $(\Lambda)_0$ be the totality of linear combinations of polynomials in Λ with polynomials for coefficients. Then $(\Lambda)_0$ is a p.i. We call $(\Lambda)_0$ *the p.i. generated by* Λ.

Let Σ be a p.i. Suppose that, whenever a polynomial A is such that some positive integral power of A is in Σ, A itself is in Σ. We shall then call Σ a *perfect* p.i. Let Λ be any system of polynomials. Let $\{\Lambda\}_0$ be the totality of those polynomials A for which a positive integer p, depending on A, exists such that A^p is in $(\Lambda)_0$. It is easy to see that $\{\Lambda\}_0$ is a perfect p.i. We call $\{\Lambda\}_0$ *the perfect p.i. determined by* Λ.

Let Σ be a p.i. We shall say that Σ is prime if, for every pair of polynomials A and B with AB in Σ, at least one of A and B is in Σ. Every prime p.i. is perfect.

For p.i., the following theorem holds.

THEOREM: *Every perfect p.i. is the intersection of a finite number of prime p.i.*

In §4, we shall show how this theorem can be proved using only material developed in the present book. Let us, however, first found a proof on Hilbert's classic basis theorem for systems of polynomials.

According to Hilbert's theorem, given an infinite system Σ of polynomials, Σ has a finite subset Φ such that $(\Phi)_0$ contains Σ. Now let Σ be a perfect ideal for which our theorem is not true. Then Σ is not prime. Let AB be in Σ while neither A nor B is. We see easily that

$$\{\Sigma + AB\}_0 = \{\Sigma + A\}_0 \cap \{\Sigma + B\}_0$$

and the proof is completed as in I, §16.

4. We may also operate as follows. Let us consider $\mathfrak{F}$ as a differential field in which all derivatives are zero and let the y be regarded as differential indeterminates. Let Σ be an infinite system of polynomials, and Φ a basis for Σ as in I, §12. We consider any polynomial A in Σ. Let A^p be linear in polynomials of Φ, and their derivatives, with d.p. for coefficients. The jth derivative of a polynomial of positive class is isobaric and of weight j. If, in the linear expression for A^p, we cast out all terms of positive weight, we have for A^p an expression linear in polynomials in Φ, with polynomials for coefficients. We secure in this way a basis theorem for systems of polynomials which, to be sure, is weaker than Hilbert's theorem, but which is adequate for the purposes of §3.

5. If Σ is a perfect p.i., a prime divisor of Σ which is not a divisor of any other prime divisor of Σ will be called an *essential prime divisor* of Σ. Every perfect p.i. has a finite number of essential prime divisors, and is the intersection of those divisors.

ALGEBRAIC MANIFOLDS

6. Let Σ be a system of polynomials $\mathfrak{F}[y_1, \cdots, y_n]$. Let $\mathfrak{F}'$ be any extension of $\mathfrak{F}$, that is, any algebraic field which contains $\mathfrak{F}$. Let there exist in $\mathfrak{F}'$ a set of elements $\eta_1, \cdots, \eta_n$ which cause every polynomial in Σ to vanish when η_i is substituted for y_i. The set $\eta_1, \cdots, \eta_n$ will be called a *zero* of Σ. If Σ has zeros, the totality of its zeros, for all extensions $\mathfrak{F}'$ of $\mathfrak{F}$, will be called the *manifold* of Σ. The manifold of a system of polynomials will be called an *algebraic manifold*.

Let an algebraic manifold $\mathfrak{M}$ be the union of two algebraic manifolds, each a proper part of $\mathfrak{M}$. We shall then call $\mathfrak{M}$ *reducible*. If $\mathfrak{M}$ is not reducible, it is called *irreducible*.

Let $\mathfrak{M}$ be an algebraic manifold. The totality Σ of polynomials which vanish over[1] $\mathfrak{M}$ is a perfect p.i., the *perfect p.i. associated with* $\mathfrak{M}$. Σ is prime if and only if $\mathfrak{M}$ is irreducible. If $\mathfrak{M}$ is irreducible, we call Σ the *prime p.i. associated with* $\mathfrak{M}$.

We see readily that *every algebraic manifold is the union of a finite number of irreducible algebraic manifolds.*

Let $\mathfrak{M}$ be the union of irreducible algebraic manifolds $\mathfrak{M}_1, \cdots, \mathfrak{M}_p$. We suppose that no $\mathfrak{M}_i$ contains any $\mathfrak{M}_j$ with $j \neq i$. We then call each $\mathfrak{M}_i$ a *component* of $\mathfrak{M}$, or of any system of polynomials whose manifold is $\mathfrak{M}$. If Σ is the perfect p.i. associated with $\mathfrak{M}$ and Σ_i the prime p.i. associated with $\mathfrak{M}_i$, Σ is the intersection of the Σ_i and the Σ_i are the essential prime divisors of Σ.

Generic zeros of prime polynomial ideals

7. Let Σ be a prime p.i. distinct from the *unit p.i.*, $(1)_0$. Let A be any polynomial, not necessarily contained in Σ. We form a class α of polynomials, putting into α every polynomial G such that $G - A$ is in Σ. We call α a *remainder class modulo* Σ. If α and β are remainder classes, $\alpha + \beta$ is defined as the remainder class which contains every $A + B$ with A in α and B in β. We define $\alpha\beta$ similarly. We call Σ, which is a remainder class, the *zero class*. Because Σ is prime, the product of two nonzero remainder classes is distinct from the zero class.

We now consider pairs (α, β) of remainder classes in which β is not the zero class. Equivalence is defined as in II, §6, and the totality of pairs of classes separates into sets of equivalent pairs. For the sets of equivalent pairs, addition and multiplication are defined, as in II, §6. Subtraction and division are then performable and unique, with the usual reservation in regard to division. The sets of equivalent pairs constitute an algebraic field $\mathfrak{F}_1$ which, after an adjustment, becomes an extension of $\mathfrak{F}$.

Let ω be the remainder class which contains 1. Let α_i, $i = 1, \cdots, n$, be the class which contains y_i. Let η_i be the set in $\mathfrak{F}_1$ which contains (α_i, ω). We find that $\eta_1, \cdots, \eta_n$ is a zero of Σ. Every polynomial in $\mathfrak{F}[y_1, \cdots, y_n]$ which vanishes when each y_i is replaced by η_i is contained in Σ.

Let Σ be as above. Every zero $\eta_1, \cdots, \eta_n$ of Σ which is such that every polynomial in $\mathfrak{F}[y_1, \cdots, y_n]$ which is annulled by the η is in Σ is called a *generic zero* of Σ.

Resolvents

8. A prime p.i. distinct from $(1)_0$ and from $(0)_0$ will be said to be *nontrivial*. Let Σ be a nontrivial prime p.i. in $\mathfrak{F}[y_1, \cdots, y_n]$. The y can be divided

[1] Language as in Chapter II.

into two sets, $u_1, \cdots, u_q$ and $y_1, \cdots, y_p$, $p + q = n$, such that no nonzero polynomial of Σ is free of the y, while, for $j = 1, \cdots, p$, there is a nonzero polynomial in Σ in y_j and the u alone. We call the u a *parametric set.* Let the *indeterminates be listed in the order*

$$u_1, \cdots, u_q; \qquad y_1, \cdots, y_p,$$

and let

$$(1) \qquad A_1, \cdots, A_p$$

be a characteristic set of Σ.

A *regular zero* of (1) is defined as a zero of (1) which does not annul the initial of any A. *Every regular zero of* (1) *is a zero of* Σ.[2]

9. Let K be any polynomial not contained in Σ. We shall prove that

$$(A_1, \cdots, A_p, K)_0,$$

which we represent by Λ, contains a nonzero polynomial in the u alone.

We start with the observation that the polynomials in Σ which involve no y_i with $i > j$, where $1 \leqq j < p$, constitute a prime p.i.; we designate this p.i. by Σ_j.

Λ contains the remainder of K with respect to (1). Of all nonzero polynomials in Λ which are reduced with respect to (1), let B be one which is of a lowest rank. We say that B is free of the y.

Suppose that this is not so, and let B be of class $q + r$ with $r > 0$. The initial C of B is not in Σ. There is a relation

$$C^m A_r = DB + E$$

where E, if not zero, is of lower degree than B in y_r. We say that E is in Σ. Let this be false. If $r > 1$, the remainder of E with respect to $A_1, \cdots, A_{r-1}$ is a nonzero polynomial contained in Λ, which is reduced with respect to (1) and of lower rank than B. If $r = 1$, a similar statement can be made of E itself. Thus E is in Σ, so that DB is in Σ. Then D is in Σ. D is of positive degree in y_r. As the initial of DB is that of $C^m A_r$, the initial I of D is not in Σ. If we had $r = 1$, D would be a nonzero polynomial in Σ which is reduced with respect to (1); this is because D is of lower degree in y_r than A_r. Thus $r > 1$. The remainder of D with respect to $A_1, \cdots, A_{r-1}$ is zero. Thus JD, with J some product of powers of the initials of $A_1, \cdots, A_{r-1}$, is linear in $A_1, \cdots, A_{r-1}$. If we write JD as a polynomial in y_r, its coefficients will be in Σ_{r-1}. Thus JI is in Σ_{r-1}. This is false because neither J nor I is in Σ_{r-1}.

Thus B is free of the y and our statement is proved.

---

[2] We are applying here, to the theory of characteristic sets, an idea due to van der Waerden. See Mathematische Annalen, vol. 96 (1927), p. 189; also *Moderne Algebra*, first edition, vol. 2, p. 56.

10. We are going to show the existence of a nonzero polynomial G, free of the y, and the existence of a polynomial

$$Q = M_1y_1 + \cdots + M_py_p$$

where the M are polynomials free of the y, such that, for two distinct zeros of Σ with the same u (if u exist) lying in the same extension of $\mathfrak{F}$ and having $G \neq 0$, Q assumes two distinct values.

We consider the system Σ' obtained from Σ by replacing each y_i by a new indeterminate z_i. Using p more indeterminates $\lambda_1, \cdots, \lambda_p$ we consider the system Λ composed of Σ, Σ' and

$$\lambda_1 (y_1 - z_1) + \cdots + \lambda_p (y_p - z_p).$$

As Λ contains Σ, Λ has, for $j = 1, \cdots, p$, a nonzero polynomial B_j in y_j and the u alone. Similarly, let C_j, $j = 1, \cdots, p$, be a nonzero polynomial of Λ in z_j and the u alone.

Let D be the product of the initials[3] of the B and C.

Consider a zero of Λ for which $(y_1 - z_1)\, D \neq 0$. For it, we have

$$\lambda_1 = - \frac{\lambda_2 (y_2 - z_2) + \cdots + \lambda_p (y_p - z_p)}{y_1 - z_1}. \tag{2}$$

Let m be the maximum of the degrees of the B_j in the y_j and of the degrees of the C_j in the z_j. Let α be any positive integer. We write, for $s = 0, \cdots, \alpha$ and for the above zero,

$$\lambda_1^s = \frac{E_s}{(y_1 - z_1)^\alpha},$$

where E_s is a polynomial. Now it is plain that, using the relations $B_j = 0$, $C_j = 0$, we can depress the degree of E_s in each y and in each z to be less than m. The new expression for each λ_1^s will be of the form

$$\lambda_1^s = \frac{F_s}{(y_1 - z_1)^\alpha D_s},$$

where D_s is a product of powers of the initials of the B and C. Let L be the least common multiple of the D_s. We write

$$\lambda_1^s = \frac{H_s}{(y_1 - z_1)^\alpha L}, \tag{3}$$

$s = 0, \cdots, \alpha$, each H_s being a polynomial of degree less than m in each y and z. Now the number of power products of the y and z, of degree less than m in each y and z, is m^{2p}. Consequently, if we take $\alpha \geqq m^{2p}$, we find a nonzero polynomial in λ_1, of degree not greater than α, whose coefficients are polynomials in $\lambda_2, \cdots, \lambda_p$ and the u, which vanishes for every zero of Λ which does not annul $(y_1 - z_1)D$. The product K_1 of this polynomial by D vanishes for every zero of Λ which does not annul $y_1 - z_1$.

[3] The initial of C_j is the coefficient of the highest power of z_j.

Similarly, for $i = 2, \cdots, p$, we find a K_i which vanishes for every zero of Λ which does not annul $y_i - z_i$.

Let M_i, $i = 1, \cdots, p$, be polynomials in the u, which, when substituted for the λ_i in $K_1 \cdots K_p$, reduce that polynomial to a nonzero polynomial G in the u. Any such set of M will furnish a Q as above. The M may be taken as integers.

11. Introducing a new indeterminate w, we let Ω represent the p.i. $(\Sigma, w - Q)_0$ in $\mathfrak{F}[u_1, \cdots, u_q; w; y_1, \cdots, y_p]$. It is easy to prove, as in II, §26, that Ω is prime. The polynomials of Ω which are free of w are precisely the polynomials of Σ.

As above, we prove that Ω has a nonzero polynomial free of the y.

We arrange the indeterminates in Ω in the order

$$u_1, \cdots, u_q; w; y_1, \cdots, y_p \tag{4}$$

and take a characteristic set for Ω,

$$A, A_1, \cdots, A_p. \tag{5}$$

Here $w, y_1, \cdots, y_p$ are introduced in succession.

We take A irreducible in $\mathfrak{F}$.

We are going to prove that each A_i is linear in y_i, so that the equation $A_i = 0$ expresses y_i rationally in terms of w and the u.

12. Let us suppose that our claim is false and let A_k be the A_i of highest subscript for which it breaks down. Then every A_i with $i > k$ which may exist is linear in y_i.

Let U be the remainder with respect to (5) of

$$I_{k+1} \cdots I_p.$$

Of course, U is free of $y_{k+1}, \cdots, y_p$. By §9,

$$(A, A_1, \cdots, A_k, U)_0$$

in $\mathfrak{F}[u_1, \cdots, u_p; w; y_1, \cdots, y_k]$ contains a nonzero polynomial B in the u alone. If $k = p$, there is no B.

Let

$$u_i = \tau_i, \qquad i = 1, \cdots, q; \qquad w = \xi; \qquad y_i = \eta_i, \qquad i = 1, \cdots, p, \tag{6}$$

be a generic zero of Ω, lying in an extension $\mathfrak{F}_1$ of $\mathfrak{F}$.

We replace the u, w and $y_1, \cdots, y_{k-1}$ in A_k by the corresponding quantities in (6). Then A_k goes over into polynomial H_k in y_k over[4] $\mathfrak{F}_1$, whose degree in y_k equals that of A_k. Let K be a factor of H_k, irreducible in $\mathfrak{F}_1$. Then $(K)_0$, in $\mathfrak{F}_1[y_k]$, is a prime p.i. Let ζ_k be a generic zero[5] of $(K)_0$.

The quantities

---

[4] That is, with coefficients in $\mathfrak{F}_1$.

[5] The irreducibility of K implies that every zero of K is a generic zero of $(K)_0$.

(7) $$\tau_1, \cdots, \tau_q; \xi; \eta_1, \cdots, \eta_{k-1}; \zeta_k$$

do not annul $I_{k+1} \cdots I_p$. If they did, they would annul U and therefore B. Now B, which is a nonzero polynomial in the u, cannot vanish for the τ. We obtain thus a zero of Ω,

(8) $$\tau_1, \cdots, \tau_q; \xi; \eta_1, \cdots, \eta_{k-1}; \zeta_k, \cdots, \zeta_p$$

lying in an extension of $\mathfrak{F}_1$. The zeros (6) and (8) do not annul G and they have the same w. They are thus identical. This means that $\zeta_k = \eta_k$. The proof that A_k is linear in y_k is now completed as in II, §30.

We shall call the equation $A = 0$ a *resolvent* of Σ.

It is now easy to prove that q, in §8, is independent of the manner in which the u are selected. We call q the *dimension* of Σ.[6] Following II, §36, we can show that if a prime p.i. Σ' is a proper divisor of Σ, the dimension of Σ' is less than that of Σ.

Hilbert's Theorem of Zeros

13. We prove the following theorem.

Theorem: *If Σ is a perfect p.i. distinct from the unit p.i., Σ has zeros and every polynomial which holds*[7] *Σ is contained in Σ.*

Let $\Sigma_1, \cdots, \Sigma_p$ be the essential prime divisors of Σ. No Σ_i is the unit p.i. If G holds Σ, G vanishes for the generic zeros of each Σ_i and is thus in each Σ_i. Then G is in Σ.

We present now

Hilbert's theorem of zeros: *Let, in $\mathfrak{F}[y_1, \cdots, y_n]$,*

(9) $$F_1, \cdots, F_s$$

be any finite system of polynomials, and G any polynomial which holds that system. Then some power of G is linear in the F, with polynomials for coefficients.

It is a matter of showing that G is contained in the perfect ideal determined by the F. If that ideal is the unit p.i., G is certainly contained in it. Otherwise, we have merely to apply the theorem which precedes.

14. The analytic case, in which $\mathfrak{F}$ consists of functions meromorphic in an open region A, needs more detailed treatment. We use analytic zeros of (9), the definition being as in Chapter II. Hilbert's theorem then becomes:

If F vanishes for every analytic zero of $F_1, \cdots, F_s$, some power of G is linear in the F, with polynomials for coefficients.

Let Σ be the perfect ideal determined by the F and suppose that G is not contained in Σ. Then Σ is not the unit ideal. Let Σ' be an essential prime divisor of Σ in which G is not contained. It will be seen that we may sup-

[6] The dimension is zero when there are no u.

[7] As in Chapter II.

pose Σ' to be distinct from the zero ideal. Let the indeterminates be written $u_1, \cdots, u_q; y_1, \cdots, y_p$ with the u parametric for Σ'.

We form a resolvent for Σ'. Let (5) be a characteristic set for the system Ω, associated with Σ' as in §11. We shall prove the legitimacy of assuming that the initials of the A_i in (5) are free of w. Let

$$A_1 = My_1 + N.$$

As A and M are relatively prime polynomials, there is a relation

$$PA + QM = L$$

where P and Q are polynomials in w and the u, and L is a nonzero polynomial in the u alone.[8] Then Ω contains $Ly_1 + QN$. If I is the initial of A, there is a relation

$$I^aQN = CA + R$$

with R reduced with respect to A. Then $I^aLy_1 + R$ is in Ω and may be used in place of A_1 in (5). We treat the other A_i similarly.

Let H be the remainder of G with respect to (5). Some linear combination of H and A is a nonzero polynomial K in the u alone. Every zero of Σ' which annuls G annuls K.

To complete our proof, we have to show that Σ' has a zero which does not annul K. We fix $u_1, \cdots, u_q$ as analytic functions which annul neither K nor any initial in (5). We can then find an analytic w which annuls A with the selected u. The equations $A_i = 0$ then determine $y_1, \cdots, y_p$.

CHARACTERISTIC SETS OF PRIME POLYNOMIAL IDEALS

15. We consider, in $\mathfrak{F}[u_1, \cdots, u_q; y_1, \cdots, y_p]$, a chain

$$(10) \qquad A_1, A_2, \cdots, A_p,$$

A_i being of class $q + i$. We are going to find a condition for (10) to be a characteristic set of a prime p.i.

Since a nontrivial prime p.i. consists of those polynomials which have zero remainders with respect to any characteristic set, (10) cannot be a characteristic set for more than one prime p.i.

16. If $\mathfrak{F}_1$ is an extension of $\mathfrak{F}$ and if $\eta_1, \cdots, \eta_r$ is a finite subset of elements of $\mathfrak{F}_1$, the totality of rational combinations of $\eta_1, \cdots, \eta_r$ with coefficients in $\mathfrak{F}$ will be denoted by $\mathfrak{F}(\eta_1, \cdots, \eta_r)$ and will be called the field obtained by the *adjunction of* the η to $\mathfrak{F}$. Thus, we represent by[9] $\mathfrak{F}(u_1, \cdots, u_q)$ the totality of the rational combinations of the u with coefficients in $\mathfrak{F}$.

17. Considering (10), we suppose first that $p = 1$. We shall show that *for* A_1 *to be a characteristic set of a prime p.i. in* $u_1, \cdots, u_q; y_1$, *it is necessary and*

[8] Chapter II, §42.

[9] Abbreviated below as $\mathfrak{F}(u)$.

sufficient that A_1, considered as a polynomial in y_1, be irreducible in $\mathfrak{F}(u)$. We first prove sufficiency. Let A_1 be irreducible, as indicated. Then $A_1 = BC$ with B free of y_1 and C irreducible in $\mathfrak{F}$ as a polynomial in y_1 and the u. Now $(C)_0$ is a prime p.i. for which C is a characteristic set. Then A_1 is also a characteristic set for $(C)_0$. For the necessity proof, let A_1 be a characteristic set for a prime p.i. Σ. Let $A_1 = BC$, where B and C are polynomials of positive degree in $\mathfrak{F}(u)$ $[y_1]$. Clearing fractions, we secure a relation $GA_1 = HK$ among polynomials in $\mathfrak{F}[u; y_1]$ with H and K of lower degree than A_1 in y_1. As one of H and K is in Σ, we have a contradiction.

18. We understand now that $p > 1$. We furnish a necessary and sufficient condition which is of an inductive type. If (10) is a characteristic set of a prime p.i. Σ_p, those polynomials in Σ_p which are free of y_p constitute a prime p.i. for which $A_1, \cdots, A_{p-1}$ is a characteristic set. Thus, *if* (10) *is a characteristic set of a prime p.i.* Σ_p, *then*

(a) $A_1, \cdots, A_{p-1}$ *is a characteristic set of a prime p.i.* Σ_{p-1} *in* $y_1, \cdots, y_{p-1}$.

Let condition (a) be fulfilled. Let

$$\tau_1, \cdots, \tau_q; \eta_1, \cdots, \eta_{p-1} \tag{11}$$

be any generic zero of Σ_{p-1}. Let $\mathfrak{F}_{p-1}$ represent the field obtained by adjoining the quantities in (11) to $\mathfrak{F}$. The initial of A_p is not in Σ_{p-1} and thus does not vanish for (11). We shall prove that *if* (10) *is a characteristic set of a prime p.i.*,

(b) A_p, *when the indeterminates other than* y_p *are replaced by their corresponding quantities in* (11), *becomes a polynomial in* $\mathfrak{F}_{p-1}[y_p]$ *which is irreducible in* $\mathfrak{F}_{p-1}$.

A few words are necessary to show that our work is not influenced by the choice which is made of a generic zero (11). For (11), let A_p become a polynomial B in $\mathfrak{F}_{p-1}$ $[y_p]$. Let $B = CD$ with C and D polynomials of positive degree in y_p, over $\mathfrak{F}_{p-1}$. A coefficient in C or D may be written in the form φ/ψ where φ is obtained by making the substitution (11) in a polynomial P in $u_1, \cdots, u_q; y_1, \cdots, y_{p-1}$ over $\mathfrak{F}$, and where ψ is obtained similarly from a polynomial Q. Then Q is not in Σ_{p-1}. Suppose now that

$$\tau_1', \cdots, \tau_q'; \eta_1', \cdots, \eta_{p-1}' \tag{12}$$

is a second generic zero of Σ_{p-1} and that the adjunction of the quantities (12) to $\mathfrak{F}$ produces a field $\mathfrak{F}_{p-1}'$. If, in the equation $B = CD$, we replace the quantities in (11) by those in (12), and bear in mind that an algebraic relation among the quantities in (11), with coefficients in $\mathfrak{F}$, holds also for the quantities (12), we secure an equation $B' = C'D'$ which shows that (12) may be used with the same effect as (11).

It will be proved that the conditions (a) and (b), which are necessary for (10) to be a characteristic set of a prime p.i., are also sufficient.

19. We prove the necessity of condition (b). Let (10) be a characteristic set of a prime p.i. Σ_p. Suppose that there is a relation $B = CD$ as in §18.

Writing each coefficient in C and D in the form φ/ψ as indicated above, we clear fractions. We obtain a relation

$$\delta B = EF \tag{13}$$

where δ is a polynomial in the quantities in (11) and E and F are polynomials in y_p, of positive degree, whose coefficients are polynomials in the quantities in (11). We write (13)

$$\delta B - EF = 0. \tag{14}$$

In the first member of (14) we replace each quantity in (11) by the indeterminate which corresponds to it. We obtain a polynomial

$$GA_p - HK. \tag{15}$$

If this polynomial is arranged according to powers of y_p, its coefficients will vanish for (11) and thus are in Σ_{p-1}. Hence HK is in Σ_p. Suppose that H is in Σ_p. The degree of H in y_p is less than that of A_p. As G and the initial of A_p are not in Σ_p, the initial of H is not in Σ_p. Let L be the remainder of H with respect to $A_1, \cdots, A_{p-1}$. Then L is reduced with respect to (10). Furthermore, L is not zero (§9). As Σ_p cannot contain a nonzero polynomial reduced with respect to (10), the necessity of (b) is proved.

20. Suppose now that (a) and (b) are satisfied. When (11) is substituted into A_p, A_p becomes a polynomial B, irreducible in $\mathfrak{F}_{p-1}$. Let η_p be a zero of B. Let Σ_p be the totality of those polynomials in $\mathfrak{F}[u; y]$ which vanish for

$$\tau_1, \cdots, \tau_q; \qquad \eta_1, \cdots, \eta_p.$$

Then Σ_p is a prime p.i. We shall prove that (10) is a characteristic set of Σ_p. Let the contrary be assumed. Then Σ_p contains a nonzero G which is reduced with respect to (10). Now G must be of class p, else, vanishing for (11), it would be in Σ_{p-1} in spite of being reduced with respect to (10). For (11), G becomes a polynomial H in $\mathfrak{F}_{p-1}[y_p]$ which is annulled by η_p and is of lower degree than B. The sufficiency of conditions (a) and (b) is thus established.

Construction of resolvents

21. Before we can give a method for the effective construction of a resolvent for a prime p.i. for which a characteristic set is given, we must have a solution of the following problem.

Let $\mathfrak{F}_0$ represent $\mathfrak{F}(u_1, \cdots, u_q)$. Let A be a polynomial in $\mathfrak{F}[u_1, \cdots u_q; w]$ irreducible as a polynomial in w over $\mathfrak{F}_0$. Let A_1 be a polynomial in $\mathfrak{F}[u_1, \cdots, u_q; w; y]$, of positive degree in y. Let $w = \eta_1$ be a zero of A considered as a polynomial in $\mathfrak{F}_0[w]$; of course, η_1 lies in an extension of $\mathfrak{F}_0$. Let $\mathfrak{F}_1$ represent $\mathfrak{F}_0(\eta_1)$. We assume that the initial of A_1 does not vanish when w is replaced by η_1. We represent by B the polynomial in $\mathfrak{F}_1$ $[y]$ obtained by replacing w by η_1 in A_1. It is required to find the irreducible factors of B over $\mathfrak{F}_1$.[10]

It will be seen that the only knowledge of η_1 which we need is that it annuls A.

Let m be the degree of A in w. We shall show the existence of an extension $\mathfrak{F}'$ of $\mathfrak{F}_1$ in which A has m distinct zeros $\eta_1, \cdots, \eta_m$. Let C be the polynomial in $\mathfrak{F}_1[w]$, of degree $m - 1$, obtained by dividing A by $w - \eta_1$. Then C has a zero η_2, lying in an extension $\mathfrak{F}_2$ of $\mathfrak{F}_1$. The irreducibility of A in $\mathfrak{F}_0$ implies that η_1 and η_2 are distinct. Let $D = C/(w - \eta_2)$. We secure a zero of D. Continuing, we obtain a set $\eta_1, \cdots, \eta_m$.

Let z be an indeterminate and let E_1 be the polynomial in $\mathfrak{F}_1[y, z]$ which results on replacing y in B by $y - z\eta_1$. Let E_i, $i = 2, \cdots, m$, result from E_1 on replacing η_1 by η_i. Let $G = E_1E_2 \cdots E_m$.

Then G is a polynomial in $\mathfrak{F}_0[y, z]$, the coefficients in G being capable of determination by the theory of symmetric functions. Let G be resolved into factors irreducible in $\mathfrak{F}_0$. This is possible, provided we are able to factor a polynomial in one indeterminate over $\mathfrak{F}$.[11] Let

$$G = H_1 \cdots H_r \tag{16}$$

with each H a polynomial in $\mathfrak{F}_0[y, z]$, irreducible in F_0.

We wish to show that, for $j = 1, \cdots, r$, E_1 and H_j have a common factor, of positive degree, over $\mathfrak{F}_1$. Let this be false for some definite j. Then there exists a relation

$$U_1E_1 + V_1H_j = W_1 \tag{17}$$

with U_1, V_1, W_1 polynomials over $\mathfrak{F}_1$ and with W_1 free of z and distinct from zero. In (17), we replace η_1 by η_i, where $1 < i \leqq m$. We secure a relation[12]

$$U_iE_i + V_iH_j = W_i.$$

This shows that H_j has no common factor over $\mathfrak{F}'$, of positive degree in z, with any E_i. Similarly H_j has no common factor over $\mathfrak{F}'$, of positive degree in y, with any E_i. On the other hand, the factors of H_j irreducible over $\mathfrak{F}'$ must be factors of the E. This proves our statement.

Let K_i, $i = 1, \cdots, r$, be the highest common factor of E_1 and H_i, the field being $\mathfrak{F}_1$. We determine K_i by the Euclid algorithm, bearing in mind that a polynomial ξ in $\eta_1, u_1, \cdots, u_q$ is zero when and only when the polynomial in w and the u, obtained by replacing η_1 by w in ξ, is divisible by A.

We shall prove that the K become, for $z = 0$, the irreducible factors of B in $\mathfrak{F}_1$.[13] Let

$$B = M_1 \cdots M_k$$

---

[10] Our treatment follows van der Waerden, *Moderne Algebra*, first edition, vol. 1, p. 210.

[11] Perron, *Algebra*, vol. 1, p. 210.

[12] Every η is a generic zero of $(A)_0$, the field being $\mathfrak{F}_0$.

[13] We do not establish a one-to-one correspondence between the K and the irreducible factors. The knowledge of the essentially distinct irreducible factors of B permits the representation of B as a product of powers of irreducible factors.

be a resolution of B into factors irreducible in $\mathfrak{F}_1$. Then

$$E_1 = N_1 N_2 \cdots N_k$$

where each N_i results from M_i on replacing y by $y - z\eta_1$. It is easy to see that each N_i, as a polynomial in y and z, is irreducible in $\mathfrak{F}_1$.

Manifestly each N_i is a common factor of E_1 and some H_j in (16). If we can prove that, in this case, N_i is the *highest common factor* of E_1 and H_j, we will have our result.

Let $N_i^{(j)}$, for $j = 2, \cdots, m$, be the polynomial obtained from N_i on replacing η_1 by η_j. Let

$$P_i = N_i N_i'' \cdots N_i^{(m)}. \tag{18}$$

Then P_i is a polynomial in $\mathfrak{F}_0\,[y, z]$ and

$$G = P_1 P_2 \cdots P_k.$$

Each H_i in (16) is a factor of some P_j.

Suppose that N_1 is a factor of H_1 and that H_1 is a factor of P_1. If we can prove that N_1 is the highest common factor of E_1 and P_1, we will have our result.

Suppose, for instance, that P_1 is divisible by $N_1 N_2$. Then by (18),

$$N_1'' \cdots N_1^{(m)} = R(y, z) N_2, \tag{19}$$

where R is a polynomial in $\mathfrak{F}_1[y, z]$.

The set of terms of highest degree in the first member of (19) is of the form

$$b(y - z\eta_2)^s \cdots (y - z\eta_m)^s \tag{20}$$

with b a rational combination of the u and η. The terms of highest degree in the second member give an expression of the type

$$S(y, z)\,(y - z\eta_1)^t. \tag{21}$$

Now (20) and (21) cannot be equal, since no $y - z\eta_i$ with $i > 1$ is divisible by $y - z\eta_1$. This completes the proof.

22. We consider a nontrivial prime p.i. Σ in $\mathfrak{F}[u_1, \cdots, u_q; y_1, \cdots, y_p]$ for which

$$A_1, \cdots, A_p \tag{22}$$

is a characteristic set, A_i introducing y_i. In §§24, 25 we show how, when the A are given, a resolvent can be constructed for Σ.

23. Let $\lambda_1, \cdots, \lambda_p$ be new indeterminates. If Σ is regarded as a system of polynomials in the u, λ, y, Σ generates a p.i. $(\Sigma)_0$ which can be seen, as in I, §27, to be prime. Furthermore $(\Sigma)_0$ contains no nonzero polynomial in the u and λ.

We see as in §10 that there exists a nonzero G in the u and λ such that, for two distinct zeros of $(\Sigma)_0$ with the same u and λ, lying in the same extension of $\mathfrak{F}$ and not annulling G,

$$Q = \lambda_1 y_1 + \cdots + \lambda_p y_p$$

assumes two distinct values.[14]

By §§11, 12, a resolvent exists for $(\Sigma)_0$ for which $w = Q$. Let $\Omega = (\Sigma, w - Q)_0$ in $\mathfrak{F}[u; \lambda; w; y]$. We consider a characteristic set for Ω

$$R, R_1, \cdots, R_p \tag{23}$$

in which $w, y_1, \cdots, y_p$ are introduced in succession and in which R is irreducible in $\mathfrak{F}$. Then $R = 0$ is a resolvent for $(\Sigma)_0$ and each R_i is linear in y_i.

24. We shall show how a characteristic set (23) can actually be constructed.

Using the polynomials in (22), and also $w - Q$, we can, by the method of elimination of II, §34, determine, by means of a finite number of rational operations, a nonzero U in w, the u, and λ, which vanishes for every generic zero of Ω. It is a matter of considering relations $w^j = Q^j$ and depressing the degrees of Q^j in the y by using the relations $A_i = 0$. Then U is in Ω. Now let

$$U = U_1 \cdots U_r$$

with each U_i irreducible in $\mathfrak{F}$. Some U_i is in Ω. The selection of such a U_i can be made as follows. Consider any U_i and let V be the polynomial obtained from it by replacing w by Q. For U_i to be in Ω, it is necessary and sufficient that V be in $(\Sigma)_0$. Let V be arranged as a polynomial in the λ. For V to be in $(\Sigma)_0$, it is necessary and sufficient that every coefficient in the polynomial be in Σ. A coefficient will be in Σ if and only if its remainder with respect to (22) is zero.

A polynomial in w, the u, and λ which is in Ω is divisible by R. Thus an irreducible factor of U which is in Ω must be the product of R in (23) by an element of $\mathfrak{F}$.

We have then a method for constructing a resolvent for $(\Sigma)_0$. It remains to show how a complete set (23) can be determined.

Let W be the polynomial which results from R on replacing w by $w + y_1$ and λ_1 by $\lambda_1 + 1$. Then W holds Ω and is thus in Ω. The degree of W in y_1 is that of R in w and the coefficient of the highest power of y_1 in W is free of w.

Let $\mathfrak{F}_0$ represent $\mathfrak{F}(u_1, \cdots, u_q; \lambda_1, \cdots, \lambda_p)$ and let R be considered as a polynomial in $\mathfrak{F}_0[w]$. Let $w = \eta$ be any zero of R. We represent by B the polynomial in y_1 over $\mathfrak{F}_0(\eta)$ obtained by replacing w in W by η. Let

$$B = B_1 \cdots B_m \tag{24}$$

be a decomposition of B into factors irreducible in $\mathfrak{F}_0(\eta)$, obtained as in §21. The coefficients in the B_i are rational in η, the u and λ. Let α be the product of the denominators of these coefficients. We write

[14] At present we have no way of determining G.

$$\alpha B = C_1 \cdots C_m.$$

The C are irreducible in $\mathfrak{F}_0(\eta)$ and their coefficients are polynomials in η, the u, and λ. Let D be the polynomial which results from α on replacing η by w. Let E_i result similarly from C_i. Let

$$F = DW - E_1 \cdots E_m.$$

Then F vanishes identically in y_1 if w is replaced by η. Hence, if F is arranged as a polynomial in y_1, its coefficients are divisible by R. Thus F is in Ω. Then one of the E is in Ω. Suppose that E_1 is found (by test) to be in Ω. We say that E_1 is linear in y_1. If I_1 is the initial of R_1 in (23), we have

$$I_1^{\mu} E_1 = HR_1 + K \tag{25}$$

where K is free of y_1. Thus, if E_1 were not linear, it would follow that C_1 is reducible in $\mathfrak{F}_0(\eta)$.[15]

It is only necessary, then, to take the remainder of E_1 with respect to R to have a polynomial which will serve as R_1 in (23).

The R_i with $i > 1$ are determined in the same way.

It can be arranged, as in §14, so that, for each i, the initial I_i of R_i is free of w. We suppose this to be done. If two zeros of Ω have the same u, λ, w, they will have the same y if no I_i vanishes for their u, λ. We may thus take G as $I_1 I_2 \cdots I_p$.

25. It remains to construct a resolvent for Σ. Let I be the initial of R in (23). Let $a_1, \cdots, a_p$ be integers for which IG, with G as above, becomes a nonzero polynomial in the u when each λ_i is replaced by a_i.

We shall show how (23) yields a resolvent for Σ with

$$w = a_1 y_1 + \cdots + a_p y_p. \tag{26}$$

Let $\Omega' = (\Sigma, w - a_1 y_1 - \cdots - a_p y_p)_0$ in $\mathfrak{F}[u; w; y]$. Then Ω' is a prime p.i. For $\lambda_i = a_i$, $i = 1, \cdots, p$, (23) becomes a system of polynomials

$$R', R_1', \cdots, R_p' \tag{27}$$

each of which holds Ω' and is therefore in Ω'. As R and R' have the same degree in w, (27) is a chain.

We are going to show that R' is not the product of two polynomials over $\mathfrak{F}$ which are of positive degree in w. Thus, if we free R' of its factors in the u, we secure a polynomial R_0 which is irreducible in $\mathfrak{F}$. The equation $R_0 = 0$ will be a resolvent for Σ.[16] Also (27) will be a characteristic set of Ω'.

If R' is a product of two polynomials of positive degree in w, Ω' will have a characteristic set

$$T, T_1, \cdots, T_p,$$

[15] We note that I_1 cannot vanish for $w = \eta$.

[16] For w as in (26), two distinct zeros of Σ with the same u and w annul G', obtained from G by putting $\lambda_i = a_i$.

with T of lower degree in w than R'. We assume that the initials of the T_i are free of w. If D is the product of those initials, we have, for a generic zero of Σ,

$$(28) \qquad y_i = \frac{E_{i0} + E_{i1}\,w + \cdots + E_{i,\,g-1}\,w^{g-1}}{D},$$

where g is the degree of T in w and the E are polynomials in the u. We understand w to be given by (26).

Let us now consider the prime p.i.

$$\Omega'' = (\Sigma, v - \lambda_1 y_1 - \cdots - \lambda_p y_p)_0$$

in $\mathfrak{F}\,[u; \lambda; v; y]$. We show that Ω'' contains a nonzero polynomial K, free of the y, which is of degree no more than g in v. We consider the relations

$$v^j = (\lambda_1 y_1 + \cdots + \lambda_p y_p)^j, \qquad j = 0, \cdots, g.$$

We replace the y by their expressions in (28) and depress the degrees in w of the second members to less than g, using the relation $T = 0$. By a linear dependence argument, we secure the polynomial K. This furnishes the contradiction that R in (23) is of degree at most g in w.

Thus $R_0 = 0$ is a resolvent for Σ.

COMPONENTS OF FINITE SYSTEMS

26. Let Φ be a finite system of polynomials in $\mathfrak{F}[y_1, \cdots, y_n]$, not all zero. We are going to show how to determine characteristic sets of a finite number of prime p.i. whose manifolds make up the manifold[17] of Φ. Later, we shall obtain finite systems whose manifolds are the components of Φ.

A system Σ of polynomials will be said to be *equivalent* to the set of systems $\Sigma_1, \cdots, \Sigma_s$ if the manifold of Σ is the union[18] of the manifolds of the Σ_i.

Let

$$(29) \qquad A_1, \cdots, A_p$$

be a characteristic set of Φ, obtained as in I, §5. If A_1 is of class zero, Φ has no zeros. We assume now that A_1 is of positive class. For every polynomial in Φ, let the remainder with respect to (29) be determined. If these remainders are adjoined to Φ, we get a system Φ' equivalent to Φ. By I, §5, if some of the remainders are not zero, Φ' will have a characteristic set lower than (29). We see, by I, §4, that after a finite number of repetitions of the above operation, we arrive at a finite system Λ, equivalent to Φ, with a characteristic set[19] (29) for which either A_1 is of class zero or for which, otherwise, the remainder of every polynomial in Λ is zero.

27. Let us suppose that we are in the latter case. We make a temporary relettering of the y. If, in the characteristic set (29) of Λ, A_i is of class j_i, we

[17] If Φ has no zeros, we obtain $(1)_0$.

[18] In this, we understand that if Σ has no zeros, no Σ_i has zeros.

[19] Naturally, (29) is not the same for Λ as for Φ.

replace the symbol y_{j_i} by y_i. The $q = n - p$ indeterminates not among the y_{j_i} we call, in any order, $u_1, \cdots, u_q$. We list the indeterminates in the order $u_1, \cdots, u_q; y_1, \cdots, y_p$.

With this change of notation, we proceed to determine, using §§17–19, whether (29) is a characteristic set for a prime p.i.

28. If A_1 is reducible as a polynomial in y_1 over $\mathfrak{F}(u_1, \cdots, u_q)$ and if $A_1 = MN$ with M and N polynomials in $u_1, \cdots, u_q; y_1$, of positive degree in y_1, then Λ is equivalent to $\Lambda + M, \Lambda + N$. Each of the latter systems, after we revert to the old notation, will have a characteristic set lower than (29).

Suppose now that A_1 is irreducible in $\mathfrak{F}(u_1, \cdots, u_q)$. We use indeterminates $\tau_1, \cdots, \tau_q$ and the field $\mathfrak{F}(\tau_1, \cdots, \tau_q)$ which we represent by $\mathfrak{F}_0$. For $u_i = \tau_i$, $i = 1, \cdots, q$, A_1 becomes a polynomial B_1 in $\mathfrak{F}_0 [y_1]$. Let $y_1 = \eta_1$ be a zero of B_1. Let B_2 be the polynomial in $\mathfrak{F}_0(\eta_1) [y_2]$ which A_2 becomes for $y_1 = \eta_1$, $u_i = \tau_i$. Suppose that B_2 is reducible in $\mathfrak{F}_0(\eta_1)$. We have, in analogy to (14),

$$\delta B_2 - EF = 0, \tag{30}$$

where δ is a polynomial in η_1 and the τ. E and F are polynomials in y_2, of positive degree, whose coefficients are polynomials in η_1 and the τ. When we replace η_1 and the τ by y_1 and the u, the first member of (30) becomes a polynomial

$$GA_2 - HK$$

which, when arranged according to powers of y_2, has coefficients which are divisible by A_1.

Thus $GA_2 - HK$ is in $(A_1)_0$ so that HK is in[20] $(A_1, A_2)_0$. Let M and N be, respectively, the remainders of H and K with respect to A_1. Because the initial of GA_2 is not divisible by A_1, the initials of H and K are not so divisible. It follows that M and N are not zero (§19). As MN is in $(A_1, A_2)_0$, we see that Λ is equivalent to $\Lambda + M, \Lambda + N$, whose characteristic sets, in the old notation, are lower than (29).

29. Suppose that B_2 is irreducible in $\mathfrak{F}_0 (\eta_1)$. By §18, A_1, A_2 is a characteristic set of a prime p.i. Σ_2 in y_1, y_2 and the u. Let η_2 be any zero of B_2. We shall show that

$$\tau_1, \cdots, \tau_q; \qquad \eta_1, \eta_2 \tag{31}$$

is a generic zero of Σ_2. Let G be a polynomial in Σ_2. The remainder of G with respect to A_1, A_2 is zero. As the initials of A_1 and A_2 do not vanish for (31), G is annulled by (31). Conversely, let G be a polynomial in y_1, y_2 and the u which is annulled by (31). The remainder R of G with respect to A_1, A_2 also vanishes for (31). Suppose that R is not zero. If R is arranged as a polynomial in y_2, its coefficients will not be divisible by A_1 and thus will not vanish for η_1 and the τ. Substituting these quantities for y_1 and the u in R, we secure

[20] In $\mathfrak{F}[u; y_1, y_2]$.

a polynomial in y_2 of lower degree than B_2 which vanishes for $y_2 = \eta_2$. This contradiction shows that $R = 0$. Then G is in Σ_2. Thus (31) is a generic zero of Σ_2.

We substitute the quantities (31) into A_3, securing a polynomial B_3 in y_3 over $\mathfrak{F}_0(\eta_1, \eta_2)$. We need a method for finding the irreducible factors of B_3 in $\mathfrak{F}_0(\eta_1, \eta_2)$. Let a resolvent be constructed for Σ_2 as in §§24, 25, with

$$w - a_1 y_1 - a_2 y_2 = 0,$$

a_1 and a_2 being integers. Now

$$\tau_1, \cdots, \tau_q; \qquad a_1\eta_1 + a_2\eta_2; \qquad \eta_1, \eta_2$$

is a generic zero of the prime p.i. for which (27), with $p = 2$, is a characteristic set. Thus $a_1\eta_1 + a_2\eta_2$ annuls R', but not the initials of R_1' and R_2'. Hence η_1 and η_2 are rational in $a_1\eta_1 + a_2\eta_2$ and the τ. Thus, to factor B_3 in $\mathfrak{F}_0(\eta_1, \eta_2)$ it suffices to factor B_3 in $\mathfrak{F}_0(a_1\eta_1 + a_2\eta_2)$. This we know how to do.

Suppose that B_3 is reducible in $\mathfrak{F}_0(\eta_1, \eta_2)$. We have, as in (30), a relation

$$\delta B_3 - EF = 0$$

where δ is a polynomial in η_1, η_2 and the τ. If, in the first member, we replace η_1, η_2 and the τ by y_1, y_2 and the u, we secure a polynomial $GA_3 - HK$ which, when arranged in powers of y_3, has its coefficients in Σ_2. Let L be any of these coefficients. Let I_i represent the initial of A_i in (29). As the remainder of L with respect to A_1, A_2 is zero, some $I_1^a I_2^b L$ is in $(A_1, A_2)_0$. Then some

$$I_1^c I_2^d (GA_3 - HK)$$

is linear in A_1 and A_2, so that $I_1^c I_2^d\, HK$ is in $(A_1, A_2, A_3)_0$. Let M and N be, respectively, the remainders of $I_1^c I_2^d\, H$ and K with respect to A_1, A_2. Then M and N are not zero and MN is in $(A_1, A_2, A_3)_0$. Thus Λ is equivalent to $\Lambda + M$, $\Lambda + N$, each of which, in the old notation, has characteristic sets lower than (29).

30. If B is irreducible in $\mathfrak{F}_0(\eta_1, \eta_2)$ then A_1, A_2, A_3 is a characteristic set of a prime p.i. Σ_3, and we continue as above.

All in all, we have a method for testing (29) to determine whether it is a characteristic set for a prime p.i. and for replacing Λ by a pair of systems with characteristic sets lower than (29) when the test is negative.[21]

In developing our method, we have recast the conditions of §§17, 18 and have secured the following theorem.

THEOREM: *A chain of polynomials of positive class fails to be a characteristic set of a prime p.i. if and only if there exist two nonzero polynomials, reduced with respect to the chain, whose product is in the p.i. generated by the chain.*

---

[21] If, when the indeterminates are $u_1, \cdots, u_q; y_1, \cdots, y_p$, (29) is a characteristic set for a prime p.i. Ω, then, when we revert to the old notation, (29) will be a characteristic set for the prime p.i. into which Ω goes.

31. Using now the old notation for the indeterminates, let us suppose that (29) has been found to be a characteristic set for a prime p.i. Σ. Then Λ is equivalent to [22]

$$(32)\qquad \Sigma, \Lambda + I_1, \cdots, \Lambda + I_p.$$

Each $\Lambda + I_j$ has characteristic sets which are lower than (29).

What precedes shows that the system Φ of §26 can be resolved into an equivalent set of prime p.i., as far as the determination of characteristic sets for the prime p.i. goes, by a finite number of rational operations and factorizations, if the same can be done for all finite systems whose characteristic sets are lower than those of Φ. The final remark of I, §4, gives a quick abstract proof that the resolution is possible for Φ. What is more, the processes used above, of reduction, factorization and isolation of prime p.i., give an algorithm for the reduction.

32. It remains to solve the following problem: Given a characteristic set

$$(33)\qquad A_1, \cdots, A_p$$

of a nontrivial prime p.i. Σ in $\mathfrak{F}[y_1, \cdots, y_n]$, each A_i being of class $q + i$ $(p + q = n)$, it is required to find a finite system of polynomials equivalent to Σ.[23]

33. Using indeterminates t_{ij}, we make the transformation

$$(34)\qquad z_i = t_{i1}y_1 + \cdots + t_{in}y_n, \qquad i = 1, \cdots, n.$$

For a zero of Σ in an extension $\mathfrak{F}_1$ of $\mathfrak{F}$, (34) gives quantities z in the field obtained by adjoining the t to $\mathfrak{F}_1$. Given any $q + 1$ of the z

$$z_{i_1}, \cdots, z_{i_{q+1}},$$

we find, by the method of elimination of II, §34, a nonzero polynomial in them and the t which vanishes when the z are replaced by their expressions in (34), with $y_1, \cdots, y_n$ a generic zero of Σ.

Let B be such a polynomial in $z_1, \cdots, z_{q+1}$ and the t. Let m be the degree of B considered as a polynomial in the z. We shall show how to obtain a relation $C = 0$ among $z_1, \cdots, z_{q+1}$ and the[24] t, where C is of degree m as a polynomial in the z and, in addition, is of degree m in each z separately.

We make in B the transformation

$$(35)\qquad z_i = a_{i1}z'_1 + \cdots + a_{i,\,q+1}z'_{q+1}, \qquad i = 1, \cdots, q + 1,$$

where the a and z' are indeterminates. Then B becomes a polynomial B' in the z' whose coefficients are polynomials in the t and the a. The degree of B'

[22] Note that Λ is contained in Σ because the remainder of every polynomial in Λ with respect to (29) is zero. Every zero of (29) which annuls no initial is a zero of Σ.

[23] Φ of §26 leads to several Σ. For each Σ, we reletter the indeterminates appropriately. After finite systems are found, equivalent to the various Σ, we revert to the original lettering.

[24] Satisfied when the y in (34) are a generic zero of Σ.

in each z'_i will be effectively m.[25] Furthermore, we can specialize the a as integers in such a way that the determinant $|a_{ij}|$ is not zero and that the coefficient of the mth power of each z'_i in B' becomes a nonzero polynomial in the t. Let this be done and let B'' be the polynomial in the z' and t into which B' thus goes.

The transformation (34), and (35) with the a as just fixed, give a transformation

$$(36) \qquad z'_i = \tau_{i1}y_1 + \cdots + \tau_{in}y_n, \qquad i = 1, \cdots, q+1,$$

where each τ is a linear combination, with rational coefficients, of the t_{ij} with $i \leqq q+1$. From (35), (36), we see that the t_{ij} with $i \leqq q+1$ are linear in the τ with integral coefficients.

In B'', we substitute for each t its expression in terms of the τ and we regard the symbols τ as indeterminates instead of linear combinations of the t. Then B'' goes over into a polynomial B''' in the z'_i, τ_{ij}, $i = 1, \cdots, q+1$. We see that B''' vanishes identically in the τ if we replace the z' by their expressions in (36), with the y a generic zero of Σ. We now replace, in B''', each τ_{ij} by t_{ij} and each z'_i by z_i. Then B''' goes over into a polynomial C in $z_1, \cdots, z_{q+1}$ and the t, C being of degree m as a polynomial in the z and of degree m in each z separately. C vanishes for the z as in (34) with the y a generic zero of Σ.

Evidently the relation $C = 0$ just described will subsist if we replace $z_1, \cdots, z_{q+1}$ by any $q+1$ of the z_i, provided that a corresponding substitution is made for the t in C.

We now specialize the t in (34) as integers with a nonvanishing determinant, in such a way that, for every set of $q+1$ indeterminates z, the polynomial over $\mathfrak{F}$ obtained from C remains of effective degree m in each z appearing in it.

34. We consider the transformation (34) with the t as just fixed. If the y are replaced in (33) in terms of the z, we get a system Φ of p polynomials in the z. Let characteristic sets be determined for a set of prime p.i. equivalent to Φ. Let $\Sigma_1, \cdots, \Sigma_s$ be those prime p.i. which do not contain the initial of any A in (33), the y being replaced in the initials in terms of the z.[26] There will be one of the Σ_i which holds the remaining Σ_i. This is because, in a resolution of (33) into an equivalent set of prime p.i., none of which is a divisor of any other, there is precisely one p.i. which contains no initial.[27] To determine which Σ_i holds the others, all we need do is to find a Σ_i whose characteristic set holds the other Σ_i. Suppose, for instance, that the characteristic set of Σ_1 holds $\Sigma_2, \cdots, \Sigma_s$. Then, if Σ_1 does not hold Σ_j, the initial of some polynomial in the characteristic set of Σ_1 must hold Σ_j. Then surely Σ_j cannot hold Σ_1. Thus, if Σ_1 does not hold all Σ_i, no Σ_j can hold all Σ_i. Then Σ_1 holds all Σ_i

Σ_1 is obtained from Σ of §32 by replacing the y in terms of the z. We shall

[25] Perron, *Algebra*, vol. 1, p. 288.

[26] The condition for a polynomial to be contained in a prime p.i. is that its remainder with respect to the characteristic set vanish.

[27] This is seen from (32).

prove that Σ_1 has the same dimension as Σ. To begin with, it is easy to see that the polynomials in any $q + 1$ of the z, found in §33, belong to Σ_1. On the other hand, if there were fewer than q indeterminates in a parametric set of Σ_1, we could use a characteristic set of Σ_1 to determine a nonzero polynomial in $\mathfrak{F}[y_1, \cdots, y_q]$ belonging to Σ.

Changing the notation if necessary, let $z_1, \cdots, z_q$ be a parametric set for Σ_1. Then Σ_1 will have a characteristic set

$$B_1, \cdots, B_p \tag{37}$$

in which B_i introduces z_{q+i}.

35. We construct a resolvent $R = 0$ for Σ_1, with

$$w = a_1 z_{q+1} + \cdots + a_p z_n, \tag{38}$$

the a being integers. Let R be of degree g in w.

We shall prove that the initial of R is an element of $\mathfrak{F}$. According to §33, each z_i, $i > q$, in a zero of Σ_1 satisfies with $z_1, \cdots, z_q$ a fixed equation of degree m in z_i, the coefficient of z_i^m being an element of $\mathfrak{F}$. The coefficient just mentioned will be assumed to be unity. Then (38) shows that w satisfies with $z_1, \cdots, z_q$ an equation in which the highest power of w is unity.[28] This implies that in the irreducible polynomial R, the coefficient of w^g is free of $z_1, \cdots, z_q$. We may and shall assume that coefficient to be unity.

Referring to §25, we see that

$$z_i = \frac{E_{i0} + E_{i1} w + \cdots + E_{i,\,g-1} w^{g-1}}{D}, \tag{39}$$

$i = q + 1, \cdots, n$, where D and the E are in[29] $\mathfrak{F}[z_1, \cdots, z_q]$.

36. Let $t_1, \cdots, t_p$; v be new indeterminates and let

$$\Lambda = (\Sigma_1, v - t_1 z_{q+1} - \cdots - t_p z_n)_0$$

in $\mathfrak{F}[z; t; v]$. Then Λ is a prime p.i. Also Λ contains an irreducible polynomial U in $v, z_1, \cdots, z_q$ and the t, the coefficient of whose highest power of v, say v^d, is unity.[30]

We shall prove that $d = g$. We see first, following §25, that $d \leqq g$. As v, in a zero of Λ, equals w if $t_i = a_i$, $i = 1, \cdots, p$, we cannot have $d < g$.[31]

Let v be replaced in U by

$$t_1 z_{q+1} + \cdots + t_p z_n. \tag{40}$$

Then U becomes a polynomial V in $z_1, \cdots, z_n$ and the t. Let V be arranged as a polynomial in the t with coefficients which are polynomials in the z.

[28] This is analogous to the fact that the sum of several algebraic integers is an integer. See Landau, *Zahlentheorie*, vol. 3, p. 71.

[29] The relations (39) hold for any zero of Σ_1 with $D \neq 0$, and for the corresponding w.

[30] Note that each $t_i z_{q+i}$ satisfies an equation in which the coefficient of the highest power of $t_i z_{q+i}$ is unity.

[31] As the coefficient of v^d in U is unity, U cannot vanish identically for $t_i = a_i$.

Let Ψ be the finite system of those coefficients (polynomials in the z). We are going to prove, in the following sections, that Ψ is equivalent to Σ_1. Thus, if the z are replaced in Ψ by their expressions (34), we get a finite system of polynomials equivalent to Σ. We shall thus have solved the problem stated in §32.

37. We begin with the observation that for given elements $z_1, \cdots, z_n$ of an extension $\mathfrak{F}_1$ of $\mathfrak{F}$ to constitute a zero of Ψ, it is necessary and sufficient that for $z_1, \cdots, z_n$ as just given, V vanish for arbitrary t in[32] $\mathfrak{F}_1$. This shows, in particular, that Ψ holds Σ_1.

Let G be the discriminant of R with respect to w and let

$$H = DG$$

where D is as in (39). We shall prove that every zero of Ψ with $H \neq 0$ is a zero of Σ_1. Let $\eta_1, \cdots, \eta_n$ be such a zero of Ψ. For $z_i = \eta_i$, $i = 1, \cdots, q$, R becomes a polynomial T in w. From §21, we see that T has g zeros in some extension of $\mathfrak{F}(\eta_1, \cdots, \eta_q)$. These zeros are distinct, because $\eta_1, \cdots, \eta_q$ do not annul G. Using each such w in (39), we get g distinct zeros,

$$\eta_1, \cdots, \eta_q; \qquad z_{q+1}^{(j)}, \cdots, z_n^{(j)}, \qquad\qquad j = 1, \cdots, g,$$

of Σ_1. Let Z be the polynomial which U becomes for $z_i = \eta_i$, $i = 1, \cdots, q$. Then[33]

$$Z = \prod_{j=1}^{g} (v - t_1 z_{q+1}^{(j)} - \cdots - t_p z_n^{(j)}). \tag{41}$$

But $v - t_1\eta_{q+1} - \cdots - t_p\eta_n$ is a factor of Z. This shows that, for some j, $z_i^{(j)} = \eta_i$, $i = q + 1, \cdots, n$, and proves our statement.

38. We have to show that a zero $\eta_1, \cdots, \eta_n$ of Ψ which annuls H is a zero of Σ_1. Our proof will employ a Newton polygon process, which we can carry out rapidly by using the material of Chapter III.

For $z_i = \eta_i$, $i = 1, \cdots, q$, R becomes a polynomial J in w. In some extension $\mathfrak{F}_1$ of $\mathfrak{F}(\eta_1, \cdots, \eta_q)$, J has g linear factors. We write

$$J = (w - \xi_1) \cdots (w - \xi_g).$$

Now let $b_1, \cdots, b_q$ be integers such that

$$H(\eta_1 + b_1, \cdots, \eta_q + b_q) \neq 0.$$

Then, if c is an indeterminate,

$$H(\eta_1 + b_1c, \cdots, \eta_q + b_qc) \tag{42}$$

is a polynomial in c which is not identically zero. We put in R,

---

[32] This means that V vanishes identically in the t.

[33] Note that Z is a polynomial in v and the t which vanishes for $v = t_1z_{q+1}^{(j)} + \cdots + t_pz_n^{(j)}$. We have thus g distinct factors of Z. As Z is of degree g in v, with unity for the coefficient of v^g, it has the expression in (41).

$$z_i = \eta_i + b_i c, \qquad i = 1, \cdots, q.$$

Then R goes over into a polynomial K in w whose coefficients are polynomials in c. In K, we put $w = \xi_1 + w_1$. Then K becomes an expression K' in w_1 and c which we write

$$K' = a'(c) + \sum_{i=1}^{g} b_i'(c)\, w_1^i. \tag{43}$$

We shall now regard $\mathfrak{F}_1$ as a differential field in which every derivative is zero. Furthermore, we regard w_1 as a differential indeterminate and c as an arbitrary constant. We wish to show that K' in (43) is annulled either by $w_1 = 0$ or by a series

$$w_1 = \varphi_2 c^{\rho_2} + \cdots + \varphi_k c^{\rho_k} + \cdots \tag{44}$$

similar to the series employed in Chapter III, with the distinction that ρ_2, while positive, need not exceed unity.

It may be that K' is annulled by $w_1 = 0$. Let us suppose that this does not happen. Then $a'(c)$ is not zero. We compare (43) with (3) of III, §7. The role of U_i' is taken over by w_1^i. Because K' vanishes when w_1 and c are replaced by zero, the lowest exponent of c in a' is positive. Again, the only exponent of c in b_g' is zero. Thus ρ_2 of III, §7, will be positive. Without further change, the work of Chapter III furnishes the series in (44).

Let

$$\alpha_1 = \xi_1 + \varphi_2 c^{\rho_2} + \cdots + \varphi_k c^{\rho_k} + \cdots.$$

We have

$$K = (w - \alpha_1)K_1$$

where K_1 is a polynomial in w of degree $g - 1$, whose coefficients are series in c. The terms free of c in K_1 are annulled by $w = \xi_2$. When w is replaced by $\xi_2 + w_1$, K_1 goes over into an expression K' like that in (43) except that the a' and b' are infinite series of fractional powers instead of polynomials. We secure a series like (44) which annuls the K' with which we are now working.

All in all, we have a representation of K

$$K = (w - \alpha_1) \cdots (w - \alpha_g)$$

where each α_i is a series of the type

$$\alpha_i = \xi_i + \varphi_2 c^{\rho_2} + \cdots. \tag{45}$$

The ρ and the φ depend on i. If we replace c by a suitable positive integral power h^r of an indeterminate h, we have, for $i = 1, \cdots, g$,

$$\alpha_i = \xi_i + \psi_{i1} h + \psi_{i2} h^2 + \cdots. \tag{46}$$

The ψ all lie in some extension of $\mathfrak{F}_1$.

From this point on, we regard our fields as algebraic fields and h as an algebraic indeterminate.

The α are distinct, since G does not vanish for

$$z_i = \eta_i + b_i h^r, \qquad i = 1, \cdots, q. \tag{47}$$

We use (39), understanding that (47) holds and that $w = \alpha_i$. We secure g distinct zeros of Σ_1,

$$\eta_1 + b_1 h^r, \cdots, \eta_q + b_q h^r; \qquad z_{q+1}^{(j)}, \cdots, z_n^{(j)},$$

$j = 1, \cdots, g$. Each $z_i^{(j)}$ is a series of integral powers of h. Such a series can contain no negative power of h. This follows from the fact that Σ_1 contains a polynomial in $z_1, \cdots, z_q, z_i$ in which one of the terms of highest degree is a term in z_i alone (§33).

Let $\zeta_i^{(j)}$ be the term of $z_i^{(j)}$ which is of zero degree in h. Then, for every j,

$$\eta_1, \cdots, \eta_q; \qquad \zeta_{q+1}^{(j)}, \cdots, \zeta_n^{(j)}$$

is a zero of Σ_1.

Let Z_h be the polynomial in v and $t_1, \cdots, t_p$ which U of §36 becomes for (47). Then

$$Z_h = \prod_{j=1}^{g} (v - t_1 z_{q+1}^{(j)} - \cdots - t_p z_n^{(j)}).$$

Letting Z_0 represent Z_h with $h = 0$, we have

$$Z_0 = \prod_{j=1}^{g} (v - t_1 \zeta_{q+1}^{(j)} - \cdots - t_p \zeta_n^{(j)}).$$

Now $v - t_1\eta_{q+1} - \cdots - t_p\eta_n$ is a factor of Z_0. This shows that $\eta_{q+1}, \cdots, \eta_n$ are the $\zeta^{(j)}$ for some j, so that, as we undertook to prove, $\eta_1, \cdots, \eta_n$ is a zero of Σ_1.

We have thus proved that Ψ is equivalent to Σ_1.

An approximation theorem

39. Working in the analytic case, we prove the following theorem.

THEOREM: *Let Σ be a prime p.i. in $y_1, \cdots, y_n$. Let B be any polynomial not contained in Σ. Given any zero of Σ, consisting of functions analytic in an open region* **B**, *there is an open region* **C**, *contained in* **B**, *in which the given zero can be approximated uniformly, with arbitrary closeness, by zeros of Σ for which B is distinct from zero throughout* **C**.

We assume, as we may, that Σ is nontrivial. If the transformation of §33 is effected, Σ may be replaced by Σ_1, while B goes over into a polynomial B_1 in $z_1, \cdots, z_n$.

B_1 is not in Σ_1. Let $z_{q+1}, \cdots, z_n$ be replaced in B_1 by their expressions (39). We find that, for every zero of Σ_1 with $D \neq 0$,

$$B_1 = \frac{M}{D^\mu} \tag{48}$$

where M is a polynomial in $w; z_1, \cdots, z_q$. Because DB_1 is not in Σ_1, M is not divisible by R of §35. Thus we have

$$XR + YM = N$$

where N is a nonzero polynomial in $z_1, \cdots, z_q$. A zero of Σ_1 which annuls B_1 annuls N.

Let $\eta_1, \cdots, \eta_n$ be a zero of Σ_1, analytic in an open region **B**, which annuls N. Shrinking **B** if necessary, we assume that every one of the polynomials in w and the z which we meet in what follows has its coefficients analytic throughout **B**.

Let $H_1 = NH$. We use constants b_i such that

$$H_1(\eta_1 + b_1, \cdots, \eta_q + b_q)$$

does not vanish for every x. Then, if h is a complex variable,

$$H_1(\eta_1 + b_1h, \cdots, \eta_q + b_qh) \tag{49}$$

is a polynomial in h of the type

$$\alpha_r h^r + \cdots + \alpha_s h^s \tag{50}$$

where the α are functions of x analytic in **B**. As H_1 in (49) vanishes for $h = 0$, we have $r > 0$. We assume that α_r is not identically zero.

Let $\mathbf{B}_1$ be a simply connected open region contained with its boundary in **B**, in which α_r is bounded away from zero. Let h be small but distinct from zero. Then (50) cannot be zero at any point of $\mathbf{B}_1$. Thus, if

$$z_i = \eta_i + b_ih, \qquad i = 1, \cdots, q, \tag{51}$$

$R = 0$ will have g distinct solutions for w, each analytic in $\mathbf{B}_1$. This is because H_1 is divisible by the discriminant of R.

As H_1 is divisible by D in (39), Σ_1 will have g distinct zeros with $z_1, \cdots, z_q$ as in (51),

$$z_1, \cdots, z_q; \quad z_{q+1}^{(k)}, \cdots, z_n^{(k)}, \qquad k = 1, \cdots, g,$$

each consisting of functions analytic in $\mathbf{B}_1$. The $z^{(k)}$ are given by (39).

Consider a sequence of nonzero values of h which tend towards zero,

$$h_1, h_2, \cdots, h_j, \cdots, \tag{52}$$

each h_j being so small that (50) is distinct from zero throughout $\mathbf{B}_1$. For each j, if

$$z_i = \eta_i + b_ih_j, \qquad i = 1, \cdots, q, \tag{53}$$

U of §36 will vanish if

$$v = t_1 z_{q+1}^{(k)} + \cdots + t_p z_n^{(k)}, \tag{54}$$

$k = 1, \cdots, g$. It is understood, of course, that the $z^{(k)}$, which are analytic throughout $\mathbf{B}_1$, depend on h_j. For any h_j, the g expressions (54) are distinct.

As the equation of degree m which a z_j, $j > q$, satisfies with $z_1, \cdots, z_q$ has unity for the coefficient of z_j^m, there is a positive number d, such that, throughout $\mathbf{B}_1$,

$$| z_j^{(k)} | < d \tag{55}$$

for $j = q + 1, \cdots, n$; $k = 1, \cdots, g$ and for every h in (52). This is because the coefficients of $z_j^{m-1}, \cdots, z_j^0$ in the above mentioned equation are bounded quantities.

For each h_j of (52), let one of the g expressions (54) be selected, and be designated by $v^{(j)}$. We form thus a sequence

$$v', v'', \cdots, v^{(j)}, \cdots. \tag{56}$$

Let $\mathbf{C}$ be any open region which lies with its boundary in $\mathbf{B}_1$. From (56) we see, using a well known theorem on bounded families of analytic functions,[34] that, for some subsequence of (56), the coefficients of each t_i, $i = 1, \cdots, p$, converge uniformly throughout $\mathbf{C}$ to an analytic function η_i'. We find thus that if

$$z_i = \eta_i, \qquad i = 1, \cdots, q, \tag{57}$$

U vanishes for

$$v = t_1 \eta_{q+1}' + \cdots + t_p \eta_n'.$$

Deleting elements of (56) if necessary, we assume that the convergence occurs when the complete sequence (56) is used, rather than one of its subsequences. For each h_j, there are $g - 1$ expressions (54) not used in (56). Let one of these be selected for each h_j and let (56) be used now to represent the sequence thus obtained. As above, we select a subsequence of (56) for which the coefficients of each t_i converge uniformly in $\mathbf{C}$. This gives a second expression which causes U to vanish when (57) holds. Continuing, we find g expressions

$$v = t_1 \eta_{q+1}^{(k)} + \cdots + t_p \eta_n^{(k)}, \qquad k = 1, \cdots, g, \tag{58}$$

which make U vanish when (57) holds.

Let v_k represent the second member of (58). Again, let w_k represent the second member of (54), it being understood that the subscripts k are assigned, for each h_j, in such a way that the coefficient of t_i in w_k converges to that in v_k as h_j approaches zero.

Then, since the g expressions w_k are distinct from one another for each h_j, we will have, representing by Z_j the polynomial which U becomes when (53) holds,

---

[34] Montel, *Les familles normales de fonctions analytiques*, p. 21; Dienes, *The Taylor Series*, p. 160.

$$Z_j = (v - w_1) \cdots (v - w_g).$$

By continuity, if we represent U, when (57) holds, by Z,

$$Z = (v - v_1) \cdots (v - v_g).$$

As $v - t_1\eta_{q+1} - \cdots - t_p\eta_n$ is a factor of Z, it must be that, for some k,

$$\eta_i = \eta_i^{(k)}, \qquad i = q + 1, \cdots, n.$$

Thus $\eta_1, \cdots, \eta_n$ can be approximated uniformly in **C**, with arbitrary closeness, by zeros of Σ_1 for which B_1 is distinct from zero throughout **C**. As the y vary continuously with the z, we have our theorem.

ZEROS AND CHARACTERISTIC SETS

40. We consider a nontrivial prime p.i. Σ in $\mathfrak{F}[u_1, \cdots, u_q; y_1, \cdots, y_p]$ with the u a parametric set. Let

$$(59) \qquad A_1, \cdots, A_p$$

be a characteristic set for Σ. We know that every zero of (59) for which no initial vanishes is a zero of Σ. We shall prove that *every zero of* (59) *for which no separant vanishes is a zero of* Σ.

Let $\eta_1, \cdots, \eta_n$ be a zero of (59) which annuls no separant.

In A_1, we replace u_i by $\eta_i + \tau_i$, $i = 1, \cdots, q$, where the τ are indeterminates, and y_1 by $\eta_{q+1} + y_1'$. Then A_1 goes over into a polynomial B_1 in y_1' and the τ which vanishes when the indeterminates are all replaced by zero. Because the separant of A_1 does not vanish for the η, B_1 contains a term $\alpha y_1'$ with α in $\mathfrak{F}(\eta_1, \cdots, \eta_n)$ and distinct from zero. We solve the equation $B_1 = 0$ for y_1' in terms of the τ, using the formal process of the implicit function theorem for securing a representation of y_1' as an infinite series of powers of the τ. We can do this because of the presence of $\alpha y_1'$. Let ξ_1 be the series thus obtained for y_1'. The terms of ξ_1 are all of positive degree.

The set

$$(60) \qquad \eta_1 + \tau_1, \cdots, \eta_q + \tau_q; \quad \eta_{q+1} + \xi_1$$

is a generic zero of the prime p.i. in y_1 and the u for which A_1 is a characteristic set.

We substitute the quantities (60) into A_2 and replace y_2 by $\eta_{q+2} + y_2'$. Then A_2 goes over into a polynomial B_2 in y_2'. The coefficients in B_2 are series of non-negative powers of the τ and the coefficient of y_2' contains a term free of the τ. We can thus solve $B_2 = 0$ for y_2', expressing y_2' as a series ξ_2 of powers of τ, the terms of ξ_2 being of positive degree. By §29,

$$\eta_1 + \tau_1, \cdots, \quad \eta_q + \tau_q; \quad \eta_{q+1} + \xi_1, \quad \eta_{q+2} + \xi_2$$

is a generic zero of the prime p.i. Σ_2 for which A_1, A_2 is a characteristic set. It follows that $\eta_1, \cdots, \eta_{q+2}$ is a zero of Σ_2. Continuing, we find that $\eta_1, \cdots, \eta_n$ is a zero of Σ.

CHAPTER V

CONSTRUCTIVE METHODS

CHARACTERISTIC SETS OF PRIME IDEALS

1. We return to differential fields and to differential polynomials. Let

$$A_1, \cdots, A_p \tag{1}$$

be a chain in $\mathfrak{F}\{y_1, \cdots, y_n\}$, A_i being of positive class j_i. We are going to find a necessary and sufficient condition for (1) to be a characteristic set of a prime ideal.

Let the order of A_i in y_{j_i} be r_i. We represent each $y_{j_i r_i}$ by z_i. The remaining y_{lm} in (1) we designate now by new symbols[1] v_k, attributing the subscripts k in any convenient way. With these replacements, (1) goes over into a chain of polynomials

$$B_1, \cdots, B_p \tag{2}$$

in algebraic indeterminates

$$v_1, \cdots, v_r; \qquad z_1, \cdots, z_p. \tag{3}$$

The passage from (1) to (2) is purely formal. Once it is effected, we treat (2) as we would any other set of polynomials in the v and z. For the B, the basic differential field $\mathfrak{F}$ is regarded as an algebraic field, its operation of differentiation being suppressed. Again, whereas in a zero of (1) $y_{l,\,m+1}$ must be the derivative of y_{lm}, any set of v, z which lie in an algebraic field containing the elements of $\mathfrak{F}$, and which annul the B, is a zero of (2).

We are going to prove that *for* (1) *to be a characteristic set of a prime ideal, it is necessary and sufficient that* (2) *be a characteristic set of a prime p.i.*[2] *in the indeterminates* (3).

2. We prove first the necessity. Suppose that (2) is not a characteristic set of a prime p.i. We refer to IV, §30. There are polynomials M and N, reduced with respect to (2), such that MN is in $(B_1, \cdots, B_p)_0$. When we replace the v and z by the y_{lm}, M and N become, respectively, d.p. P and Q, reduced with respect to (1), such that PQ is in $(A_1, \cdots, A_p)$. If (1) were a characteristic set of a prime ideal Σ, then PQ, but neither P nor Q, would be in Σ. The necessity is proved.

3. We now prove sufficiency. Let (2) be a characteristic set of a prime p.i. Let Σ be the totality of those d.p. G for which there exists a power product J of the separants and initials of the A, depending on G, such that

[1] We use only letters effectively present in (1).

[2] As has been indicated, the algebraic field used for (2) is the set of elements of $\mathfrak{F}$.

$$JG \equiv 0, \qquad [A_1, \cdots, A_p].$$

We see from Chapter I that Σ is an ideal. We shall prove that Σ is prime and that (1) is a characteristic set of Σ.

Suppose that Σ contains a d.p. PQ but neither P nor Q. Let R and T be, respectively, the remainders of P and Q with respect to (1). Then Σ contains RT but neither R nor T.

In what follows, every J_i will be a power product of the separants and initials of the A. Some J_1RT has an expression linear in the A and their derivatives. Let $A_p^{(k)}$ be the highest derivative of A_p in this expression. Suppose that $k > 0$. Then

$$A_p^{(k)} = S_p y_{j_p, r_p + k} + U$$

with S_p the separant of A_p and U of order lower than $r_p + k$ in y_{j_p}. In the expression for J_1RT, we replace $y_{j_p, r_p + k}$ by $- U/S_p$. Clearing fractions, we have an expression for some J_2RT which is free of $A_p^{(k)}$. Continuing, we find a J_tRT which is linear in the A in (1).

R and T may contain y_{lm} not effectively present in (1). If so, we adjoin corresponding letters v to (3). The set (2) will be a characteristic set of a prime p.i. for the enlarged system (3). The prime p.i. just considered will be called Σ_0. Let J_t, R, and T be regarded as polynomials in the v and z. They are not in Σ_0; neither is their product. Hence the d.p. J_tRT cannot be linear in the A. We know thus that Σ is prime.

We have just seen that if each of two nonzero d.p. is reduced with respect to (1), their product is not in Σ. Taking one of the d.p. as unity, we see that Σ contains no nonzero d.p. reduced with respect to (1). Thus (1) is a characteristic set of Σ and the sufficiency proof is completed.

4. We shall prove that *if* (1) *is a characteristic set of a prime ideal* Σ, *every zero of* (1) *for which no separant vanishes is a zero of* Σ.

Let G be any d.p. in Σ. Proceeding as in I, §6, we can find a power product J of the separants of the A such that

$$JG \equiv H, \qquad [A_1, \cdots, A_p],$$

where H is of order not more than r_i in y_{j_i}, $i = 1, \cdots, p$. As H is in Σ, its remainder with respect to (1) is zero. Hence there is a power product J_1 of the initials of the A such that

$$J_1 H \equiv 0, \qquad (A_1, \cdots, A_p).$$

We suppose, enlarging (3) if necessary, that every letter in H has a corresponding letter in (3). Let H be regarded as a polynomial in the z and v. As H is in the prime p.i. for which (2) is a characteristic set, H vanishes for all zeros of (2) which annul no separant (IV, §40). Then H as a d.p. vanishes for all zeros of (1) which annul no separant; the same is true of G. This proves our statement.

Finite systems

5. Let Φ be any finite system of d.p. in $\mathfrak{F}\{y_1, \cdots, y_n\}$, not all zero. We shall show now how to determine characteristic sets for a finite set of prime ideals equivalent[3] to Φ. In §28, we shall give a theoretical process for determining finite sets whose manifolds are the components of Φ.

Let (1) be a characteristic set of Φ. If A_1 is of class zero, Φ is equivalent to the unit ideal. We suppose now that A_1 is of positive class. For every d.p. in Φ, let the remainder with respect to (1) be determined. If these remainders are adjoined to Φ, we get a system equivalent to Φ. If the remainders are not all zero, the new system will have characteristic sets lower than (1). After a finite number of repetitions of the above operation, we arrive at a system Λ, equivalent to Φ, with a characteristic set (1) for which either A_1 is of class zero or for which, otherwise, the remainder of every d.p. in Λ is zero.

Let us suppose that we are in the latter case. We determine, by §1, whether (1) is a characteristic set of a prime ideal. If it is not, we see from §1 that Λ is equivalent to $\Lambda + P$, $\Lambda + Q$, where P and Q, reduced with respect to (1), can be obtained by calculation. Each of $\Lambda + P$, $\Lambda + Q$ will have characteristic sets lower than (1).

Let us suppose that (1) has been found to be a characteristic set for a prime ideal Σ. Then, by §4, Λ is equivalent to

$$\Sigma, \Lambda + S_1, \cdots, \Lambda + S_p \tag{4}$$

where the S are the separants for (1). Each $\Lambda + S_i$ has a characteristic set lower than (1).

What precedes shows that the given system Φ can be resolved into an equivalent set of prime ideals, as far as the determination of characteristic sets for the ideals goes, by a finite number of rational operations, differentiations and factorizations, provided that the same can be done for all finite systems whose characteristic sets are lower than those of Φ. The final remark of I, §4, gives an abstract proof that the resolution is possible for Φ. What is more, the processes used above give an algorithm for the resolution.

In the analytic case, the algorithm obtained above contains a complete elimination theory for systems of algebraic differential equations. We get all of the zeros of Φ by finding, for each characteristic set, those zeros which cause no separant to vanish. A zero of a prime ideal which causes some separant to vanish will be a zero of some system like the $\Lambda + S_i$ above, and will thus be found among the zeros of some other prime ideal, where it annuls no separant. Thus our algorithm reduces the problem of determining all solutions of a system of algebraic differential equations to a question of applying the implicit function theorem and the existence theorem for systems of differential equations.

One sees, on the basis of the algorithm obtained above, that *a system of d.p. in*

[3] We use this term as in Chapter IV.

$\mathfrak{F}\{ y_1, \cdots, y_n \}$ *in which each d.p. is linear in the* y_{ij} *has a manifold which is irreducible.*

6. The work of §§1–5 furnishes a new proof of the fact that the manifold of a finite system of d.p. is composed of a finite number of irreducible manifolds.[4] The new proof does not depend on Zermelo's axiom.

Test for a d.p. to hold a finite system

7. Let Φ be any finite system of d.p. Let it be required to determine whether a given d.p. G holds Φ. What one does is to resolve Φ into prime ideals as in §5. For G to hold Φ, it is necessary and sufficient that G hold each prime ideal. The condition for G to hold one of the prime ideals is that its remainder with respect to the characteristic set of the prime ideal be zero. This gives a test which involves a finite number of steps.

Construction of resolvents

8. Let

$$A_1, \cdots, A_p \tag{5}$$

be given as a characteristic set of a prime ideal Σ in $\mathfrak{F}\{ u_1, \cdots, u_q; y_1, \cdots, y_p \}$, A_i introducing y_i. We suppose that either $\mathfrak{F}$ does not consist purely of constants or u actually exist.

We shall show how to construct a resolvent for Σ.

We begin by showing how to obtain the d.p. G of II, §23. Let B_i be the d.p. obtained from A_i by replacing each y_j by a new indeterminate z_j. We consider the finite system Λ composed of the d.p. in (5), the d.p.

$$B_1, \cdots, B_p$$

and also

$$\lambda_1(y_1 - z_1) + \cdots + \lambda_p(y_p - z_p) \tag{6}$$

where the λ are indeterminates. We take the indeterminates in the order u; λ; y; z. We apply the process of §5 for resolving Λ into prime ideals, each prime ideal being represented by a characteristic set. The theory of II, §§23, 24, shows that each prime ideal which is not held by every $y_i - z_i$ has a characteristic set containing a d.p. in the u and λ alone. We obtain, by a multiplication of such d.p., the d.p. K of II, §§23, 24.

When $\mathfrak{F}$ contains a nonconstant element, the determination of μ which do not annul K of II, §23, is an elementary problem whose solution is sufficiently indicated in II, §22. When u exist, we find the M of II, §24, by inspection.

Let us limit ourselves now to the case in which $\mathfrak{F}$ does not consist of constants. Consider the system

---

[4] This proof, like that of §§26, 27 below, does not use the basis theorem of I, §12. It is constructive to the extent that it produces characteristic sets for the associated prime ideals.

(7) $$A_1, \cdots, A_p, \qquad w - (\mu_1 y_1 + \cdots + \mu_p y_p)$$

in $\mathfrak{F}\{u; w; y\}$.

The totality of d.p. which vanish for all zeros of (7) which annul no separant is the system Ω of II, §26. The manifold of Ω is a component of (7) and every other component is held by some separant.

We apply the process of §5 to resolve (7) into prime ideals. We test these prime ideals to see whether they are held by the separant of some A_i, and pick out those, say $\Sigma_1, \cdots, \Sigma_s$, which are held by no separant.

As (7) has only one component which is held by no separant, there must be one Σ_i which holds all other Σ_i. To find such a Σ_i, we need only find a Σ_i whose characteristic set holds all other Σ_i. For, let the set for Σ_1 hold $\Sigma_2, \cdots, \Sigma_s$. If Σ_1 does not hold Σ_j, the separant of some d.p. in the set for Σ_1 must hold Σ_j, so that Σ_j cannot hold Σ_1. Thus, if Σ_1 does not hold every Σ_i, no Σ_j can hold every Σ_i.

Σ_1 is Ω. Σ_1 has a characteristic set

$$R, R_1, \cdots, R_p$$

in which R is an algebraically irreducible d.p. Then $R = 0$ is a resolvent of Σ and each R_i is linear in y_i.

Constructive proof of theorem of zeros

9. The theorem of zeros states that if G holds a finite system Φ, some power of G is in $[\Phi]$. Richard Cohn[5] has given a proof of the theorem of zeros which provides a method for expressing a power of G as a linear combination of the d.p. in Φ and their derivatives.

First, let Φ have no zeros. We shall show constructively that unity is in $[\Phi]$. We obtain the system Λ of §5. Λ is contained in $[\Phi]$. If Λ contains a nonzero element of class zero, we have the desired expression for unity. Suppose that Λ contains no such element. Let (1) be a characteristic set for Λ. Then (1) is not a characteristic set of a prime ideal. By §1 and by IV, §30, there exist nonzero d.p. P and Q, reduced with respect to (1), such that $PQ \equiv 0$ $(A_1, \cdots, A_p)$. Neither of the systems $\Lambda + P$, $\Lambda + Q$ has a zero. Suppose that we are able to obtain relations

(8) $$1 = M_0 P + M_1 P' + \cdots + M_g P^{(g)} + C,$$

(9) $$1 = N_0 Q + N_1 Q' + \cdots + N_g Q^{(g)} + D,$$

where superscripts indicate differentiation and where C and D are in $[\Lambda]$. If we multiply (8) and (9), we secure a relation

(10) $$1 = \sum L_{ij} P^{(i)} Q^{(j)} + K$$

with K in $[\Lambda]$. We know from Chapter I how to find a power of any $P^{(i)}Q^{(j)}$

[5] Cohn, 1.

which is in $[PQ]$. Thus, if we raise the second member of (10) to a sufficiently high power, we have a representation of unity as an element of $[\Phi]$.

Our problem becomes that of finding expressions for unity in $[\Lambda + P]$ and $[\Lambda + Q]$. This is the familiar situation of systems with characteristic sets lower than that of Φ; one knows how to proceed.

We take now the general case. Let z be a new indeterminate.[6] The system

$$zG - 1, \qquad \Phi \tag{11}$$

has no zeros. Let unity be expressed linearly in the d.p. of (11) and their derivatives. In this expression, let z be replaced by $1/G$. When we clear fractions, we have a power of G expressed linearly in the d.p. of Φ and their derivatives.

A SECOND THEORY OF ELIMINATION

10. The theory of elimination for systems of algebraic differential equations given in what precedes is apparently the first accurate such theory ever to have been presented. There exist, in the treatises on differential equations, discussions of the elimination problem for systems of n equations in n unknowns, which start from the fact that a general system can be replaced by a system involving only first derivatives.[7] The unsoundness of these discussions is reflected in the reductions to normal form which they claim to effect. The representations at which they arrive are entirely unsuitable for general systems.

We shall develop, in what follows, using the principle of passing to a system involving only first derivatives, a second elimination theory for systems of equations which are algebraic in the unknowns and their derivatives. This treatment of the elimination problem may be regarded, more or less, as a rigorization, for the case of algebraic differential equations, of the discussions in the older literature.

The second elimination theory has the disadvantage, as compared with that given above, of concealing the unknowns present in a given system of equations among new unknowns, which are introduced to reduce the given equations to the first order. The first elimination theory is thus more useful for certain applications.

On the other hand, the second elimination leads, in a natural way, to theorems on the number of arbitrary constants in the solution of a system of algebraic differential equations. This subject, which is really the subject of the order of an irreducible algebraic differential manifold, will be investigated in Chapter VII.

11. We consider a finite system Φ of nonzero d.p. in $\mathfrak{F}\{y_1, \cdots, y_n\}$, each d.p. being of order not exceeding unity in each y. We shall show how to obtain

---

[6] The method used below is that given by Rabinovitch for the proof of Hilbert's theorem of zeros.

[7] See, for instance, Jordan, *Cours d'analyse*, vol. 3, §3, or Forsythe, *Differential Equations*, vol. 2, Chapter I.

the manifold of Φ, if Φ has zeros, by solving a set of systems of differential equations, each system being essentially in the Jacobi-Weierstrass normal form.[8]

12. Let $u_1, \cdots, u_m$ be those y whose derivatives are actually present in some of the d.p. in Φ. Let $v_1, \cdots, v_r$ be those y whose derivatives do not appear.[9] Then $m + r = n$.

We represent the first derivative of any u_i by u_i'.

13. We now consider the u, u', v as algebraic indeterminates. Then Φ becomes a system Ψ of polynomials in $\mathfrak{F}[u; u'; v]$, $\mathfrak{F}$ being regarded as an algebraic field.

Our first step is to find, by the method of Chapter IV, a set of finite systems $\Lambda_1, \cdots, \Lambda_s$ equivalent to Ψ, each Λ being equivalent to a prime p.i. We assume that no Λ_i holds any Λ_j with $j \neq i$. In conducting the decomposition, we order the indeterminates as follows:[10]

$$u_1, \cdots, u_m; \quad u_1', \cdots, u_m'; \quad v_1, \cdots, v_r. \tag{12}$$

Of course, Φ will be equivalent to the systems obtained by regarding the polynomials in each Λ as d.p.

The process which gives the Λ gives, for each i, a characteristic set of the prime p.i. equivalent to Λ_i.

We consider any Λ_i, calling it, simply, Λ. The prime p.i. equivalent to Λ will be denoted by Ω. In what follows, we assume that Ω has zeros.

Suppose that the characteristic set of Ω contains polynomials in the u alone, that is, polynomials free of the u' and v. Let

$$A_1, \cdots, A_p, \tag{13}$$

taken in the order in which they appear in the characteristic set, be those polynomials. Let A_j' be the polynomial in the u and u' obtained, when one regards $\mathfrak{F}$ momentarily as a differential field and u as a differential indeterminate, by differentiating A_j. Then, if u_k appears in A_j, u_k' will appear in A_j' and, indeed, will appear linearly.

14. The first case which we shall consider is that in which each A_j' is in Ω. We are going to obtain, from the characteristic set of Ω, a system of differential equations, in a normal form, whose solutions are zeros of Φ.

15. If $p < m$, there will be certain u none of which appears as a u of highest subscript in any A in (13). The totality of such u may be taken as part of a parametric set of Ω.[11] We arrange the subscripts of the u in such a way that the parametric u above become $u_1, \cdots, u_{m-p}$ and so that the u of highest subscript in each A_j in (13) goes over into u_{m-p+j}.

Now let the subscripts of the u' in (12) be rearranged in such a way that, for

[8] Forsythe, loc. cit.

[9] The separation of the u and v is for the purposes of Chapter VII.

[10] The sequence (12) corresponds to $y_1, \cdots, y_n$ in IV, §26.

[11] To complete the set, we can use those u' and v which are not rightmost indeterminates in any polynomial of the characteristic set.

the new ordering of the u, u'_j may represent the derivative of u_j.[12] The v we leave undisturbed.

For the new arrangement of the indeterminates, we write B_j for A_j, B'_j for A'_j; Λ' for Λ, Ω' for Ω. Of course, Ω' is a prime p.i.

We determine a characteristic set for Ω'. This is accomplished by decomposing Λ' into prime p.i. none of which holds any other, each prime p.i. being represented by a characteristic set. Only one prime p.i., namely Ω', will be obtained. It is easy to see that the chain

$$(14) \qquad B_1, \cdots, B_p$$

can be taken as the first p polynomials in the characteristic set of Ω'. We understand this to be done.

Of course, each B' is in Ω'.

16. We write $h = m - p$. We are going to show that

$$(15) \qquad u'_{h+1}, \cdots, u'_m$$

are not among the parametric indeterminates for Ω' as given by the characteristic set[13] Γ of Ω'. Let us consider B'_1. It involves u'_{h+1} linearly, with S, the separant of B_1, for coefficient of u'_{h+1}. We consider the polynomials of Γ which involve only indeterminates preceding u'_{h+1}. These polynomials constitute a chain Π which consists of (14) and, perhaps, of polynomials introducing certain u'_i with $i \leqq h$. Let C_1 be the remainder of B'_1 with respect to Π. Then C_1, which is in Ω', involves u'_{h+1} linearly. The coefficient D of u'_{h+1} in C_1 is found by multiplying S by powers of the initials in Π and subtracting from the result a linear combination of the polynomials in Π. If D were zero, S would be in Ω'. This shows that u'_{h+1} is not parametric; if it were, C_1 would be a nonzero polynomial in Ω', reduced with respect to Γ.

As C_1 is only of the first degree in u'_{h+1}, we may use C_1 as a polynomial in Γ to introduce[14] u'_{h+1}. We suppose this to be done.

In the same way, the remainder C_2 of B'_2 with respect to $\Pi + C_1$ involves u'_{h+2} and can be used in Γ. We continue in this way, showing that the indeterminates in (15) are not parametric, and determining a C_i which introduces u'_{h+i}, $i = 1, \cdots, p$.

It is evident that if the C and the polynomials in Π are considered as d.p. in the u, each C holds Π.

17. As given by Γ, the parametric indeterminates are $u_1, \cdots, u_h$, then perhaps some of the u'_i with $i \leqq h$ and some of the v. If the indeterminates are reordered so that the parametric ones come first and so that the relative order of the remaining indeterminates is undisturbed, Γ will remain a characteristic set.

[12] We regard the u momentarily as differential indeterminates.

[13] To be specific, the parametric indeterminates are those none of which is rightmost in any polynomial in Γ. Among them are $u_1, \cdots, u_h$.

[14] That is, we may replace the polynomial which introduces u'_{h+1} by C_1.

We reorder the indeterminates so that the parametric ones appear in the order[15]

(16) $\quad u_1, \cdots, u_k; \quad u'_1, \cdots, u'_k; \quad v_1, \cdots, v_t; \quad u_{k+1}, \cdots, u_h.$

The remaining indeterminates will appear in the order

(17) $\quad u_{h+1}, \cdots, u_m; \quad u'_{k+1}, \cdots, u'_{h+1}, \cdots, u'_m; \quad v_{t+1}, \cdots, v_r.$

For this new ordering, we write Λ'' for Λ', Ω'' for Ω', Γ' for Γ; D_i for B_i and E_i for C_i, $i = 1, \cdots, p$.

18. Those polynomials of Ω'' which are free of $u'_{h+1}, \cdots, u'_m$ constitute a prime p.i. Δ. A characteristic set of Δ is found by deleting $E_1, \cdots, E_p$ from Γ'. This is because E_i involves u'_{h+i} linearly, so that u'_{h+i} appears only in E_i in Γ'.

We build a resolvent $R = 0$ for Δ, using a w which is a linear combination of

(18) $\quad u_{h+1}, \cdots, u_m; \quad u'_{k+1}, \cdots, u'_h; \quad v_{t+1}, \cdots, v_r.$

Each indeterminate in (18) will have an expression which is rational in w and the indeterminates in (16). If R is of degree g in w, we can, by Chapter IV, write each of these expressions in the form

(19) $$\frac{H_1 + H_2 w + \cdots + H_g w^{g-1}}{L},$$

where L and the H involve only the letters in (16). The H will depend on the particular indeterminate in (18), but we may, and shall, use the same L for all of the expressions.

Let G be the resultant with respect to w of R and its separant $\partial R/\partial w$. In accordance with IV, §9, let M be a polynomial in the indeterminates in (16) which vanishes for every zero of Γ' which annuls the product of the initials[16] in Γ'. We may and shall assume that L is divisible by GM.

19. We let z represent any of the indeterminates in (18) and consider, together with $R = 0$, the system of equations

(20) $$z = \frac{H_1 + \cdots + H_g w^{g-1}}{L},$$

where z runs through all indeterminates in (18). Speaking in the language of classical analysis, we shall consider these equations as differential equations for $u_{k+1}, \cdots, u_h$ and as algebraic equations for $u_{h+1}, \cdots, u_m; v_{t+1}, \cdots, v_r$.

It is important to explain precisely what we mean by a solution of the system (20). For this, we consider $\mathfrak{F}$ again as a differential field. Suppose that, in some differential field which is an extension of $\mathfrak{F}$, there exist elements $u_1, \cdots, u_m$; $v_1, \cdots, v_r$; w, with $L \neq 0$, which satisfy $R = 0$ and (20). We shall call the elements u and v a solution of (20).

20. We are going to show that (20) has solutions. For the jth indeterminate from the left in (18), let F_j represent the polynomial

[15] For $i \leqq k$, u_i and u'_i are both parametric.

[16] The calculation of M involves no theoretical difficulty.

$$Lz - (H_1 + \cdots + H_g w^{g-1}).$$

The chain of polynomials

$$R, F_1, \cdots, F_q, \tag{21}$$

where q is the number of letters in (18), is, by the theory of resolvents, a characteristic set for a nontrivial prime p.i.

We shall now regard the polynomials in (21) as d.p. in $\mathfrak{F}\{u; v; w\}$. Let Ξ represent the system of d.p. (21) and S the separant of R. We consider those d.p. K which have the property that

$$LSK \equiv 0, \qquad \{\Xi\}. \tag{22}$$

The totality Σ of the K is seen to be an ideal. We shall prove that Σ is prime.

Let UV belong to Σ. It is easy to see that there are relations

$$L^a S^b U \equiv U_1, \qquad L^c S^d V \equiv V_1, \qquad [\Xi],$$

where U_1 and V_1 are free of $u_{h+1}, \cdots, u_m; v_{t+1}, \cdots, v_r$, and are of order at most zero in $u_{k+1}, \cdots, u_h, w$. Then U_1V_1 is in Σ. Thus some power of LSU_1V_1 is in $[\Xi]$. Given a relation

$$(LSU_1V_1)^\alpha = PR + \cdots + QF_q^{(j)},$$

we can proceed as in §3, making substitutions for the z and their derivatives, and for the derivatives of w, the substitutions producing a relation

$$L^\beta S^\gamma (U_1V_1)^\alpha = WR.$$

Thus one of U_1 and V_1 is divisible by R. Then one of U and V is in Σ, and Σ is prime. The procedure just used shows that unity is not in Σ; neither is L.

A generic zero of Σ furnishes a solution of (20).

21. In the analytic case, the solutions of (20) are found as follows. Let $u_1, \cdots, u_k; v_1, \cdots, v_t$ be taken arbitrarily as analytic functions of x, with the sole restriction that, when they are substituted into L, L becomes a function L' of $x, u_{k+1}, \cdots, u_h$ which is not identically zero. Let numerical values be assigned to $u_{k+1}, \cdots, u_h$, at some point $x = a$, so that $L' \neq 0$ for these numerical values and for $x = a$. Then $R = 0$ will determine a set of g functions w of $x, u_{k+1}, \cdots, u_h$, analytic in some neighborhood containing the chosen set of numerical values. This is because L is divisible by G. Using any of these analytic functions for w in (20), we find in those equations in (20) which correspond to $u'_{k+1}, \cdots, u'_h$, a set of differential equations which determine $u_{k+1}, \cdots, u_h$ for the initial conditions. We then use the equations in (20) whose first members are

$$u_{h+1}, \cdots, u_m; \qquad v_{t+1}, \cdots, v_r$$

to determine those unknowns.

The system (20) is essentially in the Jacobi-Weierstrass normal form.

22. A solution of (20) consists of quantities

$$(23) \qquad u_1, \cdots, u_m; \quad v_1, \cdots, v_r.$$

If we adjoin to (23) the derivatives of the quantities u, we get a set of quantities

$$(24) \qquad u_1, \cdots, u_m; \quad u_1', \cdots, u_m'; \quad v_1, \cdots, v_r.$$

We wish to show that the quantities (24) are a zero of Ω''.

If we adjoin to (23) the associated quantity w and also $u_1', \cdots, u_h'$, we get a set

$$(25) \qquad u_1, \cdots, u_m; \quad u_1', \cdots, u_h'; \quad v_1, \cdots, v_r; \quad w$$

which annuls every polynomial in (21). We can see, however, that (25) annuls no initial in (21). Firstly, L is the initial of every F. Again, L is divisible by G, which vanishes when the initial of R is zero. Thus (25) is a zero of the prime p.i. for which (21) is a characteristic set. If we suppress w in (25), we get a zero of Δ.

We know now that (24) annuls every polynomial in the characteristic set Γ' of Ω'', except perhaps the E of §17. That the E are annulled follows from the final remark of §16. Now (24) cannot annul any initial in Γ'. This is because L is divisible by M. Thus (24) is a zero of Ω''. Then (24) is a zero of Λ''.

23. Let Φ_1 represent Λ'' considered as a set of d.p. We have just seen that every solution of (20) is a zero of Φ_1. Every zero of Φ_1 with $L \neq 0$ satisfies (20) with a suitable w. Thus, to get the complete manifold of Φ_1, we have to add to the solutions of (20) the manifold of $\Phi_1 + L$. Now, by IV, §12, every prime p.i. which $\Lambda'' + L$ holds has a dimension lower than that of Ω''.

We keep the facts just adduced in reserve, while we examine again Λ of §13.

24. We suppose now, returning to §§13, 14, that some A_j', call it simply A', is not in Ω. Let Φ_2 represent Λ considered as a set of d.p. Then Φ_2 is equivalent to $\Phi_2 + A'$. Now any prime p.i. which $\Lambda + A'$ holds has a dimension lower than that of Ω.

25. From §§23, 24, it follows that, if we treat each Λ_i of §13 as Λ was treated, and then begin with the resulting systems $\Phi_1 + L$ or $\Phi_2 + A'$ as with Φ, we obtain, continuing the process sufficiently, a set of systems in the normal form (20) whose solutions make up the manifold[17] of Φ. This completes the investigation undertaken in §11.

26. We consider the prime ideal Σ of §20. The prime p.i. for which (21) is a characteristic set contains the polynomials of Δ, all of which are free of w. Every such polynomial, considered as a d.p., is in Σ. Thus Σ contains d.p. free of w. The totality of such d.p. is a prime ideal Σ' in $\mathfrak{F}\{u; v\}$.

A generic zero of Σ' is a solution of (20) and is thus a zero of Φ_1 of §23. Then Φ_1 holds Σ'. We show now that every solution of (20) is a zero of Σ'. When

[17] The u in the various systems (20) have to be reordered. Of course, if Φ has no zeros, we obtain no system (20), but are led to systems of polynomials without zeros.

we adjoin, to a solution of (20), the quantity w attached to it, we get a zero of Ξ of §20. As L is divisible by G, the solution and w do not annul S. It follows from (22) that the solution and w are a zero of Σ. This proves our statement.

We have thus another proof of the fact that the manifold of the finite system Φ of §11 is the union of a finite member of irreducible algebraic differential manifolds.

27. We now consider a finite system Ψ of nonzero d.p. in $\mathfrak{F}\{y_1, \cdots, y_n\}$, the y being involved in Ψ up to any order. If a y_i occurs up to the order $m_i \geqq 1$, we put, with prompt explanations,

$$(26) \qquad y_i = u_{i1}, \qquad y_{i1} = u_{i2}, \cdots, \qquad y_{i,\, m_i - 1} = u_{im_i}, \qquad y_{im_i} = u'_{im_i}.$$

The second subscript of a y indicates an order of differentiation. The u_{ij} are all distinct differential indeterminates and u'_{im_i} is the derivative of u_{im_i}.

If no derivative of y_i appears in Ψ, we put

$$(27) \qquad y_i = v_i.$$

Making the substitutions (26) and (27) in the d.p. of Ψ and adjoining to the resulting system the d.p.

$$(28) \qquad u'_{ij} - u_{i,\, j+1},$$

$j = 1, \cdots, m_i - 1$, we obtain a system Φ of d.p. in the u_{ij} and v_i, each d.p. of order at most unity in each indeterminate. The system Φ, aside from the notation in the subscripts, is of the type described in §11.

If A is a d.p. in the u and v, of any orders in its indeterminates, and if A goes over into a d.p. B by the substitutions

$$(29) \qquad u_{ij}^{(m)} = y_{i,\, j+m-1}; \qquad v_{im} = y_{im},$$

superscripts of u, and second subscripts of v, indicating order of differentiation, every zero of A which annuls each d.p. in (28) gives a zero of B for which $y_i = u_{i1}$ for certain i and $y_i = v_i$ for the remaining i.

It follows that if Φ is resolved into prime ideals, as in §26, the substitution (29) will produce a set of prime ideals equivalent to Ψ.

We have thus proved again that the manifold of any finite system of d.p. is the union of a finite number of irreducible manifolds.

We have also secured a second elimination theory for the system Ψ.

Theoretical process for decomposing the manifold of a finite system into its components

28. We deal with any finite system Φ in $\mathfrak{F}\{y_1, \cdots, y_n\}$. Let p be any positive integer. We denote by $\Phi^{(p)}$ the system obtained by adjoining to Φ the first p derivatives of each of its d.p.

When the d.p. in $\Phi^{(p)}$ are regarded as polynomials in the y_{ij} which they effectively involve, $\Phi^{(p)}$ goes over into a system $\Psi^{(p)}$ of polynomials. For algebraic field, we use $\mathfrak{F}$.

We decompose $\Psi^{(p)}$, with a finite number of operations, into finite systems

$$\Lambda_1, \cdots, \Lambda_r \tag{30}$$

each of which is equivalent to a prime p.i. and none of which holds any other.

Let the polynomials in the Λ be considered now as d.p. Then each Λ_i goes over into a system Φ_i of d.p. Let any Φ_i which is held by some Φ_j with $j \neq i$ be suppressed. This can be accomplished with a finite number of operations. There remain, if Φ has a manifold, systems

$$\Phi_1, \cdots, \Phi_s. \tag{31}$$

We say that, for p *sufficiently great, the manifolds of the* Φ_i *are the components of*[18] Φ.

29. Let

$$\Sigma_1, \cdots, \Sigma_t \tag{32}$$

be finite systems, no two equivalent, whose manifolds are the components of Φ. When the d.p. in the Σ are regarded as polynomials in the y_{ij}, (32) goes over into a set of systems of polynomials

$$\Gamma_1, \cdots, \Gamma_t. \tag{33}$$

Let us make any selection of t d.p., one from each Σ, and take their product. Let the products, for all possible selections, be

$$A_1, \cdots, A_g.$$

Then each A holds Φ. By the theorem of zeros, if p is large, some power of each A will be linear in the d.p. of $\Phi^{(p)}$.

Thus, if each A_i is considered as a polynomial in its y_{jk}, and if it is represented then by B_i, each B will hold $\Psi^{(p)}$ if p is sufficiently large. Let p be large enough for this.

We shall prove that each Λ_i of (30) is held by some Γ_j of[19] (33). Suppose that Λ_1 is not so held. Let C_j be a polynomial of Γ_j, $j = 1, \cdots, t$, which does not hold Λ_1. Then $C_1 \cdots C_t$, that is, some B, does not hold Λ_1. That B cannot hold $\Psi^{(p)}$. This proves our statement.

It follows that each Φ_i is held by some Σ_j.

On the other hand, each Σ_i is held by some Φ_j. Let this be false. Let D_j be a d.p. in Φ_j, $j = 1, \cdots, r$ (we restore momentarily the suppressed Φ_i) which does not hold Σ_1. Then $G = D_1 \cdots D_r$ does not hold Σ_1. Hence G does not hold Φ. Then, if G is considered as a polynomial in its y_{ij}, it does not hold $\Psi^{(p)}$. This contradicts the fact that $\Psi^{(p)}$ is equivalent to (30).

Thus, if p is sufficiently great, the manifolds of the Φ_i in (31) are the components of Φ.

---

[18] It is assumed that Φ has a manifold.

[19] The indeterminates are those which appear in (30) and (33).

For the above process to become a genuine method of decomposition, it would be necessary to have a method for determining permissible integers p. In VI, §9 we treat a special case.

Example 1. Let Φ be $y_1^2 - 4y$ in $\mathfrak{F}\{y\}$. Then $\Psi^{(p)}$ is equivalent to the system

$$y_1^2 - 4y, \qquad y_1(y_2 - 2), \qquad y_1y_3 + y_2(y_2 - 2),$$
$$y_1y_4 + 2y_2y_3 + y_3(y_2 - 2), \cdots,$$
$$y_1y_{p+1} + (p-1)\,y_2y_p + \cdots + (p-1)\,y_{p-1}y_3 + y_p(y_2 - 2).$$

Ψ' decomposes into the two systems

(34) $$y, y_1,$$

(35) $$y_1^2 - 4y, \qquad y_2 - 2,$$

in $\mathfrak{F}[y, y_1, y_2]$, each of which is equivalent to a prime p.i. If we adjoin

$$y_1y_3 + y_2\,(y_2 - 2)$$

to (34), that system decomposes into

(36) $$y, y_1, y_2,$$

(37) $$y, y_1, y_2 - 2$$

in $\mathfrak{F}[y, y_1, y_2, y_3]$. The same adjunction to (35) gives (37) and

(38) $$y_1^2 - 4y, \qquad y_2 - 2, \qquad y_3.$$

Thus (36), (37) and (38) give the decomposition of Ψ''. Continuing, we find the decomposition of $\Psi^{(p)}$ to be, for $p > 2$,

(39) $$y, y_1, y_2, \cdots, y_p,$$

(40) $$y, y_1, \qquad y_2 - 2, \qquad y_3, \cdots, y_p,$$

(41) $$y_1^2 - 4y, \qquad y_2 - 2, \qquad y_3, \cdots, y_{p+1}.$$

If we regard the last three systems as systems of d.p., (41) gives the general solution of $y_1^2 - 4y$, while (39) gives the zero $y = 0$, which is a second irreducible manifold. The system (40) of d.p. has no zeros.

We notice that the system of polynomials $y_1^2 - 4y$, $y_2 - 2$ holds the system (40) of polynomials. This is in harmony with the fact that every Λ in (30) is held by some Γ in (33).

Example 2. Let Φ be $y_1^2 - 4y^3$, whose manifold was seen in II, §19 to be irreducible. If we let

$$A_1 = 2y_2 - 12y^2$$

and represent the rth derivative of A_1 by A_{r+1}, then $\Psi^{(p)}$ will be

$$y_1^2 - 4y^3, \qquad y_1A_1, \qquad y_2A_1 + y_1A_2,$$
$$y_3A_1 + 2y_2A_2 + y_1A_3, \cdots,$$
$$y_pA_1 + (p-1)\,y_{p-1}A_2 + \cdots + (p-1)\,y_2A_{p-1} + y_1A_p.$$

Then Ψ' decomposes into

(42) $$y, y_1,$$

(43) $$y_1^2 - 4y^3, A_1.$$

We now examine Ψ''. The adjunction of $y_2A_1 + y_1A_2$ to (42) gives the single system

(44) $$y, y_1, y_2.$$

The same adjunction to (43) gives

(45) $$y_1^2 - 4y^3, A_1, A_2,$$

and also (44).

Let us examine Ψ'''. The adjunction of $y_3A_1 + 2y_2\,A_2 + y_1A_3$ to (44) gives the single system

(46) $$y, y_1, y_2$$

in $\mathfrak{F}[y, \cdots, y_4]$. The same adjunction to (45) gives

(47) $$y_1^2 - 4y^3, A_1, A_2, A_3,$$

as well as the system, held by (46), obtained by adjoining y_3 to (46).

Continuing, it is not difficult to prove that the decomposition of $\Psi^{(p)}$ is

(48) $$y, y_1, \cdots, y_q,$$

where q is the greatest integer in $1 + p/2$, and

(49) $$y_1^2 - 4y^3, \qquad A_1, \cdots, A_p.$$

The system (49) of d.p. gives the manifold of Φ, while (48) (d.p.), whose manifold is $y = 0$, is held by (49).

CHAPTER VI

ANALYTICAL CONSIDERATIONS

Normal zeros

1. We deal with the analytic case. Let Σ be a nontrivial prime ideal in $y_1, \cdots, y_n$ with a characteristic set

$$(1) \qquad A_1, \cdots, A_p.$$

A zero of (1) which annuls no separant will be called a *normal* zero of (1). By V, §4, every normal zero of (1) is a zero of Σ. A zero of (1) may annul some separant and still be a zero of Σ. One of our objects, in what follows, is to characterize such zeros of (1).

Adherence

2. Let n be a fixed positive integer. We consider sets of functions $y_1(x), \cdots, y_n(x)$, the functions of each set being analytic in some open region which depends on the set. Let $\mathfrak{A}$ be a family of such sets. Let $\bar{y}_1(x), \cdots, \bar{y}_n(x)$ be a set of functions which are analytic in an open region **B**, the set not belonging to $\mathfrak{A}$. We shall say that $\bar{y}_1, \cdots, \bar{y}_n$ *adheres* to $\mathfrak{A}$ if there exists in **B** a point a of the following description. For every positive integer m and for every $\epsilon > 0$, there exists in $\mathfrak{A}$ a set $y_1, \cdots, y_n$, the y being analytic in an open region[1] containing a, such that

$$(2) \qquad | y_{ij}(a) - \bar{y}_{ij}(a) | < \epsilon, \qquad i = 1, \cdots, n; \; j = 0, \cdots, m.$$

The point a will be called a point of contact of $\bar{y}_1, \cdots, \bar{y}_n$ with $\mathfrak{A}$.

The theorem of approximation

3. Let Σ be as in §1. Let B be any d.p. which is not in Σ, and $\mathfrak{A}$ the set of zeros of Σ which do not annul B. Let $\bar{y}_1(x), \cdots, \bar{y}_n(x)$ be a zero of B which adheres to $\mathfrak{A}$. We shall prove that the $\bar{y}$ are a zero of Σ.

Let G be any d.p. in Σ. We have to prove that G is annulled by the $\bar{y}$. Let a be a point of contact of the $\bar{y}$ with $\mathfrak{A}$. Some of the coefficients in G may have poles at a. If so, we divide G by a power of one of its coefficients and the pole is removed. We thus assume that the coefficients in G are analytic at a. If the $\bar{y}$ are substituted into G, we secure a $\gamma(x)$, analytic at a. Suppose that, choosing a large m, and then a small ϵ, we find a $y_1, \cdots, y_n$ in $\mathfrak{A}$ satisfying (2). When the y are substituted into G, we obtain a $\gamma'(x)$ with a Taylor expansion at a in which the coefficients of the $(x - a)^i$, $i = 0, \cdots, m$, are very nearly equal to the corresponding coefficients in γ. But $\gamma' = 0$. Then $\gamma = 0$ and the $\bar{y}$ annul G.

[1] The y and their region of analyticity will depend on m and ϵ.

We derive now a converse result.

THEOREM: *Every zero of B which is a zero of Σ adheres to $\mathfrak{A}$.*

We reletter the indeterminates so as to have a parametric set $u_1, \cdots, u_q$ and so that A_i in (1) introduces y_i. Let

$$\bar{u}_1(x), \cdots, \bar{u}_q(x); \qquad \bar{y}_1(x), \cdots, \bar{y}_p(x), \tag{3}$$

analytic in an open region **B**, be a zero of Σ which annuls B. We shall find points of contact of (3) with $\mathfrak{A}$.

Let R be the remainder of B with respect to (1).

Let

$$T = RS_1 \cdots S_p$$

with S_i the separant of A_i.

Let A_i be of order r_i in y_i. For every y_{is} with $s > r_i$ in a normal zero of (1), we have an expression

$$y_{is} = \frac{E}{F}, \tag{4}$$

where E is a d.p. of class at most $q + i$ and of order at most r_j in y_j, $j = 1, \cdots, i$; F is a power product in the S. The d.p.

$$Fy_{is} - E \tag{5}$$

are in Σ.

Let m be any integer greater than every r_i. We adjoin to (1) all d.p. (5) for $i = 1, \cdots, p$, with $s \leqq m$. We now consider the u_{ij} and y_{ij} as algebraic indeterminates, so that the d.p. in (1) and (5) become a system Φ of polynomials. We use here all u_{ik} and y_{ik} with $k \leqq m$ and any other u_{ik} which may occur in (1), in (5) and in T.

We shall prove that the totality Ω of polynomials which vanish for those zeros of Φ for which no S vanishes is a prime p.i. Let GH vanish for the indicated zeros. By (4) we have, for those zeros,

$$G = \frac{E_1}{F_1}, \qquad H = \frac{E_2}{F_2},$$

where E_1 and E_2 involve no y_{ij} with $j > r_i$. Then E_1E_2 vanishes for the above zeros.

By V, §1, (1), regarded as a set of polynomials, is a characteristic set of a prime p.i. The indeterminates which we use at this point are the y_{ij} with $j \leqq r_i$ and the u_{ij} in Φ. Then either E_1 vanishes for all zeros of the polynomials (1) which annul no S, or E_2 does. Suppose that E_1 does. Then G vanishes for all zeros of Ω which annul no separant, so that Ω is a prime p.i.

We shall prove that, given any zero of Σ, the u_{ij}, y_{ij} appearing in Φ, obtained from the zero, constitute a zero of Ω. This is obvious for the normal zeros of (1).

Then if G is a polynomial in Ω, G, considered as a d.p., holds Σ. This proves our statement.

We consider the given zero (3) of Σ. It annuls T. Consider the corresponding zero of Ω. By IV, §39, there is, in **B**, an open region **C** of the following description. Given any $\epsilon > 0$, we can find a zero u_{ik}, y_{jk} of Ω, analytic in **C**, for which T is distinct from zero throughout **C**, such that, for every point a in **C**,

$$(6) \qquad |u_{ik}(a) - \bar{u}_{ik}(a)| < \epsilon, \qquad |y_{jk}(a) - \bar{y}_{jk}(a)| < \epsilon,$$
$$i = 1, \cdots, q; \; j = 1, \cdots, p; \; k = 0, \cdots, m.$$

We refer to II, §10. For any point a in **C**, the $u_{ik}(a)$ and $y_{jk}(a)$ in the zero of Ω used in (6) furnish initial conditions for a normal zero of (1). It is a matter of constructing functions u with a certain number of given coefficients in their Taylor expansions at a, and then using repeatedly the implicit function theorem and the existence theorem for differential equations.[2] Thus, for every a in **C**, there is a normal zero of (1), analytic at a, for which T is not zero at a and which satisfies (6) with the given zero (3).

We repeat the above operation, using $2m$ and $\epsilon/2$ in place of m and ϵ. We find a region $\mathbf{C}_1$, in **C**, every point a of which can be used as above. For convenience we take $\mathbf{C}_1$ bounded, with its boundary in **C**. Employing $4m$ and $\epsilon/4$, we find a region $\mathbf{C}_2$ in $\mathbf{C}_1$. We continue, determining a sequence of regions $\mathbf{C}_j$. There is at least one point a common to all of these regions. Given any m and any ϵ, there is a normal zero of (1), thus a zero of Σ, analytic at a, which does not annul B at a and for which (6) holds. As a is a point of contact of the zero (3) with $\mathfrak{A}$, our theorem is proved.

4. The foregoing discussion shows that the points of contact of (3) with $\mathfrak{A}$ are dense in **B**. Thus, *if a zero of B has a point of contact with $\mathfrak{A}$, it has a dense set of points of contact.*

A point which is not a point of contact of (3) with $\mathfrak{A}$ will be said to be *exceptional* for (3) *relative to B*. That exceptional points may exist is seen from the following example. Let Σ be the prime ideal in $\mathfrak{F}\{y\}$ whose manifold is $y = c/x$ with c an arbitrary constant. Then $y = 0$ is the only zero which is analytic at $x = 0$. Thus, if $B = y$, the point $x = 0$ is an exceptional point.

Strodt has shown[3] that, when B is given, the exceptional points of all zeros of Σ which annul B lie on a fixed set which is vacuous, finite or countably infinite. Without proving Strodt's theorem, let us see that, for a particular zero $\bar{u}$, $\bar{y}$ which annuls **B**, the set of exceptional points is at most countably infinite.

We refer to IV, §39, inquiring as to the conditions which must be put on a point a of **B** so that a region **C** containing a may exist. We find that a must be distinct from the poles of the coefficients of a finite number of polynomials and must not be a zero of α_r in (50). Then, the z_j with $j > q$ will be bounded in a region containing a and **C** can be taken so as to contain a. Thus for each m,

[2] **C** is taken so that the coefficients in the A are analytic throughout **C**.

[3] Strodt, 44.

in §3, we have to avoid, in selecting a, a set of isolated points. Such a set is finite or countable. The points a which cannot be used for all m thus form at most a countable set.

5. If we take B as the product of the S, we see that *the manifold of* Σ *consists of the normal zeros of* (1) *and of the zeros which adhere to the set of normal zeros.*

We consider now an algebraically irreducible d.p. F in $\mathfrak{F}\{y_1, \cdots, y_n\}$. In the analytic case, a singular zero of F which adheres to the set of nonsingular zeros will be called an adherent singular zero. We see that *the general solution of an algebraically irreducible differential polynomial consists of the nonsingular zeros and of the adherent singular zeros.*

6. Sometimes a sequence of zeros u, y exists whose Taylor expansions at a point of contact approach those of $\bar{u}$, $\bar{y}$ in the manner indicated in (6), without the u, y converging uniformly to the $\bar{u}$, $\bar{y}$ in a neighborhood of a. We give an example, using $\mathfrak{F}\{y\}$. Let

$$A = (yy_2 - y_1^2)^2 - 4yy_1^3.$$

A is algebraically irreducible in the field of all constants because, when equated to zero, it defines y_2 as a two-branched function of y and y_1. Equating A to zero, we find, for $y \neq 0$,

$$\frac{d}{dx}\left(\frac{y_1}{y}\right) = 2\left(\frac{y_1}{y}\right)^{3/2},$$

the solutions of which are given by

$$y = be^{1/(c-x)} \tag{7}$$

and $y = b$, with b and c constants. The solution $y = 0$, suppressed above, is included among these.

The solutions (7) with $b \neq 0$ are normal zeros of A and thus belong to the general solution of A. Let b stay fixed in (7) at a value distinct from zero, while c approaches ∞ through positive values. Then y approaches b, uniformly in any bounded domain. It follows that the zeros $y = b$ with $b \neq 0$ adhere to the set of normal zeros and are in the general solution. By taking c as a small negative number, we can make the second member of (7) and an arbitrarily large number of its derivatives small at pleasure at $x = 0$. This shows that $y = 0$ adheres to the normal zeros and is in the general solution.

Of course, if we take b small, and then c large and positive, we get a sequence of normal zeros converging uniformly to zero in any preassigned bounded domain. The discussion above, in which essential singularities were used to prove adherence, shows what might conceivably happen in other examples.

All in all, it is not known whether a zero of B which adheres to $\mathfrak{A}$ can be approximated uniformly in some area by zeros in $\mathfrak{A}$. It is known[4] that such a zero of B may fail to be embedded analytically among zeros in $\mathfrak{A}$.

---

[4] Ritt, 32.

Analytic treatment of low power theorem

7. The low power theorem was first proved for the analytic case.[5] The necessity proof given was essentially that of Chapter III. We shall present here the analytic sufficiency proof, which employs ideas essentially different from those in Levi's algebraic treatment.

We refer to III, §17, and to III, §20. Let (25) of III, §17, which we rewrite

$$\sum_{j=1}^{r} C_j A^{p_i} A_1^{i_{1j}} \cdots A_{m-l}^{i_{m-l,j}}, \tag{8}$$

contain a term $C_k A^{p_k}$ which is of lower degree than every other term. We suppose, for simplicity, that $k = 1$. Let us imagine that the general solution $\mathfrak{M}$ of A is not a component of F, but rather a proper part of some component $\mathfrak{M}'$ of F. Then A does not hold $\mathfrak{M}'$.

Let $\mathfrak{A}$ be the set of points of $\mathfrak{M}'$ which are not zeros of A. By §3, every point of $\mathfrak{M}$ adheres to $\mathfrak{A}$.

Let

$$\bar{y}_1(x), \cdots, \bar{y}_n(x) \tag{9}$$

be a point of $\mathfrak{M}$ which does not annul C_1. We consider a point of contact a of (9) with $\mathfrak{A}$, produced as in §3, for which the coefficients in A, and in the C_j of (8), are analytic. We assume furthermore that C_1 is not annulled at a by the functions in (9).

A positive integer μ and an $\epsilon > 0$ being taken, let us find, as in §3, a zero $\tilde{y}_1, \cdots, \tilde{y}_n$ in $\mathfrak{A}$, analytic at a, such that

$$|\tilde{y}_{ij}(a) - \bar{y}_{ij}(a)| < \epsilon, \qquad i = 1, \cdots, n; j = 0, \cdots, \mu. \tag{10}$$

We denote by c a positive real number which later will be made small. We perform, upon the variable x, the transformation

$$z = \frac{x - a}{c}. \tag{11}$$

For the $\tilde{y}$ of (10), A becomes a function $A(\tilde{y}, x)$ of x, analytic at a and distinct from zero at a. (Note that we use a point of contact of the type produced in §3.)

Let s be a positive integer which will be fixed later, and let

$$w(z) = c^{-s} A(\tilde{y}, x), \tag{12}$$

where the x used in A is related to z as in (11). Then

$$w_1 = c^{-s+1} A_1(\tilde{y}, x), \cdots, w_{m-l} = c^{-s+m-l} A_{m-l}(\tilde{y}, x)$$

where subscripts of w indicate differentiation with respect to z.

Let $D_j(z) = C_j(\tilde{y}, x)$. The jth term in (8) goes over into

[5] Ritt, 31.

(13) $$c^{u_j}D_j(z)\, w^{p_j} w_1^{i_{1j}} \cdots w_{m-l}^{i_{m-l,j}}$$

where

$$u_j = sd_j - e_j,$$

d_j being the degree of the jth term of (8) in A and the A_i, and e_j its weight.

From the fact that $d_j > d_1$ when $j > 1$, it follows that, if s is large, every u_j with $j > 1$ will exceed u_1. Let s be fixed at a value large enough for this to occur.

As (8) vanishes for the $\tilde{y}$, we may write

(14) $$D_1(z)w^{p_1} + \sum_{j=2}^{r} c^{u_j - u_1} D_j(z)\, w^{p_j} \cdots w_{m-l}^{i_{m-l,j}} = 0.$$

Let the Taylor expansion of $A(\tilde{y}, x)$ at a be

(15) $$b_0 + b_1(x - a) + \cdots + b_i(x - a)^i + \cdots.$$

Then $b_0 \neq 0$, but, if ϵ and $1/\mu$ are small, a large number of the b, beginning with b_0, will be small. This is because the $\tilde{y}$ approximate to the $\bar{y}$ and the $\bar{y}$ annul A.

We now fix c in such a way as to make the greatest of the quantities

$$|b_i c^{-s+i}|, \qquad i = 0, \cdots, s - 1,$$

equal to unity. This is possible because $b_0 \neq 0$.

Then c tends towards zero with ϵ and $1/\mu$.

For $|z|$ small, we have, by (11), (12), (15),

(16) $$w(z) = \sum_{i=0}^{\infty} b_i c^{-s+i} z^i.$$

When μ and $1/\epsilon$ increase, the coefficient of z^i in (16), for a fixed i exceeding $s - 1$, will tend towards zero.

It follows that we can select a sequence of approximating zeros $\tilde{y}$ for which $w(z)$ tends towards a nonzero polynomial of degree $s - 1$ at most. The convergence occurs in the sense that each coefficient in (16) tends toward the corresponding coefficient in the polynomial.[6] Let $\gamma(z)$ be such a polynomial.

Let, for $|x - a|$ small, and for the particular point (9) of $\mathfrak{M}$,

$$C_j(\bar{y}, x) = \sum_{i=0}^{\infty} h_{ji}(x - a)^i, \qquad j = 1, \cdots, r.$$

Then

$$C_j(\tilde{y}, x) = \sum_{i=0}^{\infty} h'_{ji}\,(x - a)^i,$$

where, for each i, h'_{ji} approaches h_{ji} as ϵ and $1/\mu$ decrease. We have

[6] In this polynomial, the "coefficient of z^i" with $i \geqq s$ is understood to be zero.

$$D_j(z) = \sum_{i=0}^{\infty} h'_{ji} c^i z^i.$$

Turning now to (14) and remembering that the $u_j - u_1$ with $j > 1$ are positive, we recognize that

$$h_{10}\gamma^{p_1} = 0. \tag{17}$$

In short, if the first member of (17) did not have a vanishing expansion in powers of z, the first member of (14) could not have a vanishing expansion when c is small and w approximates to γ. Because $C_1(\bar{y}, x)$ does not vanish at a, we have $h_{10} \neq 0$. Then, by (17), $\gamma = 0$. This contradicts what precedes, so that the sufficiency proof is completed. The theorems of III, §§22, 23 can be obtained by modifying slightly the above procedure.

The transformation performed in (11) and (12) has the form of certain transformations which were discovered by Painlevé and which were applied by him to the study of differential equations whose solutions have fixed critical points.[7]

It might be proposed to treat the sufficiency question by making the substitution $A = \alpha^h$, with h a positive integer, in the relation $S^tF = 0$. For h large, the resulting relation could be divided through by $\alpha^{hp_1} = A^{p_1}$ and we would get a relation which could not be satisfied by a sequence of $\bar{y}$ for which the coefficients of α at a tend to vanish. There is, however, no a priori assurance that such a sequence of $\bar{y}$ exists. The proof of its existence is complicated and involves the use of the low power theorem.[8]

Poisson, in his study of singular solutions, used a transformation in which the unknown is replaced by a power of itself. A similar transformation was used by Darboux[9] in connection with the singular solutions of partial differential equations.

8. We present another theorem concerning low powers.

THEOREM: *Let*

$$y_i^{p_i} + F_i, \qquad i = 1, \cdots, n, \tag{18}$$

be d.p. in $\mathfrak{F}\{y_1, \cdots, y_n\}$ *with each* p_i *a positive integer and with each* F_i *either identically zero or else composed of terms each of which is of total degree greater than* p_i *in the* y_{jk}. *The zero* $y_i = 0$, $i = 1, \cdots, n$, *of* (18) *is a component of the system* (18).

Let $y_i = 0$, $i = 1, \cdots, n$, be a proper part of a component $\mathfrak{M}$ of (18). To fix our ideas, suppose that y_1 does not hold $\mathfrak{M}$. We use a point of contact a of the type of §3. For every m and for every $\epsilon > 0$, there is a point of $\mathfrak{M}$

$$y_i = \sum_{j=0}^{\infty} b_{ij}(x - a)^j, \qquad i = 1, \cdots, n, \tag{19}$$

[7] Bulletin de la Société Mathématique de France, vol. 28 (1900), p. 201.

[8] Ritt, 32, and Levi, 17.

[9] See Ritt, 41.

with

$$(20) \qquad | b_{ij} | < \epsilon, \qquad i = 1, \cdots, n; j = 0, \cdots, m,$$

and with $b_{10} \neq 0$.

We use a positive integer s and a positive number c, both of which will be fixed later. Considering a definite point (19), which corresponds to given m, ϵ, we let

$$(21) \qquad w_i(z) = c^{-s} y_i(x), \qquad i = 1, \cdots, n,$$

where z is related to x as in (11).

Each equation $y_i^{p_i} + F_i = 0$ goes over into an equation

$$(22) \qquad w_i^{p_i} + \sum_{j=1}^{r} c^{\mu_j s - \nu_j} \alpha_j B_j = 0,$$

where the B are power products in the w and their derivatives with respect to z; the μ are positive integers and the ν are nonnegative integers. Each α_j is the coefficient in F_i of the power product which produces B_j and we regard the α, for any c, as functions of z. It is unnecessary to express the dependence on i of $\sum$ in (22).

Let s be fixed at a value large enough for every $\mu s - \nu$ to be positive.

We have, by (19),

$$(23) \qquad w_i(z) = \sum_{j=0}^{\infty} c^{-s+j} b_{ij} z^j, \qquad i = 1, \cdots, n.$$

We now fix c in such a way that the greatest of the quantities

$$c^{-s+j} | b_{ij} |, \qquad i = 1, \cdots, n; j = 0, \cdots, s-1,$$

equals unity. This is possible because $b_{10} \neq 0$. Then, if $m \geqq s - 1$ and if ϵ is small, c will be small.

It follows that, by decreasing $1/m$ and ϵ, we can select a sequence of points (19) which yields, for every i, a sequence of w_i which tends toward a polynomial which is either identically zero or else of degree $s - 1$ at most. The selection can be made in such a way that, for some i, the w_i converge to a polynomial distinct from zero; fixing our ideas, we assume that w_1 tends towards a nonzero polynomial $\gamma(z)$.

We now consider (22) with $i = 1$. When c is small and the w_i are close to their polynomial limits, the expansion of $\sum$ in (22) will begin with a large number of small coefficients. This contradicts the fact that $\gamma^{p_1} \neq 0$ and our theorem is established.

Differential polynomials in one indeterminate, of first order

9. Let A, in $\mathfrak{F}\{y\}$, be of the first order in y and algebraically irreducible. Limiting ourselves to the analytic case, we shall show how to determine, in a

finite number of steps, a finite system of d.p. whose manifold is the general solution of A.

Let A be of degree m in y_1. We consider the system

$$A, A_1, \cdots, A_{m-1} \tag{24}$$

where A_j is the jth derivative of A. Let (24) be considered as a set of polynomials and let it be resolved into finite systems, each equivalent to a prime ideal and none holding any other. There will be precisely one system, Λ, which is not held by S, the separant of A (§3). Let the polynomials in Λ be considered now as d.p. and let Σ be the system of d.p. thus obtained.

We shall prove that *the manifold of* Σ *is the general solution of* A.

10. We know that the general solution $\mathfrak{M}$ of A is contained in the manifold of Σ. We have to show that every zero of Σ is in $\mathfrak{M}$.

We observe that A holds Σ. The zeros of A not in $\mathfrak{M}$ are zeros of S. The common zeros of A and S are zeros of the resultant of A and S with respect to y_1, which is a nonzero d.p. R of order zero. It suffices then to show that if a zero u of R is a zero of Σ, u is contained in $\mathfrak{M}$.

Let u_j be the jth derivative of u. Then $A = 0$ for $y = u$, $y_1 = u_1$. There exist an open region $\mathbf{A}_1$ and an $h > 0$ such that, for

$$x \text{ in } \mathbf{A}_1 \text{ and } 0 < |y - u| < h, \tag{25}$$

every solution of the algebraic relation $A = 0$, for y_1 considered as a function of y and x, is given by a series

$$y_1 = u_1 + a_0(y-u)^{q/s} + \cdots + a_p(y-u)^{(q+p)/s} + \cdots, \tag{26}$$

where the a are functions of x analytic in $\mathbf{A}_1$ and where q and s are integers, s being positive. The particular series used in the second member of (26) depends on the particular solution y_1 used, but, for each series, we have $s \leqq m$. We suppose that,[10] in each series, a_0 does not vanish for every x.

The system of functions

$$u, u_1, \cdots, u_m \tag{27}$$

is a zero of Λ. In some region $\mathbf{A}_2$ contained in $\mathbf{A}_1$, we can approximate to (27) arbitrarily closely by a zero of Λ with R distinct from zero throughout $\mathbf{A}_2$. We understand that the coefficients in A are analytic throughout $\mathbf{A}_2$.

It follows that, if ξ is any point in $\mathbf{A}_2$, the differential equation $A = 0$ has solutions analytic at ξ, with $R \neq 0$ at ξ, for which $y, \cdots, y_m$ differ arbitrarily slightly at ξ from $u, \cdots, u_m$ respectively.[11]

Any such solution satisfies (26), in the neighborhood of ξ, for an appropriate choice of the series in (26).[12] Hence there must be one of the series for which (26) is satisfied by a zero of A with $R \neq 0$ and with $y, \cdots, y_m$ as close as one

[10] We are setting aside the trivial case of $A = \mu(y_1 - u_1)$ with μ in $\mathfrak{F}$.

[11] If $R \neq 0$ at ξ for a zero of Λ, then $S \neq 0$ at ξ.

[12] If $R \neq 0$ at ξ, $y - u \neq 0$ for a neighborhood of ξ.

pleases at ξ to $u, \cdots, u_m$. In what follows, we deal with such a series and assume ξ to be taken so that $a_0 \neq 0$ at ξ.

We are going to prove that $q \geqq s$. We assume that $s > q$ and produce a contradiction.

We see first that $q > 0$ in (26). Otherwise $y_1 - u_1$ could not be small at ξ if $y - u$ is small at ξ. Then $s > 1$.

We show now that $2q/s - 1 > 0$. Differentiating (26), we find

$$y_2 = u_2 + \sum \frac{q+p}{s} a_p (y - u)^{(q+p)/s-1}(y_1 - u_1) + \sum \frac{da_p}{dx}(y - u)^{(q+p)/s}. \tag{28}$$

We replace y_1 in (28) by its expression in (26). As $q < s$, (28) becomes

$$y_2 = u_2 + \frac{q}{s} a_0^2 (y - u)^{2q/s - 1} + b_1(y - u)^{(2q+1)/s - 1} + \cdots, \tag{29}$$

where the b are analytic in A_1. If we had $2q/s - 1 \leqq 0$, $y_2 - u_2$ could not be small at ξ when $y - u$ is small. Thus

$$\frac{2q}{s} - 1 \geqq \frac{1}{s}.$$

Then $2q \geqq s + 1$. It follows, since $q < s$, that $s > 2$. If we differentiate (29) and use (26), it follows as above that $3q/s - 2 > 0$. We find then that $3q \geqq 2s + 1$ and that $s > 3$. Continuing, we find that s exceeds m. Then $q \geqq s$.

We are now able to show that u belongs to $\mathfrak{M}$. In (26), we replace $y - u$ by v^s. Then (26) goes over into the differential equation

$$s\frac{dv}{dx} = a_0 v^{q-s+1} + \cdots + a_p v^{q+p-s+1} + \cdots. \tag{30}$$

Since the second member of (30) is analytic in v and x for v small and x close to ξ, then, if we fix v as a small quantity at ξ, distinct from 0, (30) will have a solution analytic at ξ, not identically zero, with any desired finite number of derivatives as small as one pleases[13] at ξ. Then $y - u$, which equals v^s, while not zero at ξ will be small at ξ, together with as great a finite number of its derivatives as one may choose to consider. Zeros of A, close to u but distinct from u at ξ, cannot annul R.

Thus if u annuls S as well as R, u adheres to the nonsingular zeros of A and belongs to $\mathfrak{M}$. If u does not annul S, u certainly belongs to $\mathfrak{M}$.

Sequences of irreducible manifolds

11. Let

$$\Sigma_1, \cdots, \Sigma_p, \cdots$$

[13] Equation (30) is satisfied by $v = 0$ and its solution is analytic in the constant of integration.

be an infinite sequence of prime ideals in $\mathfrak{F}\{y_1, \cdots, y_n\}$, each Σ_i a proper divisor of Σ_{i+1}. The intersection of the Σ_i is a prime ideal Σ. Strodt has investigated[14] the relationship of the manifold $\mathfrak{M}$ of Σ to the manifolds $\mathfrak{M}_i$ of the Σ_i.

Of course, $\mathfrak{M}$ contains every $\mathfrak{M}_i$. The dimension of $\mathfrak{M}$ is shown to exceed that of any $\mathfrak{M}_i$. A point $y_1(x), \cdots, y_n(x)$ of $\mathfrak{M}$ which is not in the union $\mathfrak{N}$ of the $\mathfrak{M}_i$ adheres to $\mathfrak{N}$. For the y as just given, a point at which the y are analytic and which is not a point of contact with $\mathfrak{N}$ is called an exceptional point. The totality of exceptional points, for all zeros of Σ not in $\mathfrak{N}$, is at most countably infinite. Such a countably infinite set of exceptional points may exist, and may be dense in **A**. In fact, a given zero of Σ may have a dense set of exceptional points.

Operations upon manifolds

12. We use a single indeterminate y, and deal with the analytic case. Let $\mathfrak{M}_1$ and $\mathfrak{M}_2$ be manifolds. There exist d.p. which vanish for every sum $y_1 + y_2$ with y_1 in $\mathfrak{M}_1$ and y_2 in $\mathfrak{M}_2$.[15] The manifold of the totality of such d.p. is called the *sum*[16] of $\mathfrak{M}_1$ and $\mathfrak{M}_2$ and is denoted by $\mathfrak{M}_1 + \mathfrak{M}_2$. The *product* of the two manifolds is defined similarly. Let $\mathfrak{M}$ be any manifold. Let Σ be the totality of those d.p. which vanish for the derivative of every $y(x)$ in Σ. The manifold $\mathfrak{M}'$ of Σ is called the *derivative* of $\mathfrak{M}$.

A manifold $\mathfrak{M}$ is said to be *limited* if either $\mathfrak{M}$ consists of the single function zero, or $\mathfrak{M}$ contains nonzero functions and the function zero does not adhere to the set of reciprocals of such functions. $\mathfrak{M}$ is limited if and only if it is held by a d.p. of the form $y^p + F$, where F either is zero or else consists of terms of degree less than p.

If $\mathfrak{M}_1$ and $\mathfrak{M}_2$ are general solutions of d.p. of the first order, and are limited, $\mathfrak{M}_1 + \mathfrak{M}_2$ and $\mathfrak{M}_1\mathfrak{M}_2$ are limited. If $\mathfrak{M}_1$ and $\mathfrak{M}_2$, irreducible and of order more than unity, are limited, their limited character may not be communicated to their sum and product. This is seen from examples based on the theory of the elliptic functions. For the case of the product, the result just stated is equivalent to the fact that the product of two manifolds may contain the function zero, even if neither manifold does. The derivative of every limited manifold is limited.

---

[14] Strodt, 44.

[15] We take y_1 and y_2 with the same domain of analyticity.

[16] Ritt, 37.

CHAPTER VII

INTERSECTIONS OF ALGEBRAIC DIFFERENTIAL MANIFOLDS

Dimensions of components of intersections

1. B.L. van der Waerden has shown[1] that if two irreducible algebraic manifolds in the space of $y_1, \cdots, y_n$ have the respective dimensions p and q, every component of their intersection is of dimension at least $p + q - n$. For algebraic differential manifolds, there is no such regularity. We shall exhibit, for the case of $n = 3$, two irreducible manifolds of dimension 2 whose intersection consists of a single point.

2. Working with u, v, y, we let

$$F = u^5 - v^5 + y(uv_1 - vu_1)^2.$$

We take $\mathfrak{F}$ as the field of complex numbers. F is algebraically irreducible. We shall find its components. A component other than $\mathfrak{M}$, the general solution, must be held by the coefficient of y, therefore by $u^5 - v^5$. Let

$$A_j = u - \omega^{j-1}v, \qquad j = 1, \cdots, 5,$$

where $\omega = e^{2\pi i/5}$. As

$$uv_1 - vu_1 = v_1A_j - vA_j', \qquad j = 1, \cdots, 5,$$

it follows from the low power theorem that, for each j, the manifold of A_j is a component of F. Thus F has six components, each of dimension 2.

The manifold $\mathfrak{M}'$ of y is two-dimensional. We shall show that $\mathfrak{M}$ and $\mathfrak{M}'$ have precisely one point in common, the point $u = v = y = 0$.

We show first that $u = v = y = 0$ is in $\mathfrak{M}$. Let $\bar{u}, \bar{v}, \bar{y}$ be any point of $\mathfrak{M}$ which does not annul $u^5 - v^5$. If c is an arbitrary constant with respect to $\mathfrak{F}<\bar{u}, \bar{v}, \bar{y}>$, it follows from the homogeneity of F and $u^5 - v^5$ that $c\bar{u}, c\bar{v}, c\bar{y}$ is in $\mathfrak{M}$. Then every d.p. which holds $\mathfrak{M}$ vanishes for $u = v = y = 0$ and our statement is proved.

Now let $\tilde{u}, \tilde{v}, 0$ be a point of $\mathfrak{M}$.

For each j, we write $u^5 - v^5 = A_jB_j$. For every zero of F with $y = 0$, in particular, for every point of $\mathfrak{M}$ with y equal to zero, $u^5 - v^5$, and therefore some A_j, vanishes. By III, §23, a zero of an A_j which lies in $\mathfrak{M}$ annuls B_j, and therefore annuls some A_k with $k \neq j$. It follows that $\tilde{u} = \tilde{v} = 0$.

The anomaly which we have just found has nothing to do with "points at infinity." It would be futile to try to remove it by creating a "projective space."

Orders of components of an intersection

3. We consider, as in V, §27, a finite system Ψ of nonzero d.p. in $y_1, \cdots, y_n$. Let y_i be involved in Ψ up to the order m_i.

[1] Mathematische Annalen, vol. 115 (1938), p. 330.

Let $\mathfrak{M}$, the manifold of a prime ideal Γ, be a component of Ψ of dimension q. We are interested in securing a bound for the order of $\mathfrak{M}$ when $q = 0$, and a bound for the order of $\mathfrak{M}$ relative to any given parametric set when $q > 0$ (II, §35). We shall secure a bound for the order, or for the relative order, in terms of the m_i.

The result which we shall obtain may be regarded as a counterpart, for systems of algebraic differential equations, of Bézout's theorem on the number of solutions of a system of algebraic equations.

4. Suppose first that $q = 0$.

We consider the system Φ of d.p. in indeterminates u_{ij}, v_i, obtained from Ψ as in V, §27. Some prime ideal Σ' as in V, §26, goes over into Γ by the substitution[2] (29). Σ' is contained in a prime ideal Σ, described as in V, §20. We wish to see that Σ is of dimension zero. Suppose that Σ is of positive dimension; it will have a parametric set $u_1, \cdots, u_k; v_1, \cdots, v_t$. Suppose that v are actually present in this set. Then v_1 corresponds to some y_j in Ψ. As Γ has a d.p. in y_j alone, Σ has a d.p. in v_1 alone. Thus there are no parametric v.

Let us now consider u_1. It corresponds to some y_{js}. Γ has a nonzero d.p. N in y_j alone. We assume N to be algebraically irreducible. Suppose that N involves derivatives of y_j of order less than s. Let y_{jl} be the lowest such derivative. Then some linear combination of N and its derivative is free of y_{jl}. Continuing, we find a nonzero d.p. P in Γ, involving y_j alone, in which the derivatives of y_j are of orders at least s. To P, there corresponds in Σ a d.p. in u_1 alone.

Thus Σ is of dimension zero. The set (18) thus becomes

$$u_{h+1}, \cdots, u_m; \qquad u_1', \cdots, u_h'; \qquad v_1, \cdots, v_r.$$

We consider the system (20) which corresponds to Σ. The second members are expressions in $u_1, \cdots, u_h; w$.

We seek a bound for h. If y_i occurs up to the order m_i in Ψ, y_i yields m_i letters u. Thus

$$h \leqq m_1 + \cdots + m_n.$$

Let $\bar{u}_1, \cdots, \bar{u}_m; \bar{v}_1, \cdots, \bar{v}_r; \bar{w}$ be a generic zero of Σ. Let ζ be a derivative of any order of one of the quantities $\bar{u}, \bar{v}$. Then ζ has an expression which is rational in $\bar{u}_1, \cdots, \bar{u}_h; \bar{w}$. If ζ is one of the quantities just written, the expression is ζ itself. Otherwise, we use (20) and $R = 0$; a sufficient number of differentiations and substitutions gives the desired expression for ζ. In particular, proper derivatives of w which appear during the differentiations of the z are obtained by differentiation from $R = 0$.

Let us consider now any $h + 1$ of the letters u_{ij}, v_{ij}. They furnish $h + 1$ quantities ζ, with expressions as just described. Using these $h + 1$ expressions, and the relation $R = 0$ for $\bar{u}_1, \cdots, \bar{u}_h; \bar{w}$, we obtain, by an elimination, a non-

[2] We use, at present, equation numbers of Chapter V. The u_i of Σ' are the u_{ij} of Φ.

zero polynomial in the $h + 1$ letters u_{ij}, v_{ij} which is a d.p. in Σ. It follows that, given any $h + 1$ distinct y_{ij}, Γ contains a nonzero d.p. which involves only those y_{ij}. This means, by II, §35, that the order of Γ cannot exceed h.

We may thus state the following theorem:

THEOREM: *Let Φ be a finite system of nonzero d.p. in $\mathfrak{F}\{y_1, \cdots, y_n\}$. Let m_i be the maximum of the orders of those derivatives of y_i which appear in Φ. If a component $\mathfrak{M}$ of Φ is of dimension zero, the order of $\mathfrak{M}$ is at most $m_1 + \cdots + m_n$.*

5. We now suppose that $q > 0$. We write the indeterminates as $u_1, \cdots, u_q$; $y_1, \cdots, y_p$, with the u parametric for Γ. Let $A_1, \cdots, A_p$, with A_i of order r_i in y_i, be a characteristic set for Γ. Let B_i, $i = 1, \cdots, p$, be a nonzero d.p. in Γ involving only y_i and the u. Let C be a d.p. which is not in Γ and which holds every component of Ψ other than $\mathfrak{M}$.

Let $\bar{u}_1, \cdots, \bar{u}_q$; $\bar{y}_1, \cdots, \bar{y}_p$ be a generic zero of Γ. Let the $\bar{u}$ be substituted for the u in Ψ. Then Ψ becomes a system Ψ' in $y_1, \cdots, y_p$ over $\mathfrak{F}<\bar{u}_1, \cdots, \bar{u}_q>$. Each B_i becomes a nonzero B_i' and C a nonzero C'.

Let the components of Ψ other than $\mathfrak{M}$ be manifolds of prime ideals $\Gamma_1, \cdots, \Gamma_s$. Then Ψ' is equivalent to Γ', Γ_1', $\cdots, \Gamma_s'$, each accented system resulting from the corresponding unaccented one when the u are replaced by the $\bar{u}$.

The totality of d.p. in $\mathfrak{F} < \bar{u}_1, \cdots, \bar{u}_q > \{y_1, \cdots, y_p\}$ which vanish for $\bar{y}_1, \cdots, \bar{y}_p$ is a prime ideal Δ held by Ψ'. Each Γ_i' is held by C', while Δ is not. Thus, the manifold of Δ is contained in a component $\mathfrak{M}'$ of Ψ' which is held by Γ'. $\mathfrak{M}'$ must be of dimension zero, since each B' is in Γ'. Then Δ is of dimension zero and, by II, §36, its order h does not exceed the order of $\mathfrak{M}'$.

Now Δ contains no d.p. involving only y_{ij} with $j < r_i$; otherwise, there would be a nonzero d.p. reduced with respect to $A_1, \cdots, A_p$ which vanishes for the generic zero of Γ. By II, §35, $h \geqq r_1 + \cdots + r_p$. By §4, if the highest derivative of y_i in Ψ is of order m_i, the order of $\mathfrak{M}'$ does not exceed $m_1 + \cdots + m_p$. Thus

$$r_1 + \cdots + r_p \leqq m_1 + \cdots + m_p.$$

We may thus formulate the following theorem:

THEOREM: *Let Φ be a finite set of d.p. in $\mathfrak{F}\{u_1, \cdots, u_q; y_1, \cdots, y_p\}$, the u being a parametric set for a component $\mathfrak{M}$ of Φ. Let m_i, $i = 1, \cdots, p$, be the maximum of the orders of those derivatives of y_i which appear in Φ. Then the order of $\mathfrak{M}$ relative to $u_1, \cdots, u_q$ cannot exceed $m_1 + \cdots + m_p$.*

In what precedes, the condition that $\mathfrak{M}$ be a component of Φ is essential. For instance, taking Φ as $y_{10} + y_{20}$, the manifold of $y_{1n} + y_{10}$, $y_{10} + y_{20}$, which is of order n, is, for every n, held by Φ.

6. Jacobi examined, from the heuristic standpoint, the problem of determining the number of arbitrary constants in the solution of a system of n differential equations in n unknowns.[3] Taking the system in the form

[3] See Ritt, 29.

$$(1) \qquad u_i = 0, \qquad i = 1, \cdots, n,$$

where each u involves the unknowns $y_1, \cdots, y_n$, a certain number of their derivatives and the independent variable x, Jacobi considers the derivatives of y_j appearing in u_i and denotes the maximum of the orders of those derivatives by a_{ij}. He forms all sums

$$(2) \qquad a_{1j_1} + \cdots + a_{nj_n}$$

where $j_1, \cdots, j_n$ is a permutation of $1, \cdots, n$. He arrives at the conclusion that *the number of arbitrary constants in the solution of* (1) *does not exceed the greatest sum* (2).

After our study of algebraic differential manifolds, it is unnecessary to insist on the fact that the notion of the number of constants in the solution of a general system never was a notion which was definite in advance. For algebraic systems, the concept is made definite by the theory of orders of irreducible manifolds which has been developed here. It is thus not surprising that Jacobi's work on this question, in spite of its daring and ingenious quality, should not have firm logical structure.

One would be disposed to regard Jacobi's work as conjectural and to expect that his bound would be found valid in a rigorous theory. We shall see later that Jacobi's bound, like weaker ones given before his time, does not have the broad applicability which one might anticipate for it. We shall treat now a situation in which Jacobi's bound is found to hold.

We deal with two nonzero d.p. A and B in y and z. We represent by a and b the respective orders of A in y and z; by c and d the orders of B in y and z. Let

$$h = \text{Max}\,(a + d,\, b + c).$$

We prove the following theorem:

THEOREM: *If $\mathfrak{M}$, of dimension zero, is a component of the system A, B, the order of $\mathfrak{M}$ is at most*[4] *h.*

We assume that $\mathfrak{M}$ is of order greater than h and produce a contradiction. Fixing our ideas, we assume that $b \geqq d$.

There exist nonzero d.p. C whose orders in y and z do not exceed c and d respectively and which hold $\mathfrak{M}$, such that the system A, C has no component of dimension unity containing $\mathfrak{M}$. B is such a d.p. From among all such d.p. C, we select one which, for the order y, z of the indeterminates, is of a least rank. The d.p. selected will be denoted by D.

We are going to prove that D is free of z. We assume that z is present in D and force a contradiction.

Let D be of order e in y and of order f in z. Let S be the separant of D. There is a relation

[4] A better bound can be given in the case in which one of y and z is absent from one of A and B. For instance, if B is free of z, it can be shown as below that the order of M does not exceed $b + c$.

$$S^tA \equiv E, \qquad [D],$$

where E has an order in z not exceeding f and an order in y not exceeding

$$\text{Max } (a, e + b - f).$$

Suppose that S does not hold $\mathfrak{M}$. Let $\mathfrak{M}'$ be a component of the system D, E which contains $\mathfrak{M}$. Then $\mathfrak{M}'$ is a component of A, D and is thus of dimension zero. Applying the theorem of §4 to D, E and using II, §36, we find that the order of $\mathfrak{M}$ does not exceed[5]

$$\text{Max } (a, e + b - f) + f = \text{Max } (a + f, e + b).$$

As $f \leqq d$ and $e \leqq c$, the order of $\mathfrak{M}$ cannot exceed h.

Thus S holds $\mathfrak{M}$. If D is of degree q in z_f, then

$$qD = z_f S + T, \tag{3}$$

where T, like S, is of lower rank than D in z. Also T holds $\mathfrak{M}$.

By I, §29, we may assume that $\mathfrak{F}$ has a nonconstant element.[6] We shall prove the existence of an element μ in $\mathfrak{F}$ such that all components of the system

$$A, \qquad S + \mu T \tag{4}$$

which contain $\mathfrak{M}$ are of dimension zero. As $S + \mu T$ will be of lower rank than D in z, our statement that D is free of z will be proved.

By (3), the system A, D holds the system

$$A, S, T. \tag{5}$$

Let u be an indeterminate. We consider the system

$$A, \qquad S + uT \tag{6}$$

in y, z, u. Let the essential prime divisors of the perfect ideal determined by the system (6) be $\Sigma_1, \cdots, \Sigma_r$. Let $\Sigma_1, \cdots, \Sigma_s$ be those Σ which are not held by (5). We say that each of these ideals contains a nonzero d.p. in y and u alone and a nonzero d.p. in z and u alone.

Suppose that Σ_1 contains no d.p. in y and u alone. Then, if the indeterminates are taken in the order u, y, z, Σ_1 has a characteristic set composed of one d.p., so that the manifold of Σ_1 is the general solution of a d.p. F (II, §§18, 33). Now F cannot involve u, for F will continue to be a characteristic set for Σ_1 if the indeterminates are taken in the order y, z, u, and A, which is in Σ_1, does not involve u. We take the remainder of $S + uT$ with respect to F for the order u, y, z. We secure a relation

---

[5] As $b \geqq d \geqq f$, we have $e + b - f \geqq e$.

[6] Suppose that $\mathfrak{F}$ consists purely of constants. The ideal $\{A, B\}$ has essential prime divisors $\Sigma_1, \cdots, \Sigma_s$. When an element x, of derivative unity, is adjoined to $\mathfrak{F}$, we secure a larger $\{A, B\}$. Its essential prime divisors can easily be shown to be the prime ideals generated by the Σ in $\mathfrak{F} < x >$. The new prime ideals have the same characteristic sets as the old ones.

$$J(S + uT) \equiv 0, \qquad [F],$$

with J a power product in the initial and separant of F. This means, since F is free of u, that

$$JS \equiv 0, \qquad JT \equiv 0, \qquad [F].$$

It follows that each d.p. in (5) is in Σ_1.

This proves that Σ_i, for $i \leqq s$, contains a d.p. H_i in y and u alone. Similarly each such Σ_i contains a d.p. K_i in z and u alone. Let M be the product of the d.p. H and N the product of the K. Let u be fixed as an element μ in F so that M goes over into a nonzero d.p. U in y alone, N into a nonzero d.p. V in z alone.

Then those zeros of

(7) $$A, \qquad S + \mu T$$

which are not zeros of (5) must annul U and V. A fortiori, all zeros of (7) which are not zeros of A, D annul U and V.

This shows that a component of (7) which is not contained in a component of A, D is held by U and V. Then every component of (7) which contains $\mathfrak{M}$ is of dimension zero. This proves that D is free of z.

D must involve y effectively, since A, D has zeros. Denoting still by S the separant of D, we secure a relation

$$S^q A \equiv L, \qquad [D],$$

where the orders of L in y and z do not exceed e and b respectively. We reason with D, L as with D, E, above, to show that S holds $\mathfrak{M}$. Then we follow the method above to find a system similar to (4), with $S + \mu T$ of lower rank than D. Thus it is not possible to choose a d.p. of least rank among the d.p. C. This completes the proof that the order of $\mathfrak{M}$ does not exceed h.

Intersections of general solutions

7. By all the rules of play, the bound h of §6 should, when A and B are algebraically irreducible, apply to the components of dimension zero in the intersection of the general solutions of A and B. The general solution of a d.p. F in y and z can be regarded as the solution of the differential equation obtained by solving for the highest derivative of one of y and z in the equation $F = 0$. To be sure, we would then be dealing with irrational differential equations. However, as Jacobi's considerations are detached from questions of the theory of functions, one would not expect irrationality to have a bearing on the problem. It might be suggested that Jacobi's heuristic work, as well as previous work which yielded bounds like that of §4, was intended to apply to the "general case." If so, the heuristic history of differential equations has been different from that of algebraic equations. Bézout's work of the middle eighteenth century, on the number of solutions of a system of algebraic equations, was entirely heuristic. His conjecture was validated, late in the nineteenth century, not for a "general case" but for all systems.

The actual situation is as follows. If the orders of A and B in each of y and z do not exceed unity, we get the bound of §6 for a component of the intersection of the general solutions. For higher orders, that bound need not hold. We shall show how to construct, for every $n > 3$, a d.p. of order n in y and in z whose general solution intersects the manifold of y in an irreducible manifold of dimension zero and order $2n - 3$.

8. We consider A and B, as in §6, assuming them to be algebraically irreducible, with each of a, b, c, d not greater than unity. We prove the following theorem.

THEOREM: *If $\mathfrak{M}$, of dimension zero, is a component of the intersection of the general solutions of A and B, the order of $\mathfrak{M}$ does not exceed h.*

Thus the order of $\mathfrak{M}$ does not exceed 2.

We represent by $\mathfrak{N}$ the intersection of the general solutions of A and B.

If a, b, c, d are all zero, the general solutions of A and B are their complete manifolds and we have merely to apply the theorem of §4.

Suppose now that $a = b = 0$ and that at least one of c and d is 1. We consider first the intersection $\mathfrak{M}'$ of the complete manifolds of A and B. Every component of $\mathfrak{M}'$ of dimension zero has an order not exceeding unity. By II, §36, if $\mathfrak{M}$ is not contained in a component of $\mathfrak{M}'$ of dimension unity, the order of $\mathfrak{M}$ does not exceed unity.

We have now to consider the case in which $\mathfrak{M}$ is contained in a component $\mathfrak{M}''$ of $\mathfrak{M}'$ of dimension unity. $\mathfrak{M}''$ is the general solution of a d.p. C. Because A holds $\mathfrak{M}''$, C must be of order zero in each of y and z; this implies that $\mathfrak{M}''$ is the manifold of A. Then $\mathfrak{M}''$ must be a component of the manifold of B. Otherwise $\mathfrak{M}''$ would be contained in the general solution of B and $\mathfrak{M}$ would not be a component of $\mathfrak{N}$.[7]

We suppose, as we may, that A involves z effectively. As $\mathfrak{M}''$ is a component of B other than the general solution, we have $d = 1$ (III, §15). Let S be the separant of A. We have, by the low power theorem, a relation

$$S^t B = C_0 A^p + C_1 A^{p_1} A_1^{q_1} + \cdots + C_r A^{p_r} A_1^{q_r}.$$

Here A_1 is the derivative of A and, for every i, $p_i + q_i > p$. The orders of the C in z and in y do not exceed 0 and 1 respectively, and no C is divisible by A. By III, §23, as $\mathfrak{M}$ is in the intersection of $\mathfrak{M}''$ and the general solution of B, C_0 must hold $\mathfrak{M}$. The manifold of the system C_0, A is a proper part of $\mathfrak{M}''$ and thus, by II, §36, has components which are all of dimension zero. By §6, the order of such a component cannot exceed unity. Then the order of $\mathfrak{M}$ does not exceed unity; this is what was to be proved.

Suppose now that at least one of a and b is unity and that at least one of c and d is unity. We take up immediately the case in which $\mathfrak{M}$ is contained in a component $\mathfrak{M}''$ of $\mathfrak{M}'$ of dimension unity; when $\mathfrak{M}$ is not so contained, it follows

[7] By III, §15, the components of B other than its general solution are manifolds of d.p. of orders zero in y and z.

from §6 that its order does not exceed h. As $\mathfrak{M}$ is a component of $\mathfrak{N}$, $\mathfrak{M}''$ is not part of $\mathfrak{N}$. Let, then, $\mathfrak{M}''$ fail to be contained in the general solution of B. Then some other component of B contains $\mathfrak{M}''$ and is thus identical with $\mathfrak{M}''$. By the case which precedes, the components of the intersection of $\mathfrak{M}''$ with the general solution of B are of dimension zero and of order at most unity. This completes the proof.

9. We are going to present a d.p. F in y and z, of order 4 in y and in z, whose general solution will be shown to intersect the manifold of $y = 0$ in an irreducible manifold of dimension zero and order 5.

Through §13, K_1 will represent, for any d.p. K, the derivative of K. We let

$$A = y_1 - z_3y^2, \tag{8}$$

$$B = A^4 - y_3^8, \tag{9}$$

$$C = y_3A_1 - 2y_4A, \tag{10}$$

$$F = B - y^6C^2 = A^4 - y_3^8 - y^6C^2. \tag{11}$$

We use the field of rational numbers. Let us see first that F is algebraically irreducible. If we consider the equation $F = 0$ as an algebraic equation for y_4, we secure a function y_4 of two branches. Thus, if F were factorable, it would have a factor of positive degree free of y_4. Such a factor would have to be a factor of y^6A^2. As F is not divisible by y or by A, F is algebraically irreducible.

Let us now determine the components of F other than the general solution.

Let $\mathfrak{N}$ be such a component. As $\partial F/\partial y_4 = 4y^6AC$, $\mathfrak{N}$ must be held by yC or by A. Suppose that A holds $\mathfrak{N}$. By (10) and (11), y_3 holds $\mathfrak{N}$. In every case then, B holds $\mathfrak{N}$.

Now B is the product of the four d.p.

$$E^{(j)} = y_1 - z_3y^2 - jy_3^2, \qquad j = \pm 1, \qquad \pm(-1)^{1/2}, \tag{12}$$

each of which is algebraically irreducible. For what follows, it is important to know that the manifold of each E is irreducible. From the manner in which z_3 figures in (12), one sees that a component of $E^{(j)}$ other than the general solution is held by y. Such a component, being of dimension unity, must be the manifold of y. But the low power theorem shows that the manifold of y is not a component. This proves the irreducibility of the manifolds of the E.

We have, for every j,

$$C = y_3E_1^{(j)} - 2y_4E^{(j)}.$$

Referring to (11), and applying the low power theorem, we see that the manifold of each E is a component[8] of F.

It will be proved that the intersection of the general solution of F with the manifold of $y = 0$ is the manifold of the system $y = 0$, $z_5 = 0$. The latter manifold is of dimension zero and order 5.

[8] For the order y, z of the indeterminates, F as it stands is in the form (25) of III, §17.

10. We refer to I, §26. We use any positive integer p and any power product P in y and its derivatives. The degree of P is denoted by d and its weight by w. The second member of (31) of I, §26, will be represented by $\delta(p, w)$. Let $U = y^p$. We shall prove that P has a representation as a homogeneous polynomial in U and derivatives of U, whose coefficients are homogeneous polynomials[9] in y and derivatives of y of a common degree not greater than $\delta(p, w)$.

If $d \leqq \delta(p, w)$, P itself is the representation sought. Otherwise, by I, §26, P is a linear combination of U and its derivatives, with coefficients all of degree $d - p$ and none of weight exceeding w. If $d - p \leqq \delta(p, w)$, we have the desired representation. Otherwise, the coefficients of U and its derivatives will be in $[U]$. Continuing, we have P expressed as in our statement.

11. Let Σ be an ideal of d.p. in y and z; M a d.p. in y and z; α a nonnegative number. We shall say that M *admits* α *as a multiplier with respect to* Σ if, for every $\epsilon > 0$, there exists an integer $n_0(\epsilon)$ such that, for every $n > n_0(\epsilon)$,

$$M^n \equiv P, \qquad (\Sigma),$$

where P is a d.p. depending on M and n which, arranged as a polynomial[10] in the y_i, contains no term of degree less than $n(\alpha - \epsilon)$. P may be zero. If α is a multiplier for M and if $0 \leqq \gamma < \alpha$, γ is also a multiplier.

We prove the following properties of multipliers:

(a) Let M and N admit α and β, respectively, as multipliers with respect to Σ. Let $\gamma = \text{Min}\ (\alpha, \beta)$. Then $M + N$ admits γ as a multiplier.

(b) For M and N as in (a), MN admits $\alpha + \beta$ as a multiplier.

(c) Let M^p, where p is a positive integer, admit α as a multiplier. Then M admits α/p.

(d) Let M admit α as a multiplier. Then M_1, the derivative of M, also admits α.

(e) If $M \equiv N$, (Σ), M and N admit the same multipliers.

Proving (a), we take an $\epsilon > 0$. Let $n_0(\epsilon/2)$ serve as above for both M and N with respect to $\epsilon/2$. We consider $(M + N)^n$ for any $n \geqq 1$. Let $R = M^aN^b$ where $a + b = n$. If a and b both exceed $n_0(\epsilon/2)$, we have $R \equiv P$, (Σ), where no term of P is of degree less than

$$a(\alpha - \epsilon/2) + b(\beta - \epsilon/2),$$

which quantity is not less than $n(\gamma - \epsilon/2)$. If $b \leqq n_0(\epsilon/2) < a$, we have $R \equiv P$, (Σ), with no term of P of degree less than

$$[n - n_0(\epsilon/2)]\ (\alpha - \epsilon/2).$$

The last quantity, if n is large in comparison with $n_0\ (\epsilon/2)$, exceeds $n(\alpha - \epsilon)$. The truth of (a) is now clear.

The proofs of (b), (c), and (e) are trivial.

[9] Over the field of rational numbers.

[10] When P is thus arranged, its coefficients are d.p. in z. The definition of multiplier thus gives a special role to y.

Proving (d), we take an $\epsilon > 0$ and, relative to M, an $n_0(\epsilon/2)$. Let m be a fixed integer which exceeds $n_0(\epsilon/2)$. We consider an $n > 0$ and use $\delta(m, n)$ as in §10. Then M_1^n is a polynomial in M^m and its derivatives, with coefficients which are d.p. in M of degree not greater than $\delta(m, n)$. In this expression, every power product in M^m and its derivatives is of degree not less than

$$q = [n - \delta(m, n)]/m. \tag{13}$$

Now if n is large, $\delta(m, n)$, as one sees from I, §26, is small in comparison with n, so that q is only slightly less than n/m. Each power product in M^m and its derivatives is congruent to a d.p. whose terms have degrees in the y_i not less than $qm(\alpha - \epsilon/2)$. If n is large, this quantity exceeds $n(\alpha - \epsilon)$, q.e.d.

12. We return to F of §9, denoting the general solution of F by $\mathfrak{M}$. We show now that a point in $\mathfrak{M}$ with $y = 0$ satisfies $z_5 = 0$. Later we shall prove that every z with $z_5 = 0$ is admissible.

We determine first a d.p. G which holds $\mathfrak{M}$, but no other component of F. We have, by (9) and (10),

$$AB_1 - 4A_1B = 4y_3^7C. \tag{14}$$

Thus, by (11) (first representation of F), we have when $F = 0$

$$4y_3^7B^{1/2} = y^3(AB_1 - 4A_1B). \tag{15}$$

Again, letting $K = y^3C$, we have by (11), when $F = 0$, the relation $B^{1/2} = K$. Thus, for $F = 0$, $B \neq 0$,

$$B^{-1/2}B_1 = 2K_1. \tag{16}$$

Substituting into (15) the expression which (16) furnishes for B_1, we find, for $F = 0$, $B \neq 0$,

$$4y_3^{14} + L = 0, \tag{17}$$

where

$$L = -4y^3y_3^7AK_1 + y^6A^2K_1^2 - 4y^6A_1^2B. \tag{18}$$

We designate the first member of (17) by G. Then G holds $\mathfrak{M}$.

13. In what follows, all multipliers will operate with respect to $[F, G]$.

In (11), y_3^8 and y^6C^2 contain no terms of degree less than 8 in the y_i. Thus A^4 admits 8 as a multiplier so that, by (c) of §11, A admits 2. Now z_3y^2 admits 2. By (a) of §11, y_1 admits 2. Then, by (d), every y_i with $i \geqq 1$ admits 2. From (10), using (a), (b), (d), we find that C admits 4. Referring to (11) and using (e), we see now that A^4 admits 14 so that A admits 3. By (10), now, C admits 5 and we find from (11) that A admits 4. We return to (10) and see that C admits 6. Also, by (11), B admits 18. Finally, K of §12 admits 9.

By (18), L admits 30. By (17), y_3 admits 15/7. Now $y_2 - z_4y^2 - 2z_3yy_1$, which is A_1, admits 4. As y_1 admits 2, $y_2 - z_4y^2$ admits 3. Then $y_3 - z_5y^2 - 2z_4yy_1$ admits 3 so that $y_3 - z_5y^2$ admits 3. As y_3 admits 15/7, z_5y^2 admits 15/7.

We infer that $[F, G]$ contains a d.p. of the type $(z_5y^2)^m + M$ where every term of M is of degree greater than $2m$ in the y_i. It follows from III, §23, that a point in $\mathfrak{M}$ cannot have $y = 0$ unless $z_5 = 0$.

14. Let $(0, \alpha)$ be a generic point in the manifold of $y = 0$, $z_5 = 0$. We shall prove that $\mathfrak{M}$ contains $(0, \alpha)$. This will imply that $\mathfrak{M}$ contains the manifold of y, z_5, and our investigation of F will be completed.

Representing by c an arbitrary constant with respect to $\mathfrak{F} <\alpha>$ and by v a new indeterminate, we make in F the substitution[11]

$$y = \sum_{j=1}^{6} c^j \alpha_2^{j-1} + c^6 v. \tag{19}$$

We represent by A', A_1', B', C', F' the expressions into which A, A_1, B, C, F are transformed when z is replaced by α and y by the second member of (19).

We find from (19)

$$A' = c^6 v_1 + c^7 P, \tag{20}$$

with P a polynomial in α_2, α_3, c, v. Then we may write

$$A_1' = c^6 v_2 + c^7 Q, \tag{21}$$

with Q a polynomial in α_2, α_3, α_4, c, v, v_1.

From (19), we have, remembering that $\alpha_5 = 0$,

$$y_3 = 6c^3\alpha_3\alpha_4 + \cdots; \qquad y_4 = 6c^3\alpha_4^2 + \cdots. \tag{22}$$

By (20), (21), (22), we have, putting $\beta = 6\alpha_3\alpha_4$ and $\gamma = 12\alpha_4^2$,

$$C' = c^9(\beta v_2 - \gamma v_1) + c^{10} R,$$

with R a polynomial in α_2, α_3, α_4, c and the v_j with $j \leqq 4$. We find thus

$$F' = c^{24}\,[v_1^4 - \beta^8 - (\beta v_2 - \gamma v_1)^2] + c^{25} T, \tag{23}$$

with T of the type of R.

Let V represent the coefficient of c^{24} in F'. As $\beta \neq 0$, the differential equation $V = 0$ for v is effectively of the second order. Let then $v = \xi$ be a zero (constructed by the abstract method) of V which does not annul $v_1^4 - \beta^8$.

We wish to show that F' is annulled by a series

$$v = \xi + \varphi_2 c^{\rho_2} + \varphi_3 c^{\rho_3} + \cdots \tag{24}$$

of the usual type, with $\rho_2 > 0$.

It will suffice to show that $G = F'/c^{24}$ is annulled by a series (24). If G vanishes for $v = \xi$, then $v = \xi$ is an acceptable series (24). In what follows, we assume that such vanishing does not occur. We put, in G, $v = \xi + u_1$. Then G goes over into an expression K' in c and u_1

$$K' = a'(c) + \sum b_i'(c)\, u_{10}^{\alpha_{0i}} \cdots u_{14}^{\alpha_{4i}}. \tag{25}$$

[11] Subscripts of α indicate differentiation.

Here $\sum$ contains the terms of K' which are not free of the u_{1j} and i ranges from unity to some positive integer. As to a' and the b', they are polynomials in c with coefficients in $\mathfrak{F} <\alpha_2, \xi>$. Because ξ does not annul G, a' is not zero. On the other hand, because G vanishes for $v = \xi$, $c = 0$, the lowest power of c in a' is positive. Because the bracketed terms in (23) contribute effectively to $\sum$ in (25), certain of the b' contain terms of zero power in c.

Let σ' be the lowest exponent of c in a' and σ_i' the lowest exponent of c in b_i'. Let

$$\rho_2 = \operatorname{Max} \frac{\sigma' - \sigma_i'}{\alpha_{0i} + \cdots + \alpha_{4i}},$$

where i has the range which it has in $\sum$. As $\sigma' > 0$ and certain σ_i' equal 0, $\rho_2 > 0$. We may now suppose ourselves to be working with K' of III, §7. We obtain the series (24).

We have shown, all in all, that F, for $z = \alpha$, is annulled by a series

$$y = c + c^2\alpha_2 + \cdots + c^5\alpha_2^4 + c^6(\alpha_2^5 + \xi) + \cdots, \tag{26}$$

where the unwritten terms have rational exponents greater than 6. The series (26) does not annul B for $z = \alpha$. Indeed,

$$B' = c^{24}(v_1^4 - \beta^8) + \cdots$$

and the coefficient of c^{24} does not vanish for $v = \xi$.

It follows that every d.p. which holds $\mathfrak{M}$ vanishes for $z = \alpha$ and for y as in (26). This means that $y = 0$, $z = \alpha$ is in $\mathfrak{M}$.

15. If, in (8) to (11), we replace z_3, y_3, y_4 wherever they occur by z_{n-1}, y_{n-1}, y_n, with $n \geqq 4$, we obtain a d.p. F with a general solution which intersects the manifold of $y = 0$ in that of $y = 0$, $z_{2n-3} = 0$; the proofs require only the slightest changes.

In F of §9, if one replaces z_3 by z, one obtains a d.p. which is of the first order in z and whose general solution intersects the manifold of $y = 0$ in that of $y = 0$, $z_2 = 0$. This, in itself, is sufficiently anomalous. However, if it is desired to secure a d.p. F whose order in z cannot be reduced, it suffices to replace y_3 and y_4, in (9), (10), (11), by zy_3 and its derivative, respectively.

Intersections of Components of a Differential Polynomial

16. Dealing with the analytic case, we prove the following theorem:

THEOREM: *Let F be a d.p. in $y_1, \cdots, y_n$. A zero of F which is contained in more than one component of F annuls $\partial F/\partial y_{ij}$ for $i = 1, \cdots, n$ and for every*[12] *j.*

Thus, in particular, if F vanishes for $y_i = 0$, $i = 1, \cdots, n$, and, considered as a polynomial in the y_{ij}, contains a term of the first degree, the zero $y_i = 0$ belongs to only one component of F.

Let

$$\bar{y}_1, \cdots, \bar{y}_n \tag{27}$$

[12] The j for which this result is significant are those for which y_{ij} appears effectively in F.

be a zero for which some $\partial F/\partial y_{ij}$ fails to vanish. We shall prove that (27) is contained in only one component of F.

We know that systems defining the components can be secured by choosing a sufficiently large positive integer p and resolving the system of derivatives

$$F, F_1, \cdots, F_p, \tag{28}$$

the F being considered as polynomials in the y_{ij}, into prime p.i. none of which holds any other. We shall show that, for any $p \geqq 1$, (28) yields only one prime p.i. whose polynomials vanish when each y_{ij} in (28) is replaced by $\bar{y}_{ij}$ as determined by (27). This will prove our theorem.

Reassigning the subscripts of the y_i if necessary, we assume that one or more $\partial F/\partial y_{1j}$ do not vanish for (27) and let m be the greatest value of j for which the vanishing does not occur. Putting the polynomials in (28) equal to zero, we secure a set of equations which we shall regard as equations to be solved for those $y_{1,\,m+j}$ for which $0 \leqq j \leqq p$, in terms of x and the other y_{ik} in (28).

Let ξ be a value of x at which the coefficients in F and the functions in (27) are analytic, and at which $\partial F/\partial y_{1m}$ does not vanish for (27). Let $[\eta]$ represent, collectively, the values at ξ of the $\bar{y}_{ij}$ in the zero of (28) derived from (27).

The polynomials in (28) vanish at the point ξ, $[\eta]$ in the space of x and the y_{ij} in (28). We shall examine, at ξ, $[\eta]$, the jacobian with respect to $y_{1m}, \cdots, y_{1,\,m+p}$ of the polynomials in (28). In the first row of this jacobian, which row we understand to consist of partial derivatives of F, only the first term $\partial F/\partial y_{1m}$ fails to vanish at ξ, $[\eta]$. To treat the other rows, let us imagine the polynomials in (28) to be expanded in powers of the various differences $y_{ij} - \bar{y}_{ij}$. The expansion of F will contain a term $\alpha(y_{1m} - \bar{y}_{1m})$, where α is the function of x to which $\partial F/\partial y_{1m}$ reduces for (27). By the nature of m, F_1 must contain the term $\alpha(y_{1,\,m+1} - \bar{y}_{1,\,m+1})$ and can have no term $\beta(y_{1j} - \bar{y}_{1j})$ with $j > m + 1$. Thus, in the second row of the jacobian, the value of the second element at ξ, $[\eta]$ is that of $\partial F/\partial y_{1m}$, and the elements which follow have zero values. Continuing, we find the value of the jacobian at ξ, $[\eta]$ to be the $(p + 1)$th power of the value of $\partial F/\partial y_{1m}$.

Thus, for the neighborhood of ξ, $[\eta]$, $y_{1m}, \cdots, y_{1,\,m+p}$ are determined by our equations as analytic functions $f_m, \cdots, f_{m+p}$ of x and the remaining y_{ij}. By specializing the y_{ij} in the f as functions of x, we can construct zeros of (28). Indeed, we secure in this way all zeros of (28) which, in an area contained in a small neighborhood of $x = \xi$, approximate closely to the zero of (28) derived from (27).

Some prime p.i. in the decomposition of (28), call it Σ, is such that all its polynomials vanish when $y_{1m}, \cdots, y_{1,\,m+p}$ are replaced by their f. Then Σ must admit the $\bar{y}_{ij}$ as a zero. If a prime p.i. Σ' which Σ does not hold vanishes for the $\bar{y}_{ij}$, Σ' has, by IV, §39, zeros which are not in the manifold of Σ and which approximate closely to the $\bar{y}_{ij}$. Thus, by what precedes, Σ is the only prime p.i. in the decomposition of (28) which has the $\bar{y}_{ij}$ as a zero. The theorem is proved.

If one allows all the $\partial F/\partial y_{ij}$ to vanish and requires the nonvanishing of one or more partial derivatives of the second order, there is no upper bound to the number of components to which a zero of F may belong. We illustrate this by an example in $\mathfrak{F}\{ y \}$. Let

$$F = y_2^2 + \prod_{j=1}^{m} [(x + j) y_1 - y],$$

where m is any integer greater than unity. Now $(x + j)y_1 - y$ has $(x + j)y_2$ as derivative, and therefore has, for every j, a manifold which is a component of F. The zero $y = 0$ belongs to every such component.

Analogue of a theorem of Kronecker

17. It is a theorem of Kronecker that, given any system of polynomials in n indeterminates, there exists an equivalent system containing $n + 1$ or fewer polynomials.[13] We present an analogous theorem for d.p.

Theorem: *Let $\mathfrak{F}$ contain a nonconstant element. Let*

$$F_1, \cdots, F_r \tag{29}$$

be any finite system of d.p. in $\mathfrak{F}\{ y_1, \cdots, y_n \}$. There exists a system composed of $n + 1$ linear combinations of the F, with coefficients in $\mathfrak{F}$, whose manifold is identical with that of (29).

We introduce $r(n + 1)$ new indeterminates $u_j^{(i)}$, $i = 1, \cdots, n + 1$; $j = 1, \cdots, r$ and consider the system Λ,

$$u_1^{(i)}F_1 + \cdots + u_r^{(i)}F_r, \qquad i = 1, \cdots, n + 1,$$

in the u and y.

Consider a zero of Λ for which $F_1 \neq 0$. For it, we have

$$u_1^{(i)} = - \frac{u_2^{(i)} F_2 + \cdots + u_r^{(i)} F_r}{F_1}, \tag{30}$$

$i = 1, \cdots, n + 1$. If we differentiate the relations (30) often enough, the $u_{1j}^{(i)}$ will be more numerous than the y_{ij}. By an elimination, we obtain a d.p. K_1 in the u which is annulled by every zero of Λ for which $F_1 \neq 0$. We find, similarly, a K_i for each F_i with $i > 1$. We fix the $u_j^{(i)}$ as elements μ_{ij} in $\mathfrak{F}$ which do not annul the product of the K. Then the manifold of the $n + 1$ d.p.

$$\mu_{i1}F_1 + \cdots + \mu_{ir}F_r, \qquad i = 1, \cdots, n + 1,$$

in $y_1, \cdots, y_n$ is identical with that of (29).

The proof just given does not involve the notion of irreducible manifold. It is considerably shorter than the proof given in A.D.E. However, the older proof gives information on the degree to which one can approximate to the representation of a manifold with a system of p equations with $1 \leqq p \leqq n + 1$.

[13] Koenig, *Algebrasiche Grössen*, p. 234.

CHAPTER VIII

RIQUIER'S EXISTENCE THEOREM FOR ORTHONOMIC SYSTEMS

1. In Chapter IX, we shall extend some of the main results of the preceding chapters to systems of partial differential polynomials. In treating the analytic case, we shall use an important existence theorem due to Riquier. This existence theorem will now be developed.

For §§1–19 of Chapter IX, only §2 and §8 of the present chapter are necessary.

MONOMIALS

2. We deal with m independent variables, $x_1, \cdots, x_m$. By a *monomial* is meant an expression $x_1^{i_1} \cdots x_m^{i_m}$, where the i are non-negative integers. If $\alpha = \gamma\beta$, with α, β, γ monomials, then α is called a *multiple* of β. Given two distinct monomials,

$$x_1^{i_1} \cdots x_m^{i_m}, \qquad x_1^{j_1} \cdots x_m^{j_m},$$

the first is said to be *higher* or *lower* than the second according as the first nonzero difference $i_k - j_k$ is positive or is negative.

The following theorem, due to Riquier, is used only in Chapter IX.

THEOREM: *Let*

$$(1) \qquad \alpha_1, \alpha_2, \cdots, \alpha_q, \cdots$$

be an infinite sequence of monomials. Then there is an α_i which is a multiple of some α_j with $j < i$.

Let β_1 be one of those α for which the exponent of x_1 is a minimum. Consider the monomials which come after β_1 in (1). Let β_2 be a monomial of this class whose degree in x_1 does not exceed that of any other monomial of the class. Of the monomials which follow β_2, let β_3 be one of minimum degree in x_1. Continuing, we form an infinite sequence of monomials

$$(2) \qquad \beta_1, \quad \beta_2, \quad \beta_3, \cdots$$

whose degrees in x_1 are nondecreasing. We extract similarly, from (2), a sequence in which the degrees in x_2 do not decrease. We arrive finally at an infinite subsequence of (1) in which each monomial is a multiple of all which precede it.

Dissection of a Taylor series

3. Let

$$\sum \frac{a_{i_1 \cdots i_m}}{i_1! \cdots i_m!} x_1^{i_1} \cdots x_m^{i_m} \tag{3}$$

be the Taylor expansion at

$$x_i = 0, \qquad i = 1, \cdots, m, \tag{4}$$

of a function u of $x_1, \cdots, x_m$ analytic at the point (4). Let $[\alpha]$ be any given finite and nonvacuous set of distinct monomials. We are going to separate (3), with respect to $[\alpha]$, into a set of components.

Let a be the greatest exponent of x_1 in the set $[\alpha]$. We write

$$u = f_0 + x_1 f_1 + \cdots + x_1^{a-1} f_{a-1} + x_1^a f_a, \tag{5}$$

where, for $i < a$, $x_1^i f_i$ contains all terms in (3) in which the exponent of x_1 is precisely i. As to $x_1^a f_a$, it contains all terms divisible by x_1^a. Then $f_1, \cdots, f_{a-1}$ are series in $x_2, \cdots, x_m$, while f_a involves also x_1.[1]

We define sets of monomials $[\alpha]_\lambda$, $\lambda = 0, \cdots, a$, as follows. If $[\alpha]$ contains monomials in which the exponent of x_1 does not exceed λ, then $[\alpha]_\lambda$ is to consist of all such monomials in $[\alpha]$. If there are no such monomials, then $[\alpha]_\lambda$ is to be unity. Let $[\beta]_\lambda$ be the set of monomials in $x_2, \cdots, x_m$ obtained by putting $x_1 = 1$ in $[\alpha]_\lambda$. We now give to each f_λ, with respect to x_2, the treatment accorded to u, above, with respect to x_1. For $\lambda < a$, we get a representation of the type

$$f_\lambda = f_{\lambda 0} + x_2 f_{\lambda 1} + \cdots + x_2^b f_{\lambda b}, \tag{6}$$

where b depends upon λ, the $f_{\lambda i}$ with $i < b$ involving $x_3, \cdots, x_m$, while $f_{\lambda b}$ involves also x_2. For $\lambda = a$, each f_{ai} involves x_1. That is, in the dissection of f_a, we treat x_1 like $x_3, \cdots, x_m$.

We now operate on each $f_{\lambda\mu}$ with respect to x_3. We use a set of monomials $[\gamma]_{\lambda\mu}$, where, if $[\beta]_\lambda$ has monomials of degree not exceeding μ in x_2, $[\gamma]_{\lambda\mu}$ is obtained by putting $x_2 = 1$ in all such monomials, and where, otherwise, $[\gamma]_{\lambda\mu}$ is unity.

Continuing, we find an expression for u,

$$u = \sum x_1^{i_1} \cdots x_m^{i_m} f_{i_1 \cdots i_m}, \tag{7}$$

the summation extending over a finite number of terms.

Example: Let u be a function of x, y, z. Let $[\alpha]$ be

$$xz^2, \qquad xy, \qquad x^2yz.$$

For x, we find

$$u = f_0(y, z) + xf_1(y, z) + x^2 f_2(x, y, z).$$

[1] We consider every combination $i_1, \cdots, i_m$ to occur in (3), using zero coefficients if necessary.

We now treat each f_i with respect to y, the set of monomials being that indicated below:

$$\begin{array}{ll} f_0(y, z) & 1; \\ f_1(y, z) & z^2, y; \\ f_2(x, y, z) & z^2, y, yz. \end{array}$$

Hence

$$\begin{aligned} f_0(y, z) &= f_{00}(y, z), \\ f_1(y, z) &= f_{10}(z) + yf_{11}(y, z), \\ f_2(x, y, z) &= f_{20}(x, z) + yf_{21}(x, y, z). \end{aligned}$$

The final step is

$$\begin{array}{lll} f_{00}(y, z) & = f_{000}(y, z) & 1; \\ f_{10}(z) & = f_{100} + zf_{101} + z^2f_{102}(z) & z^2; \\ f_{11}(y, z) & = f_{110}(y) + zf_{111}(y) + z^2f_{112}(y, z) & 1, z^2; \\ f_{20}(x, z) & = f_{200}(x) + zf_{201}(x) + z^2f_{202}(x, z) & z^2; \\ f_{21}(x, y, z) & = f_{210}(x, y) + zf_{211}(x, y) + z^2f_{212}(x, y, z) & 1, z, z^2. \end{array}$$

Thus the dissection of u is

$$\begin{aligned} u = f_{000}(y, z) &+ xf_{100} + xzf_{101} + xz^2f_{102}(z) \\ &+ xyf_{110}(y) + xyzf_{111}(y) + xyz^2f_{112}(y, z) \\ &+ x^2f_{200}(x) + x^2zf_{201}(x) + x^2z^2f_{202}(x, z) \\ &+ x^2yf_{210}(x, y) + x^2yzf_{211}(x, y) + x^2yz^2f_{212}(x, y, z). \end{aligned}$$

4. Consider any monomial $\alpha = x_1^{j_1} \cdots x_m^{j_m}$ in $[\alpha]$ and any monomial β in the expansion of u which is a multiple of α. Of course, β appears in one and in only one of the terms in the second member of (7). Let it appear in $x_1^{t_1} \cdots x_m^{t_m}$ $f_{t_1 \cdots t_m}$. We shall prove that $x_1^{t_1} \cdots x_m^{t_m}$ is a multiple of α. For $m = 1$, this result certainly holds. Let the result be true for $m = r - 1$. We shall prove it for $m = r$. We observe first that in the resolution (5) of u, β appears in a term $x_1^{t_1}f_{i_1}$ with $i_1 \geqq j_1$.

Suppose first that $i_1 < a$ in (5). Then $\beta/x_1^{t_1}$ is free of x_1. Among the monomials used in the dissection of f_{i_1} will be $x_2^{j_2} \cdots x_r^{j_r}$ and $\beta/x_1^{t_1}$ will be a multiple of $x_2^{j_2} \cdots x_r^{j_r}$. As there are only $r - 1$ variables involved now, $\beta/x_1^{t_1}$ will appear in a term $\epsilon f_{t_1 t_2 \cdots t_r}$ in the dissection (7) of f_{t_1} with ϵ divisible by $x_2^{j_2} \cdots x_r^{j_r}$. Thus $x_1^{t_1} \cdots x_r^{t_r}$ is divisible by α.

Suppose now that $i_1 = a$. Then β/x_1^a is contained in f_a. Among the monomials used in the dissection of f_a will be $x_2^{j_2} \cdots x_r^{j_r}$. Now the formal scheme in (7) of the dissection of f_a can be obtained by taking a function g of $x_2, \cdots, x_r$, dissecting g with respect to the monomials associated with f_a and then adjoining x_1 to the variables in the series yielded by g. That is, the monomials $x_2^{i_2} \cdots x_r^{i_r}$ in the dissections, analogous to (7), of f_a and g, will be the same. Let γ result from β on putting $x_1 = 1$. Then γ is found in the dissection of g with an $x_2^{i_2} \cdots x_r^{i_r}$ divisible by $x_2^{j_2} \cdots x_r^{j_r}$. The same would therefore be true for β/x^a in the dissection of f_a. This completes the proof.

It follows that every monomial in $[\alpha]$ is an $x_1^{i_1} \cdots x_m^{i_m}$ in (7).

5. The set of monomials consisting of all $x_1^{i_1} \cdots x_m^{i_m}$ in (7) which are multiples of monomials in $[\alpha]$ will be called the *extended set arising from* $[\alpha]$. The set of monomials $x_1^{i_1} \cdots x_m^{i_m}$ in (7) not in the extended set will be called the set *complementary* to $[\alpha]$.

If $[\alpha]$ is identical with the extended set arising from $[\alpha]$, then $[\alpha]$ will be called *complete*.

Consider a set $[\alpha]$ which is not complete. We shall prove that it is possible to form a complete set by adjoining to $[\alpha]$ multiples of monomials in $[\alpha]$.

Let p be the maximum of all exponents in all monomials in $[\alpha]$. Then, in (7), no i_k exceeds p.

Let $[\alpha]'$ be the extended set arising from $[\alpha]$. Then if $[\alpha]'$ is not complete, it is a proper subset of its extended set $[\alpha]''$ (§4). Since we can never get more than $(p + 1)^m$ monomials $x_1^{i_1} \cdots x_m^{i_m}$ in (7), this process of taking extended sets must bring us eventually to a complete set.

6. In (7), the variables in an $f_{i_1 \cdots i_m}$ will be called the *multipliers* of the corresponding $x_1^{i_1} \cdots x_m^{i_m}$, and all other variables will be called *nonmultipliers* of $x_1^{i_1} \cdots x_m^{i_m}$. Of course, if $f_{i_1 \cdots i_m}$ is a constant, $x_1^{i_1} \cdots x_m^{i_m}$ has no multipliers.

Let $\beta = x_1^{i_1} \cdots x_m^{i_m}$ be a monomial in the extended set arising from $[\alpha]$. Let x_k be a nonmultiplier of β. Then βx_k, as a multiple of some monomial in $[\alpha]$, is the product of a monomial γ in the extended set by unity or by multipliers of γ (§4).

We shall prove that γ is higher than β. Let $\gamma = x_1^{j_1} \cdots x_m^{j_m}$. If $j_1 < i_1$, x_1 cannot be a multiplier for γ since j_1 is certainly not the maximum of the degrees in x_1 of the monomials in $[\alpha]$. Hence $j_1 \geqq i_1$. It remains to examine the case in which $j_1 = i_1$. When we dissect f_{i_1}, we find that if $j_2 < i_2$, x_2 cannot be a multiplier for $x_2^{j_2} \cdots x_m^{j_m}$. Hence $j_2 \geqq i_2$ and we have to study the case in which $j_2 = i_2$. Continuing, we see that γ is not lower than β so that, since $\gamma \neq \beta$, γ is higher than β.

7. We associate with every monomial $x_1^{j_1} \cdots x_m^{j_m}$ the differential operator

$$\frac{\partial^{j_1 + \cdots + j_m}}{\partial x_1^{j_1} \cdots \partial x_m^{j_m}}. \tag{8}$$

Then the product of two operators corresponds to the product of the corresponding monomials.

Consider any monomial

$$\beta = x_1^{i_1} \cdots x_m^{i_m} \tag{9}$$

in (7). Let the corresponding differentiation be performed upon u, and after the differentiation, let the nonmultipliers of β be given zero values. Every term in the expansion of u which is not divisible by β will disappear during the differentiation. Any term divisible by β whose quotient by β contains nonmultipliers of β will disappear when the nonmultipliers are made zero. Hence the above operation gives identical results when applied to u and to $\beta f_{i_1 \cdots i_m}$.

Marks

8. Let $y_1, \cdots, y_n$ be analytic functions of $x_1, \cdots, x_m$. Riquier effects an ordering of the y and their partial derivatives in the following wav.

Let s be any positive integer. We associate with each x_i any ordered set of s nonnegative integers

$$u_{i1}, \cdots, u_{is}. \tag{10}$$

With each y_i, we associate any ordered set of nonnegative integers

$$v_{i1}, \cdots, v_{is} \tag{11}$$

taking care that y_i and y_j with $i \neq j$ do not have identical sets (11). The jth integer in (10) is called the jth *mark* of x_i, and the jth integer in (11), the jth mark of y_i.

If

$$w = \frac{\partial^{k_1 + \cdots + k_m}}{\partial x_1^{k_1} \cdots \partial x_m^{k_m}} y_i \tag{12}$$

we define the jth mark of w, $j = 1, \cdots, s$, to be $v_{ij} + k_1 u_{1j} + \cdots + k_m u_{mj}$.

Consider all of the derivatives[2] of all y_i. Let w_1 and w_2 be any two of these derivatives. Let the marks of w_1 and w_2 be

$$a_1, \cdots, a_s; \qquad b_1, \cdots, b_s$$

respectively. Suppose that the two sets of marks are not identical. We shall say that w_1 is *higher* than w_2 or is *lower* than w_2 according as the first nonzero difference $a_i - b_i$ is positive or is negative. If the two sets of marks are identical, no relation of order is established between w_1 and w_2.

If w_1 is higher than w_2, $\partial w_1/\partial x_i$ is higher than $\partial w_2/\partial x_i$.

When the marks in (10) and (11) are such that a difference in order exists between any two distinct derivatives, the derivatives of the y are said to be *completely ordered.*

Suppose that the ordering is not complete. We shall show how to adjoin new marks, after u_{is} and v_{is}, so as to effect a complete ordering. Clearly, the adjunction of such new marks will not disturb any order relationships which may already exist.

Let m additional marks be assigned, as in the following table:

---

[2] Each y_i will be considered as a derivative of zero order of itself.

	$x_1\, x_2 \cdots x_m$	$y_1\, y_2 \cdots y_n$
$s+1$	$1\ 0 \cdots 0$	$0\ 0 \cdots 0,$
$s+2$	$0\ 1 \cdots 0$	$0\ 0 \cdots 0,$
$\cdots\cdots$	$\cdots\cdots\cdots\cdots$	$\cdots\cdots\cdots,$
$s+m$	$0\ 0 \cdots 1$	$0\ 0 \cdots 0.$

Now, let w_1 and w_2 be two derivatives with the same set of $s + m$ marks. The $(s + i)$th mark of w_1 or w_2, $i = 1, \cdots, m$, is the number of differentiations with respect to x_i in w_1 or w_2. Hence the same differentiations are effected in w_1 as in w_2. From the definition of the marks of w_1 and w_2, it follows now that the functions of which w_1 and w_2 are derivatives have the same sets (11). Thus w_1 and w_2 are identical, so that the new ordering is complete.

In everything which follows, we shall deal only with complete orderings. Thus, with w as in (12), $\partial w/\partial x_i$ is higher than w.

9. Let $\xi_1, \cdots, \xi_m; \zeta_1, \cdots, \zeta_n$ be variables. We associate with w, in (12), the power product $\xi_1^{k_1} \cdots \xi_m^{k_m} \zeta_i$.

Let $w_1, \cdots, w_t$ be any finite number of distinct derivatives of the y. Let the power product associated above with w_i, $i = 1, \cdots, t$, be α_i. Let g be any positive number. We shall show how to assign, to the ξ, ζ, real values, not less than unity, in such a way that, if w_i is higher than w_j, we have, for the assigned values, $\alpha_i > g\alpha_j$.

We introduce s new variables $z_1, \cdots, z_s$. With each ξ_i we associate the power product $z_1^{u_{i1}} \cdots z_s^{u_{is}}$ where the u_{ij} are the marks of x_i. With each ζ_i we associate $z_1^{v_{i1}} \cdots z_s^{v_{is}}$ where the v_{ij} are the marks of y_i. Then each α_i goes over into a power product $\beta_i = z_1^{a_1} \cdots z_s^{a_s}$ with a_j the jth mark of w_i.

It will evidently suffice to prove that we can attribute to the z real values not less than unity in such a way that $\beta_i > g\beta_j$ if w_i is higher than w_j.

Let r be the maximum of the degrees (total) of the β. Let k be any positive number, greater than unity and greater than g. We put

$$z_i = k^{(rs+1)^{s-i}}, \qquad i = 1, \cdots, s. \tag{13}$$

Then, if

$$\beta_i = z_1^{a_1} \cdots z_{h-1}^{a_{h-1}} z_h^{a_h} \cdots z_s^{a_s},$$

$$\beta_j = z_1^{a_1} \cdots z_{h-1}^{a_{h-1}} z_h^{b_h} \cdots z_s^{b_s},$$

with $a_h > b_h$, we have, for (13),

$$\frac{\beta_i}{\beta_j} \geqq \frac{z_h}{(z_{h+1} \cdots z_s)^r} \geqq \frac{k^{(rs+1)^{s-h}}}{k^{r(s-h)(rs+1)^{s-h-1}}} \geqq k > g.$$

Orthonomic systems

10. From this point on, we assume that the first mark of each x is unity. Let $y_1, \cdots, y_n$ be unknown functions of $x_1, \cdots, x_m$, whose derivatives have

been completely ordered by marks. We consider a finite system σ of differential equations,

$$\frac{\partial^{i_1 + \cdots + i_m} y_j}{\partial x_1^{i_1} \cdots \partial x_m^{i_m}} = g_{i_1 \cdots i_m, j} \tag{14}$$

where

(a) *in each equation, g is a function of $x_1, \cdots, x_m$ and of a certain number of derivatives of the y_i, every derivative in g being lower than the first member of the equation;*

(b) *the first members of any two equations are distinct;*

(c) *if w is a first member of some equation, no derivative of w appears in the second member of any equation;*

(d) *the functions g are all analytic at some point in the space of the arguments involved in all of them.*[3]

We do not assume that every y_i appears in a first member.

Riquier calls such a system of equations *orthonomic.*

The derivatives of the y which are derivatives of first members in the orthonomic system are called *principal derivatives.* All other derivatives are called *parametric derivatives.*

11. Given an orthonomic system, σ, we shall show how to obtain an orthonomic system with the same solutions, in which, for each y_i appearing in the first members, the monomials corresponding as in §7 to those first members which are derivatives of y_i form a complete set (§5).

Let equations be adjoined to (14), by differentiating the equations in (14), so that, for each y which occurs in some first member, the monomials corresponding to the enlarged set of first members constitute a complete set. By §5, this can be done. We obtain thus a system σ_1 of equations. Certain first members in σ_1 may be obtainable from more than one of the first members in σ. In that case, we use any one of the first members in σ which is available.

Consider any one of the equations in σ. Let w represent its first member, and v the highest derivative in the second member. If we differentiate the equation with respect to x_i, the first member becomes $\partial w/\partial x_i$. The highest derivative in the new second member will be $\partial v/\partial x_i$, which is lower than $\partial w/\partial x_i$ (§8).

It is clear, on this basis, that σ_1 satisfies condition (a).

We attend now to (c). Let **C** be an open region in the space of the arguments in the second members in σ in which the second members are analytic. We consider those solutions of σ for which the indicated arguments lie in **C**.

The second members in σ_1 may involve derivatives not in the second members in σ. The second members in σ_1 will be polynomials in the new derivatives, with coefficients analytic in **C**.

---

[3] Thus, in (d), derivatives not effectively present in a g may be regarded as arguments in that g. This does not conflict with (a), in which the arguments considered are supposed to be effectively present.

Let w be the highest derivative present in a second member in σ_1 which is a derivative of a first member in σ_1. Then w is not present in any second member in σ, so that it appears rationally and integrally in the second members in σ_1. Let w be a derivative of v, the first member of the equation $v = g$ in σ_1. Then w can be replaced, in the second members in σ_1, by its expression obtained on differentiating g. We obtain thus a system σ_2 with the same solutions as σ_1 (or σ) and with the same first members as σ_1. The system σ_2 satisfies condition (a). The derivatives higher than w which appear in the second members in σ_2 also appear in the second members in σ_1. Hence, if w_1, present in the second members in σ_2, is a derivative of a first member in σ_2, then w_1 is lower than w. We treat w_1 as w was treated. Since there cannot be an infinite sequence of derivatives each lower than the preceding one, we must arrive, in a finite number of steps, at a system τ, with the same solutions as σ, which satisfies (a), (b), (c), and which has complete sets of monomials corresponding to its first members. The second members in τ will be polynomials in any derivatives not present in the second members of σ. Hence assumption (d) is satisfied for **C** and for any values of the new derivatives. Thus τ is orthonomic and has the same solutions as σ.[4]

Of course, whether we employ σ or τ, we get the same set of principal derivatives and the same parametric derivatives.

12. We consider an orthonomic system, σ, whose first members, as in §11, yield complete sets of monomials. We are going to seek solutions of σ, analytic at some point, which, with no loss of generality, may be taken as $x_i = 0$, $i = 1, \cdots, m$.

Consider any y_i. Let numerical values be assigned to the parametric derivatives of y_i, at the origin, with the sole conditions that the second members in σ are analytic for the values given to the derivatives in them and that the series

$$\sum \frac{a_{j_1 \cdots j_m}}{j_1! \cdots j_m!} x_1^{j_1} \cdots x_m^{j_m}, \tag{15}$$

where the a are the values of the parametric derivatives, the subscripts indicating the type of differentiation, converges in a neighborhood of the origin. The series (15) is called the *initial determination* of y_i. If y_i does not appear in a first member, (15) is a complete Taylor series.

In what follows, we suppose an initial determination to be given for each y_i. We shall then develop a process for calculating the values of the principal derivatives at the origin. There will result analytic functions y_i which satisfy each equation of σ on the spread obtained by equating to zero the nonmultipliers of the monomial corresponding to the first member. Later we shall obtain a condition for the y_i to give an actual solution of σ.

In the dissection (7) of each y_i which we shall obtain,[5] those terms whose monomials are multiples of monomials in the complementary set will constitute

[4] With the values of the arguments in the second members in σ lying in **C**.

[5] This dissection is based on the complete set of monomials corresponding to y_i.

the initial determination of y_i. Thus the initial determination of each y_i is a linear combination of a certain number of arbitrary functions, with monomials for coefficients, the variables in the arbitrary functions being specified. This description of the degree of generality of the solution of a system of equations is one of the most important items of Riquier's work.

We replace each y_i which does not figure in any first member in σ by an arbitrarily selected initial determination. Then σ becomes an orthonomic system in the remaining y_i, with the same principal derivatives as before for the remaining y_i. On this basis, we assume, with no loss of generality, that every y_i figures in a first member.

13. We use the symbol δ to represent differential operators. Any principal derivative, δy_i, which is not a first member in σ, can be obtained from one and only one first member in σ by differentiation with respect to multipliers of the monomial corresponding to that first member. This is because the first members yield complete sets. We have thus a unique expression for δy_i,

$$\delta y_i = g, \tag{16}$$

where the derivatives in g are lower than δy_i.

The infinite system obtained by adjoining all equations (16) to σ will be called τ. Let p be any nonnegative integer. The system of equations in τ whose first members have p for first mark will be called τ_p. Since the first mark of a derivative is the sum of the order of the derivative and of the first mark of the function differentiated, each τ_p has only a finite number of equations.

Let a be the minimum, and b the maximum, of the first marks in the first members in σ. For the values assigned, in §12, to the parametric derivatives, the equations $\tau_a, \tau_{a+1}, \cdots, \tau_b$ determine uniquely the values at the origin of the principal derivatives whose first mark does not exceed b. In short, the lowest such derivative has an equation which determines it in terms of parametric derivatives; the principal derivative next in ascending order is determined in terms of parametric derivatives, and, perhaps, the first principal derivative, and so on.

We subject the unknowns y_j to the transformation

$$y_j = \bar{y}_j + \varphi_j + \sum \frac{c_{j,\, i_1 \cdots i_m}}{i_1! \cdots i_m!} x_1^{i_1} \cdots x_m^{i_m} \tag{17}$$

where φ_j is the chosen initial determination of y_j and where the c are the principal derivatives at the origin of y_j, of first mark not exceeding b, found as above.

Then σ goes over into a system σ' in the $\bar{y}_j$. In the new system, we transpose the known terms in the first members (these come from the known terms in (17)) to the right. The new system will be orthonomic in the $\bar{y}_j$, with the same monomials for its first members as in σ. The second members will be analytic when each x_i and each parametric derivative is small.

The system τ' for σ', analogous to τ for σ, is obtained by executing the transformation (17) on the equations of τ.

Thus, if we give to the $\bar{y}_i$, in σ', initial determinations which are identically zero, the principal derivatives at the origin, of first mark not exceeding b, will be determined as zero by $\tau'_a, \cdots, \tau'_b$.

On this account, we limit ourselves, without loss of generality, to the search for solutions $y_1, \cdots, y_n$, of σ, with initial determinations identically zero, assuming that the system $\tau_a, \cdots, \tau_b$ yields zero values at the origin for the principal derivatives whose first marks do not exceed b.

14. In the second members in τ_{b+1}, no derivatives appear whose first marks exceed $b + 1$. Those derivatives whose first marks are $b + 1$ enter linearly, because they come from the differentiation of derivatives of first mark b in τ_b.

We denote by $\delta_k y_i$ the second member of (12). Then every equation in τ_{b+1} is of the form

$$\delta_i y_\alpha = \sum p_{i\alpha j\beta} \delta_j y_\beta + q_{i\alpha}, \tag{18}$$

where the $\delta_j y_\beta$ are of first mark $b + 1$ and where the p and q involve the x_i and derivatives whose first marks are b or less.

In (18), we consider every derivative of first mark $b + 1$ which is lower than $\delta_i y_\alpha$ to be present in the second member. If necessary, we take $p_{i\alpha j\beta} = 0$.

Consider any $\delta_i y_\alpha$ in (18). Suppose that there is a β such that y_β has derivatives of first mark $b + 1$ which are lower than $\delta_i y_\alpha$. For every such β, we let $r_{i\alpha\beta}$ represent the number of derivatives of y_β, of first mark $b + 1$, which are lower than $\delta_i y_\alpha$. For every other β, we let $r_{i\alpha\beta} = 1$, and we suppose that a single derivative of y_β of first mark $b + 1$ appears in the second member of (18), with a zero coefficient. We can thus not continue to say that every derivative in the second member of (18) is lower than the first member, but no difficulty will arise out of this; only a question of language is involved.

Let r be the maximum of the $r_{i\alpha\beta}$.

The p and q in (18) are analytic for small values of their arguments. Let the p and q be expanded as series of powers of their arguments.

Let $\epsilon > 0$ be such that each of the above series converges for values of its arguments which all exceed ϵ in modulus. Let $h > 0$ be such that each p and each q has a modulus less than h when the arguments do not exceed ϵ in modulus.

Let λ be any positive number less than $1/n$.

Following §9, we determine positive numbers ξ_i, ζ_i, not less than unity such that, if $\delta_i y_\alpha$ and $\delta_j y_\beta$ are of first mark $b + 1$, with $\delta_i y_\alpha$ higher than $\delta_j y_\beta$, we have

$$\frac{\xi_1^{i_1} \cdots \xi_m^{i_m} \zeta_\alpha}{\xi_1^{j_1} \cdots \xi_m^{j_m} \zeta_\beta} > \frac{hr}{\lambda}. \tag{19}$$

In what follows, we associate with each y_i a new unknown function u_i.

Let

$$\rho = \frac{\xi_1 x_1 + \cdots + \xi_m x_m + \sum \delta u}{\epsilon},$$

where $\sum$ ranges over all derivatives of $u_1, \cdots, u_n$ whose first mark does not exceed b($\delta_i u_\alpha$ is supposed to have the same marks as $\delta_i y_\alpha$).

We consider the system of equations

$$\delta_i u_\alpha = \frac{1}{1-\rho} \sum \frac{\lambda}{r_{i\alpha\beta}} \frac{\xi_1^{i_1} \cdots \xi_m^{i_m} \zeta_\alpha}{\xi_1^{j_1} \cdots \xi_m^{j_m} \zeta_\beta} \delta_j u_\beta + \frac{h \, \xi_1^{i_1} \cdots \xi_m^{i_m} \zeta_\alpha}{1-\rho} \tag{20}$$

which has the general form of (18), with alterations of the form of the p and q.

The function

$$\frac{h}{1 - \dfrac{x_1 + \cdots + x_m + \sum \delta u}{\epsilon}}$$

is a majorant for every p and every q. As each ξ_i is at least unity, the same is true of $h/(1-\rho)$.

Thus, in virtue of (19), wherever a $\delta_j y_\beta$ is lower than $\delta_i y_\alpha$ in an equation in (18), the coefficient of $\delta_j u_\beta$ in the corresponding equation of (20) will be a majorant for the coefficient of $\delta_j y_\beta$. In the exceptional case where a $\delta_j y_\beta$ is not lower than $\delta_i y_\alpha$ and thus has a zero coefficient, the corresponding coefficient in (20) is certainly a majorant. Evidently the terms in (20) which correspond to the q in (18) are majorants of the q.

15. We shall show that (20) has a solution in which each u_i is a function of

$$\xi_1 x_1 + \cdots + \xi_m x_m. \tag{21}$$

Consider, in (20), all derivatives of a particular u_α whose first marks are $b + 1$. The first mark of any such derivative is the order (total) of the derivative, plus the first mark of u_α. Hence all of the derivatives of u_α which are of first mark $b + 1$ are of the same order, say g_α.

Let the u_α, in what follows, represent functions of (21). Put $u_\alpha = \zeta_\alpha u'_\alpha$ and let $u'_{\alpha i}$ be the ith derivative of u'_α with respect to (21). Then with $i = i_1 + \cdots + i_m$,

$$\frac{\partial^{i_1 + \cdots + i_m}}{\partial x_1^{i_1} \cdots \partial x_m^{i_m}} u_\alpha = \xi_1^{i_1} \cdots \xi_m^{i_m} \zeta_\alpha u'_{\alpha i}.$$

When the u_α are functions of (21), ρ becomes a function ρ' of (21) and of the derivatives of the u'_α of order less than g_α, $\alpha = 1, \cdots, n$. Equations (20) reduce to

$$u'_{\alpha g_\alpha} = \lambda \sum_{\beta=1}^{n} \frac{1}{1-\rho'} u'_{\beta g_\beta} + \frac{h}{1-\rho'}. \tag{22}$$

There will be n equations in (22), one for each α. All equations in (20) in which a given u_α appears in the first member yield the same equation (22). We write (22) as

$$u'_{\alpha g_\alpha} = \rho' u'_{\alpha g_\alpha} + \lambda \sum_{\beta=1}^{n} u'_{\beta g_\beta} + h. \tag{23}$$

When (21) is zero and when the $u'_{\alpha i}$, $i = 0, \cdots, g_\alpha - 1$, for each α, are given zero values, the determinant of (22) with respect to the $u'_{\alpha g_\alpha}$ is

$$\begin{vmatrix} 1-\lambda, & -\lambda, & \cdots, & -\lambda \\ -\lambda, & 1-\lambda, & \cdots, & -\lambda \\ \cdots & \cdots & \cdots & \cdots \\ -\lambda, & -\lambda, & \cdots, & 1-\lambda \end{vmatrix}.$$

This determinant is not zero. In short, the equations

$$(24) \qquad \begin{aligned} (1-\lambda)\, z_1 - \lambda z_2 - \cdots - \lambda z_n &= c_1, \\ \cdots\cdots\cdots\cdots\cdots\cdots&\cdots, \\ -\lambda z_1 - \lambda z_2 - \cdots + (1-\lambda) z_n &= c_n, \end{aligned}$$

imply

$$(1 - n\lambda) z_i = \lambda(c_1 + \cdots + c_n) + (1 - n\lambda) c_i,$$

so that the determinant cannot vanish for $\lambda < 1/n$.[6]

Then the $u'_{\alpha g_\alpha}$ can be expressed as functions of the other quantities in (23), analytic when the arguments are small. By the existence theorem for ordinary differential equations, (23) has a solution with the $u'_{\alpha i}$ zero, for $i < g_\alpha$, when (21) is zero. The functions in this solution will be analytic for (21) small.

16. We shall prove that, in the solution just found, all $u'_{\alpha i}$ with $i \geqq g_\alpha$ are positive for (21) zero. For (21) zero, we have

$$u'_{\alpha g_\alpha} - \lambda \sum_{\beta=1}^{n} u'_{\beta g_\beta} = h.$$

Referring to (24), we see that, since $\lambda < 1/n$, the z_i are positive if the c_i are all positive. Then the $u'_{\alpha g_\alpha}$ are positive for every α.

Differentiating (23), we find, for (21) zero,

$$u'_{\alpha, g_\alpha + 1} - \lambda \sum_{\beta=1}^{n} u'_{\beta, g_\beta + 1} = k_\alpha,$$

where the k_α are positive. Again, the solution consists of positive numbers Continuing, we obtain our result.

What precedes shows that (20) has a solution, analytic at the origin, with every derivative of first mark less than $b + 1$ equal to zero and every other derivative positive, at the origin.

17. We now return to the system σ. With the procedure employed, in §13 for the determination, at the origin, of the principal derivatives of first mark not greater than b, we determine the values of all principal derivatives at the

[6] For $i = 1$, subtract each equation from the first, in succession, and substitute the result nto the first.

origin. We can ascend, step by step, through all the principal derivatives, because each τ_p in §13 has only a finite number of equations.

We obtain thus a complete power series for each y_i. We are going to prove that these power series converge for small values of the x_i.

Let $\delta_i y_\alpha$ be any principal derivative. We shall prove that the modulus of this derivative at the origin does not exceed the value at the origin found for $\delta_i u_\alpha$ in §16.

For derivatives of first mark less than $b + 1$, this is certainly true; those derivatives have zero values. Let the result hold for all derivatives lower than some $\delta_i y_\gamma$ of first mark greater than b. The equation in τ for $\delta_i y_\gamma$ is either in (18) or is found by differentiating some equation in (18). Consider the corresponding equation for $\delta_i u_\gamma$, which is either in (20), or obtained from (20) by differentiation.

We shall consider the expressions for $\delta_i y_\gamma$ and $\delta_i u_\gamma$ as power series in the x_i and in the derivatives in terms of which $\delta_i y_\gamma$ and $\delta_i u_\gamma$ are expressed.

We see that, for every term in the series for $\delta_i y_\gamma$, there is a dominating term in the series for $\delta_i u_\gamma$. What is more, the series for $\delta_i u_\gamma$ may have other terms, involving $\delta_i u_\gamma$ itself, or even higher derivatives. This is because of the exceptional terms in (20), introduced in §14.[7]

Each term in $\delta_i u_\gamma$ which has a corresponding term in $\delta_i y_\gamma$ is at least as great as the modulus of that term at the origin, for such terms involve only lower derivatives than $\delta_i y_\gamma$ or $\delta_i u_\gamma$. Terms in $\delta_i u_\gamma$ which have no corresponding terms in $\delta_i y_\gamma$ are zero or positive at the origin. They will be positive if they involve no x_i, and contain only derivatives of first mark at least $b + 1$ (§16). This proves that the value determined for each $\delta_i y_\alpha$ by τ has a modulus not greater than the value at the origin of $\delta_i u_\alpha$.

Thus the series obtained for the y_i converge in a neighborhood of the origin.

18. We shall now see to what extent the analytic functions y_i, just obtained, are solutions of σ.

Consider any equation $\delta y_i = g$ in σ. This equation, and all equations obtained from it by differentiation with respect to multipliers of the monomial corresponding to the first member, are satisfied, at the origin, by the derivatives of $y_1, \cdots, y_n$ at the origin. Hence, if we substitute $y_1, \cdots, y_n$ into $\delta y_i - g$, we obtain a function k of $x_1, \cdots, x_n$ which vanishes at the origin, together with its derivatives with respect to the above multipliers. Thus, in the expansion of k, only nonmultipliers occur. Then k vanishes when the nonmultipliers are zero.

Hence $y_1, \cdots, y_n$ satisfy each equation of σ on the spread obtained by equating to zero the nonmultipliers corresponding to the first member of the equation.

19. Let us return now to the most general orthonomic system σ whose first members give complete sets of monomials. We do not suppose that every y_i appears in some first member.

[7] In our present language, all derivatives in a second member in (18) are lower than the first member.

We consider any point $x_i = a_i$, $i = 1, \cdots, m$, subject to obvious conditions of analyticity. Let any values be given to the parametric derivatives of the y_i at $a_1, \cdots, a_m$, so as to yield convergent initial determinations. Then the principal derivatives are determined uniquely by σ in such a way as to yield analytic functions $y_1, \cdots, y_n$ which satisfy each equation in σ on the spread obtained by equating to a_i each nonmultiplier x_i corresponding to the first member of the equation.

This is an immediate consequence of the preceding sections.

Passive orthonomic systems

20. Let σ be an orthonomic system, described as in the preceding section. Let the equations in σ be listed so that their first members form an ascending sequence, and let them be written

$$v_i = 0, \qquad i = 1, \cdots, t. \tag{25}$$

If v_i is $\delta y_j - g$, we attribute to v_i the s marks of δy_j. This establishes order relations among the v, according to the convention of §8. To all of the derivatives of v_i, we attribute marks as in §8. Thus, the marks of δv_i will be the marks of the highest derivative in δv_i. By the *monomial corresponding to* v_i, we mean the monomial corresponding to δy_j. We shall refer to δy_j as the *first term* in v_i. By the first term of a derivative of v_i, we shall mean the corresponding derivative of δy_j.

Consider a v whose corresponding monomial, α, has nonmultipliers. Let x_i be such a nonmultiplier. By §6, $x_i\alpha$ is the product of a β, in the same complete set as α and higher than α, by unity or by multipliers of β. Hence, there is a v_p, higher than v, such that some δv_p has the same first term as $\partial v/\partial x_i$. Then, in the expression

$$\frac{\partial v}{\partial x_i} - \delta v_p \tag{26}$$

all derivatives effectively present are lower than the first term of $\partial v/\partial x_i$.

It is clear that (26) is a polynomial in such principal derivatives as it may involve. Let w be the highest such principal derivative. Then w is the first term of some expression δv_q, where δv_q is lower than $\partial v/\partial x_i$. We choose v_q so that w is obtained from it by differentiation with respect to multipliers of the corresponding monomial. This makes v_q unique. Let then, identically,

$$w = \delta v_q + k, \tag{27}$$

where the derivatives in k are all lower than w. We replace w in (26) by its expression in (27) and find, identically,

$$\frac{\partial v}{\partial x_i} = \delta v_p + h_1 (\delta v_q, \cdots),$$

where h_1 is a polynomial in δv_q whose coefficients involve no principal derivative as high as w. Let w_1 be the highest principal derivative in h_1. We give it the treatment accorded to w and find

$$\frac{\partial v}{\partial x_i} = \delta v_p + h_2(\delta v_q, \delta v_r, \cdots),$$

where h_2 is a polynomial in δv_q, δv_r. Continuing, we find in a unique manner an identity

$$\text{(28)} \qquad \frac{\partial v}{\partial x_i} = \delta v_p + h(\delta v_q, \cdots, \delta v_z),$$

in which the coefficients in h involve only parametric derivatives. We now write (28) in the form

$$\text{(29)} \qquad \frac{\partial v}{\partial x_i} = \delta v_p + \gamma(\delta v_q, \cdots, \delta v_z) + \mu,$$

where μ is the term of zero degree in h. Then μ is an expression in the parametric derivatives alone. The expression γ vanishes when $\delta v_q, \cdots, \delta v_z$ are replaced by 0.

It is clear that, for any solution of σ, we must have $\mu = 0$. The totality of equations $\mu = 0$, obtained from all equations of σ for which the monomial corresponding to the first member has nonmultipliers, all nonmultipliers being used, are called the *integrability conditions* for σ.

21. If every expression μ is identically zero, the system σ is said to be *passive*. We shall prove that, if σ is passive, the n functions $y_1, \cdots, y_n$, described in §19, which satisfy each equation in σ on a certain spread, constitute an actual solution of σ.

What we have to show is, that for these functions, every v_i in (25) vanishes identically.

When the y_j above are substituted into v_i, we obtain a function u_i of $x_1, \cdots, x_m$. If v_i has no nonmultipliers, $u_i = 0$. Otherwise, u_i vanishes when the nonmultipliers of the monomial corresponding to v_i are equated to their a.

If, in (29), where μ is now identically zero, the parametric derivatives in γ are replaced by their expressions as functions of the x_i, found from the y_i, (29) becomes a system φ of differential equations in the *unknowns* v_i. Since (29) consisted of identities, before these replacements, φ is satisfied by $v_i = u_i$, $i = 1, \cdots, t$.

We now attribute to each x_i an additional mark 0, and to each v_i an additional mark $t - i$. With this change, the derivatives of the v_i will be completely ordered and the first member in each equation in φ will be higher than every derivative in the second member.

If the second members in φ contain derivatives of the first members, we can get rid of such derivatives, step by step. Then φ goes over into an orthonomic system ψ, with the same first members as φ.

For our purposes, it is unnecessary to adjoin new equations to ψ as in §11.

Consider any unknown v_i which appears in a first member. The derivatives of v_i in the first members will be taken with respect to certain variables

$$x_a, \cdots, x_d. \tag{30}$$

The variables (30), when equated to their a_i, give a spread on which u_i vanishes.

The parametric derivatives of v_i will be the derivatives taken with respect to the variables not in (30). For the corresponding u_i, each of these parametric derivatives is zero. Now we know that, for given values of the parametric derivatives, there is at most one solution of ψ. But $v_i = 0$, $i = 1, \cdots, t$, is a solution of ψ for which all parametric derivatives vanish. Hence $u_i = 0$, $i = 1, \cdots, t$.

This proves that, *given a passive orthonomic system, there is one and only one solution of the system for any given initial determinations.*

CHAPTER IX

PARTIAL DIFFERENTIAL ALGEBRA

Partial differential polynomials. Ideals and manifolds

1. We use an algebraic field $\mathfrak{F}$ of characteristic zero which admits m operations of differentiation. Each element a of F has m partial derivatives $\partial a/\partial x_i$, $i = 1, \cdots, m$. In this, the x are not necessarily variables. They may merely be symbols which distinguish the derivatives. Each of the m operations satisfies (1) and (2) of I, §1. In addition,

$$\frac{\partial}{\partial x_j}\left(\frac{\partial a}{\partial x_i}\right) = \frac{\partial}{\partial x_i}\left(\frac{\partial a}{\partial x_j}\right)$$

for every i and j. We call F a *partial differential field.*

In our work below, definitions will usually be as for the case of one operation and will be given, formally, only when there is some necessity for it.

2. We employ indeterminates $y_1, \cdots, y_n$. With each y_i are associated symbols

$$\frac{\partial^{i_1 + \cdots + i_m} y_i}{\partial x_1^{i_1} \cdots \partial x_m^{i_m}}, \tag{1}$$

where the i_j are any nonnegative integers; these are the *partial derivatives*[1] of y_i.

$\mathfrak{F}$ being given, we understand by a *partial differential polynomial* (p.d.p. or d.p.), a polynomial in derivatives of the y with coefficients in $\mathfrak{F}$.

3. We understand marks to be attributed to the symbols x and y as in VIII, §8, in such a way as to effect a complete ordering.

By the *leader* of a p.d.p. A which actually involves indeterminates,[2] we shall mean the highest of those derivatives of the y which are present in A.

Let A_1 and A_2 be p.d.p. which actually involve indeterminates. If A_2 has a higher leader than A_1, then A_2 will be said to be of *higher rank* than A_1. If A_1 and A_2 have the same leader, and if the degree of A_2 in the common leader exceeds that of A_1, then again A_2 will be said to be of higher rank than A_1. A d.p. which effectively involves indeterminates will be of higher rank than one which does not. Two d.p. for which no difference in rank is created by what precedes will be said to be of the same rank.

As in I, §3, we see that every aggregate of p.d.p. contains a d.p. which is not higher than any other d.p. of the aggregate.

4. If A_1 involves indeterminates, A_2 will be said to be *reduced with respect to*

[1] When the i_j are all zero, (1) represents y_i.

[2] We mean that A is not an element of $\mathfrak{F}$.

A_1 if A_2 contains no proper derivative of the leader of A_1 and if A_2 is either zero or of lower degree than A_1 in the leader of A_1. A set of p.d.p.

$$A_1, \cdots, A_r \tag{2}$$

will be called a *chain* if either

(a) $r = 1$ *and* $A_1 \neq 0$, or

(b) $r > 1$, A_1 *involves indeterminates and, for* $j > i$, A_j *is of higher rank than* A_i *and reduced with respect to* A_i.

When (b) holds, the leader of A_j is higher than that of A_i for $j > i$.

Relative rank for chains is defined exactly as in I, §4. If Φ_1, Φ_2, Φ_3, are chains with $\Phi_1 > \Phi_2$ and $\Phi_2 > \Phi_3$, then $\Phi_1 > \Phi_3$.

We prove that, *in every aggregate of chains, there is a chain which is not higher than any other chain of the aggregate.* Let α be the aggregate. We form a subset α_1 of α, putting a chain Φ into α_1 if the first d.p. of Φ is not higher than the first d.p. of any other chain in α. It may be that the chains in α_1 are merely elements of $\mathfrak{F}$; if so, any of them is a chain of least rank in α. Let us suppose that the first d.p. in the chains of α_1 actually involve indeterminates. These first d.p. will all have the same leader; we represent that leader by the symbol p_1. If the chains in α_1 all consist of one d.p., any chain in α_1 meets our requirements. Suppose that there are chains in α_1 which have more than one d.p. We form the subset α_2 of them whose second d.p. are of a lowest rank and indicate the common leaders of these second d.p. by p_2. Now p_2 is not a proper derivative of p_1. As we saw above, p_2 is higher than p_1. If the chains in α_2 all have just two d.p., any of these chains serves our purpose. If not, we continue. Our result will hold unless there is an infinite sequence

$$p_1, p_2, \cdots, p_q, \cdots$$

of derivatives which increase steadily in rank, no p_q being a derivative of a p_i with $i < q$. The existence of such a sequence would contradict Riquier's theorem of VIII, §2.

5. Let Σ be a system containing nonzero d.p. We define a *characteristic set* of Σ to be a chain in Σ of least rank.

If A_1 in (2) involves indeterminates, a d.p. F will be said to be *reduced with respect to* (2) if F is reduced with respect to A_i, $i = 1, \cdots, r$.

Let Σ be a system for which (2), with A_1 not free of the indeterminates, is a characteristic set. Then no nonzero d.p. in Σ can be reduced with respect to (2). If a nonzero d.p., reduced with respect to (2), is adjoined to Σ, the characteristic sets of the resulting system are lower than (2).

6. In this section we deal with a chain (2) in which A_1 involves indeterminates.

If a d.p. G has a leader, p, we shall call the d.p. $\partial G/\partial p$ the *separant* of G. The coefficient of the highest power of p in G will be called the *initial* of G.

Let S_i and I_i be, respectively, the separant and initial of A_i in (2).

We prove the following result.

Let G be any d.p. There exist nonnegative integers s_i, t_i, $i = 1, \cdots, r$, such that, when a suitable linear combination of the A and their derivatives is subtracted from

$$S_1^{s_1} \cdots S_r^{s_r} I_1^{t_1} \cdots I_r^{t_r} G,$$

the remainder, R, is reduced with respect to (2).

Let p_i be the leader of A_i. We limit ourselves, as we may, to the case in which G involves derivatives, proper or improper, of the p. Such derivatives will be called *p-derivatives.* Let the highest p-derivative in G be q and let q be a derivative of p_j. For the sake of uniqueness, if there are several possibilities for j, we use the largest j available. To fix our ideas, we assume q higher than p_r. Then

$$S_j^g G = CA_j' + B$$

where A_j' is a derivative of A_j with q for leader and where B is free of q. Because A_j' and S_j involve no derivative higher than q, B involves no p-derivative which is as high as q. For uniqueness, we take g as small as possible.

If B involves a p-derivative which is higher than p_r, we give B the treatment accorded to G. After a finite number of steps, we reach a d.p. D which differs by a linear combination of derivatives of the A from a d.p.

$$S_1^{g_1} \cdots S_r^{g_r} G.$$

D contains no p-derivative which is higher than p_r.

We find then a relation

$$I_r^{t_r} D = HA_r + K,$$

where K is reduced with respect to A_r. K may involve p_r. Aside from p_r, the only p-derivatives present in K are derivatives of $p_1, \cdots, p_{r-1}$. Such p-derivatives are lower than p_r. Let q_1 be the highest of them.

Suppose that q_1 is higher than p_{r-1}. We give K the treatment received by G, obtaining a unique d.p. L which differs from some

$$S_1^{h_1} \cdots S_{r-1}^{h_{r-1}} I_{r-1}^{t_{r-1}} K$$

by a linear combination of A_{r-1} and proper derivatives of $A_1, \cdots, A_{r-1}$. The d.p. L is reduced with respect to A_r and A_{r-1}. Aside from p_r and p_{r-1}, the p-derivatives in L are derivatives of $p_1, \cdots, p_{r-2}$, and all such p-derivatives are lower than p_{r-1}.

Continuing, we determine, in a unique manner, a d.p. R as described in our statement. We call R the *remainder of G with respect to* (2).

7. Ideals of p.d.p. are defined as in I, §7. In (b) of I, §7, one requires that the m partial derivatives of any d.p. in Σ belong to Σ.

We define *basis* as in I, §12. The basis theorem,[3] the decomposition theorem

[3] In dealing with I, §10, one uses the fact that

$$u^2 \frac{\partial v}{\partial x_i} \equiv 0, \quad \left(uv, \frac{\partial uv}{\partial x_i}\right).$$

of I, §16, and the theorem on relatively prime ideals of I, §19, go over immediately to the case of several differentiations.

Manifolds are defined as in II, §1. The decomposition theorem of II, §3, then carries over.

The *analytic case* is formulated as follows. $\mathfrak{F}$ is a set of functions of m complex variables $x_1, \cdots, x_m$. There is given an open region **A** in the space of the x. The functions in $\mathfrak{F}$ are meromorphic at each point of **A**. An analytic zero consists of functions which are analytic in an open region contained in **A**.

To illustrate the decomposition theorem, we let

$$A = z - (px + qy) + p^2 + q^2, \tag{3}$$

where $p = \partial z/\partial x$, $q = \partial z/\partial y$. Putting $A = 0$, and differentiating with respect to x, we find

$$-(rx + sy) + 2(pr + qs) = 0, \tag{4}$$

where $r = \partial^2 z/\partial x^2$, $s = \partial^2 z/\partial x \partial y$. Similarly,

$$-(sx + ty) + 2(ps + qt) = 0, \tag{5}$$

where $t = \partial^2 z/\partial y^2$. From (4) and (5) we obtain

$$(rt - s^2)(x - 2p) = 0; \qquad (rt - s^2)(y - 2q) = 0.$$

Thus, either $rt - s^2 = 0$ or $z = (x^2 + y^2)/4$. The latter zero of A does not annul $rt - s^2$. Thus the manifold of A is reducible. The zero $(x^2 + y^2)/4$ is a component of A. As one will see later, there is one other component, the *general solution* of A.

8. The question of generic zeros is treated as in II, §6. Given a prime ideal Σ of p.d.p. in $y_1, \cdots, y_n$, distinct from the unit ideal, one finds a zero $\eta_1, \cdots, \eta_n$ of Σ which annuls no d.p. not contained in Σ. The abstract theorem of zeros of II, §7, then carries over. The analytic case will be treated later.

The theoretical method of V, §28, for resolving a finite system of d.p. into finite systems equivalent to prime ideals is seen to hold for p.d.p.

General solutions

9. Let F be an algebraically irreducible p.d.p. and S its separant. We see as in II, §12, that the totality Σ_1 of those d.p. A which are such that

$$SA \equiv 0, \qquad \{F\}, \tag{6}$$

is an ideal. We shall prove that Σ_1 is prime. Let p be the leader of F. Let AB be in Σ_1. There exist relations

$$S^a A \equiv R, \qquad S^b B \equiv T, \qquad [F],$$

where R and T involve no proper derivatives of p. Then SRT is in $\{F\}$. Let then

$$(SRT)^c = MF + M_1F_1 + \cdots + M_qF_q,$$

where the F_i are distinct partial derivatives of F. The leaders of the F_i are distinct. We may thus, and shall, assume that the F_i increase in rank as their subscripts increase. Let p' be the leader of F_q. We have

$$F_q = Sp' + U,$$

where the leader of U is lower than p'. We replace p' in F_q and in the M by $-U/S$. The proof is completed as in II, §12.

As in II, §13, we prove that Σ_1 consists of those d.p. which have zero remainders with respect to[4] F. In particular, Σ_1 does not contain S.

As in II, §§14, 15, we find that $\{F\}$ has a decomposition into essential prime divisors

$$\{F\} = \Sigma_1 \cap \Sigma_2 \cap \cdots \cap \Sigma_s \tag{7}$$

in which Σ_1 is the only divisor which does not contain S.

A change of marks may give F a new separant. Any such separant involves only derivatives present in F and is not divisible by F. Hence, for the original marks, such a separant has a remainder which is not zero. Thus, in (7), Σ_1 contains no separant of F, while $\Sigma_2, \cdots, \Sigma_s$ contain every separant.

We call the manifold of Σ_1 the *general solution of F*.

Components of a partial differential polynomial

10. Let F be a nonzero p.d.p. We shall prove that every essential prime divisor of $\{F\}$ has a characteristic set consisting of a single d.p. Such a d.p., call it A, can be taken as algebraically irreducible; the prime divisor consists of those d.p. which have zero remainders with respect to A. It will follow that *every component of a nonzero p.d.p. is the general solution of some p.d.p.*[5]

11. Let

$$A_1, \cdots, A_r \tag{8}$$

be a chain with A_1 not an element of $\mathfrak{F}$. Let A_i have S_i for separant and I_i for initial. Let G be any p.d.p. We shall prove that *there exists a power product J of the S and I such that JG is a polynomial in the A and their partial derivatives, with coefficients which are d.p. reduced with respect to* (8).

Let p_i be the leader of A_i. We limit ourselves, as we may, to the case in which G involves p-derivatives. Let the highest p-derivative in G be q_1 and let q_1 be a derivative of p_j. For uniqueness, we use the largest j available. To fix our ideas, we assume q_1 higher than p_r. For some partial derivative A_j' of A_j, we have

$$A_j' = S_jq_1 + T,$$

[4] We obtain B as in (12) of II, §13, with B free of proper derivatives of p.

[5] The case of $m > 1$ is essentially different from that of $m = 1$. For instance, for $m = 1$, every irreducible manifold in one indeterminate is a general solution. This is not so for p.d.p.

where T involves no derivative as high as q_1. Let G be of degree a in q_1. Then $S_j^a G$ can be written as a polynomial in $A'_j - T$, and hence as a polynomial in A'_j, with coefficients in which all p-derivatives are lower than q_1. Suppose that, among the coefficients just mentioned, there are one or more which involve p-derivatives higher than p_r. Let q_2 be the highest such p-derivative. We give the coefficients which involve q_2, with respect to q_2, the treatment accorded above to G with respect to q_1. We see now that there is a power product J_1 in one or two of the S such that J_1G is a polynomial in two derivatives of the A, with coefficients involving no p-derivative as high as q_2. We reach ultimately a J_uG, with J_u a power product in the S, in the coefficients of which the p-derivatives actually present are not higher than p_r. Some $I_r^v J_u G$ is a polynomial in A_r and proper derivatives of the A with coefficients which are reduced with respect to A_r. Aside from p_r, the only p-derivatives present in the coefficients are derivatives of $p_1, \cdots, p_{r-1}$. How to complete the proof is now obvious.

Let us examine the expression found for JG. In our discussion, there appeared a finite sequence of derivatives

$$q_1, q_2, \cdots, q_t \tag{9}$$

with q_i higher than q_{i+1}, $i = 1, \cdots, t-1$, each q_i being the leader of a derivative B_i, proper or improper, of some A. JG is a polynomial in the B, with coefficients reduced with respect to (8).

12. Let F be a nonzero d.p. and let (7) be a decomposition of $\{F\}$ into essential prime divisors. Suppose that some Σ_i in (7) has a characteristic set consisting of more than one d.p. We let Λ stand for such a Σ_i and consider a characteristic set (8) of Λ.

Treating F as G was treated in §11, we obtain a J as in §11 and let $H = JF$. Then H is a polynomial in the A and their partial derivatives.

Let $\eta_1, \cdots, \eta_n$ be a generic zero of Λ contained in an extension of $\mathfrak{F}_0$ of $\mathfrak{F}$. We make in H and in the A the substitution

$$y_i = \eta_i + z_i, \qquad i = 1, \cdots, n, \tag{10}$$

using the same marks for z_i as for y_i. Each A_i goes over into a d.p. C_i over $\mathfrak{F}_0$. Let us study C_i as a polynomial in the z and their derivatives. C_i admits the zero $z_j = 0$, $j = 1, \cdots, n$. We examine the terms of the first degree in C_i. To p_i, the leader of A_i, there corresponds a derivative r_i of some z. The coefficient of r_i in C_i is what S_i becomes when the η are substituted into it. Because S_i is not in Λ, S_i does not vanish for the η. Thus C_i contains effectively terms of the first degree. We represent the sum of these terms by D_i. The leader of D_i is r_i.

We now consider H. Let K represent what H becomes under (10). Our object is to describe the terms of lowest degree in K considered as a polynomial in the z and their derivatives.

Referring to the final remarks of §11, we consider H as a polynomial in the B_i, $i = 1, \cdots, t$. Let L be the sum of those terms of H which are of a lowest total degree in the B. Then every term of L is of the form MN with M reduced with respect to (8) and N a power product in the B. Under (10), let M and N go over into P and Q respectively. Then P contains an effective term which is in $\mathfrak{F}_0$, while the terms of Q which are of a lowest total degree in the z and their derivatives constitute a product of powers of the D and their derivatives. Let us select, from L, those terms which are of a highest degree in B_1. From these latter terms we select those which are of a highest degree in B_2. Continuing, we are led to a definite term MN of L which goes over under (10) into an expression PQ. Let

$$N = B_a^\alpha B_b^\beta \cdots B_c^\gamma,$$

where $a < b < \cdots < c$ and $\alpha, \beta, \cdots, \gamma$ are positive. If s_i is allowed to represent that derivative of a z whose marks are those of q_i in (9), we find that PQ contains effectively a term in $s_a^\alpha\, s_b^\beta \cdots s_c^\gamma$. This term is one of the terms of lowest degree in K.

Thus the leader of W, the sum of the terms of lowest degree in K, is a derivative, proper or improper, of the leader of some D.

13. Changing the notation if necessary, we assume that the leader of W is a derivative of z_1. We decompose W into irreducible factors in $\mathfrak{F}_0$ and consider an irreducible factor V which effectively involves the leader of W.

V is a d.p. over $\mathfrak{F}_0$. Let $\zeta_1, \cdots, \zeta_n$ be a generic point in the general solution of V, contained in an extension $\mathfrak{F}_1$ of $\mathfrak{F}_0$.

Then W vanishes for the ζ. On the other hand, not every D_i can so vanish. Let us assume that D_1 vanishes. We shall prove that D_2 does not. By the final statement of §12, the leader of V is not lower than that of D_1. If D_1 had a lower leader than V, D_1 would be reduced with respect to V and would not vanish for the ζ. Thus D_1 has the same leader as V. Then D_1 is divisible by V. As D_1 is linear, D_1 is the product of V by an element of $\mathfrak{F}_0$. Thus the general solution of V is the general solution of D_1. By §12, the leaders of A_i and D_i have the same marks for every i. Thus the leader of D_2 is not a derivative of that of D_1. Then the remainder of D_2 with respect to D_1 is not zero so that D_2 does not vanish for the ζ.

14. We say that K is annulled by expressions

$$(11)\qquad \begin{aligned} z_i &= \zeta_i c, \qquad\qquad\qquad\qquad i = 2, \cdots, n, \\ z_1 &= \zeta_1 c + \varphi_2 c^{\rho_2} + \cdots + \varphi_k c^{\rho_k} + \cdots, \end{aligned}$$

with $\rho_2 > 1$.

If K vanishes for $z_i = \zeta_i c$, $i = 1, \cdots, n$, we have the desired expressions. Let the vanishing fail to occur. We put in K

$$z_i = \zeta_i c, \qquad i = 2, \cdots, n; \qquad z_1 = \zeta_1 c + u_1,$$

where u_1 has the same marks as z_1. The work of III, §§6–13, carries over with very slight changes. Where, in Chapter III, one uses derivatives of an indeterminate up to a certain order, one employs here a set of partial derivatives.

Leaders serve here as derivatives of highest order do in Chapter III. In treating (11) of III, §10, we represent the derivatives of u_1 appearing in K' by $v_1, \cdots, v_g$ and the corresponding derivatives of u_2 by $w_1, \cdots, w_g$. Assuming that, for certain l,

$$\frac{\partial^{l_1 + \cdots + l_g} L'(u_1)}{\partial^{l_1} v_1 \cdots \partial^{l_g} v_g}$$

does not vanish for $u_1 = \varphi_2$, we prove that $w_1^{l_1} \cdots w_g^{l_g}$ is present in K''.

15. The series (11) being obtained, we find that H is annulled by expressions

$$\text{(12)} \qquad \begin{aligned} y_i &= \eta_i + \zeta_i c, \qquad\qquad i = 2, \cdots, n, \\ y_1 &= \eta_1 + \zeta_1 c + \varphi_2 c^{\rho_2} + \cdots . \end{aligned}$$

These expressions do not annul J, since the η do not. Thus F vanishes for (12). Because the D of §12 do not all vanish for the ζ, the C do not all vanish for (11), so that the A in the characteristic set (8) of Λ of §12 do not all vanish under (12). Now some Σ_i in (7) must admit (12) as a zero. Such a Σ_i is necessarily distinct from Λ. On the other hand, such a Σ_i must admit $\eta_1, \cdots, \eta_n$ as a zero, and thus is contained in Λ. As this is impossible, it is established that every prime ideal in the second member of (7) has a characteristic set consisting of one d.p.

16. Suppose now that F of §10 is algebraically irreducible. Let Σ_1 in (7) be the prime ideal associated with the general solution of F. Consider any Σ_i with $i > 1$. Its manifold is the general solution of a d.p. A. We say that *F effectively involves some proper derivative of the leader of A.*

If this were not true, F would be divisible by A, since F is in Σ_i and the remainder of F with respect to A is zero.

Let y_j be any indeterminate of which some derivative appears effectively in A and let r be the maximum of the orders of the derivatives of y_j in A. Marks can be chosen for which the leader of A is a derivative of y_j of order r. Thus *F is of higher order than A in every indeterminate appearing in A.*

The low power theorem

17. Let F and A be two p.d.p. in $\mathfrak{F}\{y_1, \cdots, y_n\}$, neither an element of $\mathfrak{F}$. Let S be the separant, and p the leader, of A. Proceeding as in III, §17, and as in IX, §11, one proves the existence of a nonnegative integer t such that $S^t F$ has a representation

$$\text{(13)} \qquad \sum_{j=1}^{l} C_j A^{p_j} A_1^{i_{1j}} \cdots A_h^{i_{hj}}$$

where the A_i are distinct proper derivatives of A and no two sets $i_{1j}, \cdots, i_{hj}$ are identical; the C involve no proper derivative of p and are not divisible by A. If F involves no proper derivative of p, there are no A_i in (13); otherwise the leader of A_h is the highest of the derivatives of p which appear in F. For a given admissible t, the representation (13) of $S^t F$ is unique.

In what follows, we assume A to be algebraically irreducible and we use the smallest admissible t.

The low power theorem has the wording of III, §20, except that one uses the representation in (13).

18. We use an indeterminate y and the field of rational numbers.[6] Let p be any positive integer. We shall show that every power product of degree $2p - 1$ in the $\partial y/\partial x_i$, $i = 1, \cdots, m$, is in $[y^p]$.

We may assume that $p > 1$. We have, for every i, $y^{p-1}\partial y/\partial x_i \equiv 0$, $[y^p]$. Thus, for every i and j,

$$(p-1)\, y^{p-2} \frac{\partial y}{\partial x_j} \frac{\partial y}{\partial x_i} + y^{p-1} \frac{\partial^2 y}{\partial x_j\, \partial x_i} \equiv 0, \qquad [y^p].$$

We multiply by any $\partial y/\partial x_k$. Then, for any i, j, k,

$$y^{p-2} \frac{\partial y}{\partial x_i} \frac{\partial y}{\partial x_j} \frac{\partial y}{\partial x_k} \equiv 0, \qquad [y^p].$$

Continuing, we verify our statement.

Let k be any positive integer. We consider the derivatives of y of order k, and form power products in those derivatives. We shall show that every such power product which is of degree $2^k m^{k-1} p$ is in $[y^p]$.

For $k = 1$, we observe that $2^k m^{k-1} p = 2p > 2p - 1$, and use the result proved above. We suppose the proof carried through for $k < q$, where $q > 1$, and consider the case of $k = q$. Among $2^q m^{q-1} p$ derivatives of order q, there must be at least $2^q m^{q-2} p$ which are derivatives of order $q - 1$ of some one $\partial y/\partial x_j$. By the case of $k = q - 1$, a product of $2^q m^{q-2} p$ derivatives as just mentioned is in $[(\partial y/\partial x_j)^{2p}]$, thus in $[y^p]$.

The weight of a product of powers of derivatives of y will be understood to be the sum of the orders of the derivatives in the product.

Let a be a positive integer. Let

$$f(a, p, m) = p(a+1)\, \frac{(2m)^{a+1} - 1}{2m - 1}.$$

We shall show that a power product in y and its derivatives whose degree is $f(a, p, m)$ and whose weight does not exceed $af(a, p, m)$ is in $[y^p]$.

Let P be a power product of degree $f(a, p, m)$ which is not in $[y^p]$. For each nonnegative integer k, the product P, by what precedes, must involve fewer than $(2m)^k p$ derivatives of order k.[7] Thus P involves fewer than

$$\frac{(2m)^{a+1} - 1}{2m - 1}\, p = \frac{f(a, p, m)}{a+1}$$

[6] In §§18, 19, we do not use marks; the order of a partial derivative is the only index of rank which is employed.

[7] We count each derivative of order k as many times as it appears in P.

derivatives of order not exceeding a. Therefore P has more than $f - f/(a+1)$ derivatives of orders exceeding a. Then the weight of P exceeds af.[8]

19. We can now carry over the lemma of III, §21. Let r be the maximum of the weights of the B. The cases of $r = 0$ and $r = 1$ are trivial. We therefore assume that $r > 1$ and put

$$d = f(r-1, p, m), \qquad t = d(r-1).$$

Every power product in z and its derivatives which is of degree d and of weight not more than t is in $[z^p]$. The work of III, §21, needs only minor changes. Where one uses there the ith derivative of a d.p., one employs here appropriate partial derivatives of order i. The lemma having been extended, one finds the theorems of III, §§22, 23, to hold for p.d.p.

20. The necessity proof can be conducted as follows. We assume that the terms of lowest degree in (13) involve proper derivatives of A. If we let A take the place of the chain (8), (13) is an expression for S^tF like that of JG in §10, with the difference that the C are not reduced with respect to A. For our purposes, it is enough that the C do not hold the general solution of A.

We let $\eta_1, \cdots, \eta_n$ be a generic zero in $\mathfrak{M}$, the general solution of A, and make the substitution (10) in S^tF and in A. Then A goes over into a d.p. E in the z. To p, the leader of A, there corresponds a derivative r of some z. E has terms of the first degree and their sum has r for leader.

The substitution (10) converts S^tF into a d.p. K in the z. Considering K as a polynomial in the z and their derivatives, we let W be the sum of the terms of lowest degree in K. The leader of W is seen to be a proper derivative of r. We then proceed as in §§13, 14 and find expressions (12) which annul F but neither S nor A. Those expressions furnish a zero in a component $\mathfrak{M}'$ of F which is not held by A. Then $\eta_1, \cdots, \eta_n$ is in $\mathfrak{M}'$ and $\mathfrak{M}$ is not a component of F.

Characteristic sets of prime ideals

21. Let Σ be a nontrivial prime ideal for which

$$(14) \qquad A_1, A_2, \cdots, A_r$$

is a characteristic set. One shows, as in V, §1, that when the A are regarded as ordinary polynomials in the symbols which they involve, (14) is a characteristic set[9] for a prime p.i. Λ. One then proves as in V, §4, that *every zero of the p.d.p.* (14) *which annuls no separant is a zero of* Σ.

22. From this point on we limit ourselves to the consideration of the analytic case. Through §25, it will be assumed that the first mark of each x is unity.

A being the region in which the functions in $\mathfrak{F}$ are given, we represent by

[8] The result is due to Kolchin.

[9] As we shall see below, we do not have in this a sufficient condition for (14) to be a characteristic set of a prime ideal.

$\xi_1, \cdots, \xi_m$ or, more briefly, by ξ, a point in **A** at which the coefficients in (14) are analytic. We use the symbol $[\eta]$ to designate any set of numerical values which one may choose to associate with the derivatives appearing in (14).

We wish to show that there are sets ξ, $[\eta]$ which annul every A but none of the separants of the A. If we consider the A as ordinary polynomials, Hilbert's theorem of zeros, as derived for the analytic case in IV, §14, holds for them. As no power of the product of the separants is linear in the A, we can find a system of analytic functions of $x_1, \cdots, x_m$ which annul the A when substituted for the various derivatives, without annulling any separant. The existence of a set ξ, $[\eta]$, described as above, follows. We shall deal with such a set.

Let p_i be the leader of A_i. The equation $A_1 = 0$, treated as an algebraic equation for p_1, determines p_1 as a function of the x and the derivatives lower than p_1 in A_1, the function being analytic for x_i close to ξ_i and for the derivatives lower than p_1 close to their values among the $[\eta]$. The value of the function p_1 for the special arguments just mentioned will be the value for p_1 in $[\eta]$. Let the expression for p_1 be substituted into A_2. We can then solve $A_2 = 0$ for p_2, expressing p_2 as a function of the x and of the derivatives other than p_1 and p_2 appearing in A_1 and A_2. We substitute the expressions for p_1 and p_2 into A_3, solve $A_3 = 0$ for p_3, and continue in this manner for all d.p. in (14).

We find thus a set of expressions for the p, each p being given as a function of the x and of the derivatives other than $p_1, \cdots, p_r$ in (14). We write

$$p_i = g_i, \qquad i = 1, \cdots, r. \tag{15}$$

If the equations in (15) are considered as differential equations for the y, they will form an orthonomic system. We shall prove that *if* (15) *is extended into an orthonomic system whose first members give complete systems of monomials* (VIII, §11), *the extended orthonomic system is passive.*

We consider the prime p.i. Λ of §21. The parametric indeterminates in Λ will be those which correspond to the parametric derivatives in (15). We form a resolvent for Λ with

$$w = b_1p_1 + \cdots + b_rp_r, \tag{16}$$

where the b are integers. Let the resolvent be

$$B_0w^s + \cdots + B_s = 0, \tag{17}$$

and let the expressions for the p be

$$p_i = \frac{E_{i0} + \cdots + E_{i,\,s-1}w^{s-1}}{D}. \tag{18}$$

Suppose that, in (16), the p are replaced by the g of (15). Then w in (16) becomes a function of the arguments in the g, analytic at ξ, $[\eta]$. We wish to see that the functions g_i and w satisfy (17) and (18). We can form a zero of the characteristic set (14) of Λ, in which the leaders of the A are put equal to the g and in which the other letters in the A are represented by the complex variables of which the g are functions. This zero of (14) annuls no separant; it is thus a zero of Λ. This is enough to show that the g and w satisfy (17) and (18).

We consider each g in (15) to be expressed by the second member of (18), where w is a function of the x and the parametric derivatives, analytic when the arguments are close to their values[10] in ξ, $[\eta]$.

Let us show how an orthonomic extension σ of (15), described as in VIII, §11, is formed. We can calculate each $\partial p_i/\partial x_j$ from (18). In this calculation $\partial w/\partial x_j$ appears, and can be found from (17). Higher derivatives of the p are calculated similarly. If principal derivatives appear in an expression for a δp, we can get rid of them step by step. We secure in this way the desired extension σ. Its equations will be of the form (IV, §14)

$$\delta y = \frac{F_0 + \cdots + F_{s-1}w^{s-1}}{T}, \tag{19}$$

where T involves only parametric derivatives. There may be, in the second members of (19), parametric derivatives which do not appear in (15). Such derivatives enter rationally and integrally. We shall allow these derivatives to vary in the neighborhood of any set of numerical values $[\zeta]$.

If we refer now to VIII, §20, we see that every μ has an expression like the second member of (19). To establish the passivity of σ for the neighborhood of ξ, $[\eta]$, $[\zeta]$, we have to show that every μ, as a function of the x and of the parametric derivatives, is identically zero.

Consider some μ, say μ_1. Let Z be the numerator in the expression for μ_1 and let P represent the first member of (17). Suppose that Z is not identically zero. Then the resultant W of P and Z with respect to w is not zero. If we can show that W is in Σ, we will have a contradiction. Working in the abstract, let us form a generic zero of Σ; with it is associated a quantity w as in (16). The generic zero and w satisfy (19) and thus annul Z. Then the generic zero annuls W. Hence Z is identically zero and σ is passive at ξ, $[\eta]$, $[\zeta]$.

23. Let (14), with A_1 not a function in $\mathfrak{F}$, be a chain. We shall find necessary and sufficient conditions for (14) to be a characteristic set of a prime ideal.

As a first necessary condition, we have the condition that (14), when regarded as a set of polynomials, be a characteristic set for a prime p.i. This implies the existence of r functions g_i, as in (15), which annul the A when substituted for the p, without annulling any separant.

Let ξ, $[\eta]$ be some set of values as above, for which no separant vanishes. A second necessary condition is that the extended system (19) be passive for the neighborhood of ξ, $[\eta]$, $[\zeta]$.

We shall prove that, *if* (14), *considered as a set of polynomials, is a characteristic set of a prime p.i., and if, for some set* ξ, $[\eta]$, $[\zeta]$, (19) *is passive, then* (14) *is a characteristic set of a prime ideal.*

Let (14) satisfy the stated conditions. As the expressions for the μ vanish

[10] It may be that D vanishes at ξ, $[\eta]$, but this is not a matter for concern.

identically, (19) developed for *any values at all* ξ, $[\eta]$ which annul no separant will be passive.

The passivity of (19) implies that (14) has zeros which annul no separant. We shall prove that the system Σ of d.p. which vanish for all zeros of (14) annulling no separant is a prime ideal for which (14) is a characteristic set.

Let GH be in Σ. Let $J_1G \equiv G_1$, $J_2H \equiv H_1$, $[A_1, \cdots, A_r]$, where the J are power products in the separants and G_1, H_1 involve no proper derivatives of the p. There may be, in G_1 and H_1, parametric derivatives not present in (14). But (14), considered as a set of polynomials, will be a characteristic set for a prime p.i. Λ, even after the adjunction of the new parametric derivatives to the indeterminates in (14).

Let us consider any zero of Λ which annuls no separant in (14). By the passivity of (19) for arbitrary sets ξ, $[\eta]$, $[\zeta]$, the mentioned zero furnishes, at a point free to vary in a region in A, initial conditions for a zero $\eta_1, \cdots, \eta_n$ of the d.p. in (14) which annuls no separant. Σ admits $\eta_1, \cdots, \eta_n$ as a zero. It follows that the zero of Λ annuls G_1H_1. Then G_1H_1, considered as a polynomial, is in Λ. Suppose then that G_1 is in Λ. Then G is in Σ. Thus Σ, which we know to be an ideal, is prime. To prove that (14) is a characteristic set for Σ, it suffices to show that Σ contains no nonzero d.p. reduced with respect to (14); such a d.p., by what precedes, would, considered as a polynomial, belong to Λ.

24. Given a set (14) which satisfies the first condition in §23, we can determine, with a finite number of rational operations and differentiations, whether or not (19) is passive. If (19) is not passive, we secure a d.p. involving only parametric derivatives which vanishes for all zeros of (14) which annul no separant.[11]

Algorithm for decomposition

25. Let Φ be any finite system of p.d.p., not all zero. As in Chapter V, we can obtain, by a finite number of differentiations, rational operations and factorizations, a set, equivalent to Φ, of finite systems $\Lambda_1, \cdots, \Lambda_s$ which have the following properties:

(a) The characteristic sets of the Λ_i are not higher than those of Φ.

(b) If the characteristic set of a Λ_i involves indeterminates, the remainder of any d.p. of Λ_i with respect to the characteristic set is zero.

(c) The characteristic set of a Λ_i, considered as a set of polynomials, is a characteristic set of a prime p.i.

Suppose that Λ_1 has a characteristic set (14) with A_1 not in $\mathfrak{F}$. If (19) is not passive, Λ_1 is equivalent to

$$\Lambda_1 + G, \Lambda_1 + S_1, \cdots, \Lambda_1 + S_r,$$

where the S are the separants, and G, involving only parametric derivatives,

[11] In (19) and in the analogous expressions for the μ, we may use a single T. If Z of §22 does not vanish. TW will serve our purpose.

vanishes for every zero of (14) which annuls no S. Now all of the systems just obtained have characteristic sets lower than (14). If (19) proves passive, Λ_1 is equivalent to

$$\Sigma, \Lambda_1 + S_1, \cdots, \Lambda_1 + S_r,$$

where Σ is the prime ideal for which (14) is a characteristic set.

It is clear that, by this process, we arrive in a finite number of steps at a finite number of chains which are characteristic sets of a set of prime ideals equivalent to Φ.

The above constitutes an elimination theory for systems of algebraic partial differential equations.

26. The assumption that the first mark of each x is unity prevents us from using, in the case of one independent variable, the ordering employed in the earlier chapters. Thus, when the first mark is unity, no derivative of y_2 will be higher than every derivative of y_1. Now, in the case of $m = 1$, no two p in (15) are derivatives of the same y. Thus, with any marks, when $m = 1$, the equations (15) are a set of ordinary differential equations for which the standard existence theorem can be used. We see that, when $m = 1$, (14) will be a characteristic set of a prime ideal if it is a characteristic set of a prime p.i.; one may use any marks which effect a complete ordering. In this way, the theory of characteristic sets of prime ideals is so framed as to include, in the case of $m = 1$, our earlier considerations.

The theorem of zeros

27. We treat the theorem of zeros in the analytic case. Let there be given p.d.p. $F_1, \cdots, F_p$, and a G which vanishes for every analytic zero of the F. We have to show that G is contained in $\{F_1, \cdots, F_p\}$. Let Σ be an essential prime divisor of the perfect ideal. Suppose that Σ does not contain G. Let (14) be a characteristic set for Σ. Let R be the remainder of G with respect to (14) and let $K = RS_1 \cdots S_r$. Then K, as a polynomial, is not in Λ of §21. A zero of Λ which does not annul K furnishes initial conditions for a zero of (14) which is a zero of Σ and does not annul G.

APPENDIX. QUESTIONS FOR INVESTIGATION

IDEALS

1. Levi's work shows the nonexistence of a theory of ideals of d.p. possessing the scope of the Lasker-Noether theory of p.i. For d.p., it will be necessary either to use special types of ideals or to use other combinations than intersections and products.

2. Given a finite set of d.p., $F_1, \cdots, F_r$, and a d.p. G, is it possible to determine whether G is contained in $[F_1, \cdots, F_r]$? The methods of Chapter V permit one to decide whether some power of G is in $[F_1, \cdots, F_r]$. It is thus a question of determining a smallest admissible exponent.

3. Kolchin's theory of exponents should admit of extension in several directions. The chief problem examined by Kolchin is that of the exponent of $\{ A \}$ relative to $[A]$, where A is a d.p. in y of the first order. In the theorems obtained by Kolchin, the relative exponents are 1, 2, ∞. For instance, if $A = y^2 + y_1^3$, the exponent is ∞. Now

$$[A] = [y^p] \cdot \Sigma,$$

with p a positive integer and Σ an ideal whose manifold is the general solution of A. One may inquire as to the exponent of $\{ \Sigma \}$ relative to Σ. That exponent may easily be finite. This problem can, of course, be formulated for d.p. A admitting many singular zeros.

The problem of exponents may be examined for d.p. of order higher than the first and for p.d.p.

4. For $F = y^p + y_1^q$, in $\mathfrak{F}\{ y \}$, with $q > p$, what is the smallest integer r such that

$$y^r G \equiv 0, \qquad [F],$$

where G does not vanish for $y = 0$? This problem can be extended to general classes of d.p.

5. For $p > 0$, $i > 0$, what is the least q such that $y_i^q \equiv 0$, $[y^p]$? For $i = 1$, it is not hard to show that $q = 2p - 1$. In $\mathfrak{F}\{ u, v \}$, what is the least power of $u_i v_j$ which is contained in $[uv]$?

6. The ideals generated by various differential expressions may be examined. One may study the wronskian, the jacobian, the expression $EG - F^2$ of differential geometry, etc.

7. One may study d.p. over a field of characteristic p.

THE DECOMPOSITION PROBLEM

8. The basic problem has been met in Chapter V. It is that of determining the number of times which the d.p. in a finite system Φ must be differentiated

before eliminations will produce finite systems whose manifolds are the components of Φ. One would hope to secure a bound which depends on the number of d.p. in Φ, their orders and degrees.

9. Attached to the decomposition problem is the first problem of Laplace, mentioned in III, §37. Let F and A be algebraically irreducible and let F hold the general solution of A. It is required to determine whether the general solution of A is contained in that of F. The author has shown how to settle this question for d.p. F of the second order.[1] The methods can perhaps be extended to cover the case in which F, in $\mathfrak{F}\{ y \}$, is of order n, and A of order $n - 2$. One might perhaps undertake to develop a test for the presence of $y = 0$ in the general solution of a d.p. of the third order. Other problems of this type will readily suggest themselves.

Intersections

10. One can see from Chapter VII that if there is regularity in the theory of intersections of algebraic differential manifolds, that regularity is not immediately visible. In VII, §1, an anomaly is found in the dimension of the intersection of a general solution with a second irreducible manifold. One might try to use complete manifolds of d.p. rather than general solutions. Thus, let $F_1, \cdots, F_r$ be d.p. in $\mathfrak{F}\{ y_1, \cdots, y_n \}$. Suppose that $r < n$. Is every component of the system $F_1, \cdots, F_r$ of dimension at least $n - r$? For $r = 1$, we see from III, §1, that the answer is affirmative.

11. One may seek to extend the result of VII, §6, on Jacobi's bound to systems of n d.p. in n indeterminates.

The anomaly met in connection with the order of a component of the intersection of two general solutions raises the following problem. Let A and B be algebraically irreducible d.p. in y and z. Let $\mathfrak{M}$ be a component of dimension zero in the intersection of the general solutions of A and B. It is required to find a bound for the order of $\mathfrak{M}$ in terms of the orders of A and B in y and z. It is conceivable, of course, that no bound exists.

12. One may generalize the problem of III, §1, as follows. Let Σ be a nontrivial prime ideal in $\mathfrak{F}\{ u_1, \cdots, u_q; y_1, \cdots, y_p \}$ with the u parametric and with

$$A_1, \cdots, A_p \tag{1}$$

a characteristic set. Let Σ_0 be the prime p.i. for which (1), with the A considered as polynomials, is a characteristic set. Let Σ' be the system of d.p. obtained from Σ_0 when the polynomials in Σ_0 are regarded as d.p. What are the dimensions of the components of Σ'? Does the low power theorem have a generalization for this situation?

Differential power series

13. This subject has been mentioned in III, §39. Only one paper has been

[1] Ritt, 31. In connection with §65 of this paper, see the final remarks of §51 of Ritt, 32.

written on it. The entire program awaits development, both for ordinary differential equations and for partial. In the analytic case, the procedure will depend on whether one works in the neighborhood of a point in the space of the independent variables or in the neighborhood of a set of functions constituting a point of a manifold.

Birational transformations

14. The theory of the resolvent furnishes an instance of the birational equivalence of two irreducible manifolds. The general problem is that of finding conditions for such equivalence. The results of algebraic geometry should be a guide.

In studying birational transformations, one will meet *differential Cremona transformations.* For instance, let

$$Y = y\frac{d}{dx}\left(\frac{z}{y}\right), \qquad Z = z\frac{d}{dx}\left(\frac{z}{y}\right).$$

We find

$$y = Y\frac{d}{dx}\left(\frac{Z}{Y}\right), \qquad z = Z\frac{d}{dx}\left(\frac{Z}{Y}\right).$$

Is there a theorem on the structure of such transformations of y and z similar to M. Noether's theorem on ordinary Cremona transformations?

The analogue of Lüroth's theorem presented in Chapter II may have an extension to fields formed by the adjunction of two indeterminates.

Singular solutions of partial differential equations

15. For simplicity, we use two independent variables, x and y. Let F be an algebraically irreducible d.p. in $\mathfrak{F}\{z\}$, of order n in z. Let the components of F be $\mathfrak{M}, \mathfrak{M}_1, \cdots, \mathfrak{M}_s$, with $\mathfrak{M}$ the general solution. Each $\mathfrak{M}_i$ is the general solution of a d.p. F_i. Suppose that, for some i, F_i is of order $n - 1$ in z. Considering Hamburger's results for ordinary differential equations, one would expect the functions in $\mathfrak{M}_i$ to be envelopes, with a contact of some natural order, of functions in $\mathfrak{M}$. For $n = 1$, this question has been studied by the author.[2] For $n > 1$, the matter should be more difficult, since there is no theory of characteristics.

Difference algebra

16. This subject has been treated in papers of J. L. Doob, W. C. Strodt, F. Herzog, H. W. Raudenbush, Richard Cohn and the author.[3] The theory is open for cultivation.

---

[2] Ritt, 41.

[3] See bibliography.

BIBLIOGRAPHY

1. Cohn, R. M. *On the analog for differential equations of the Hilbert-Netto theorem*, Bulletin of the American Mathematical Society, vol. 47 (1941), pp. 268–270.

2. ——— *Manifolds of difference polynomials*, Transactions of the American Mathematical Society, vol. 64 (1948), pp. 133–172.

3. Doob, J. L., and Ritt, J. F. *Systems of algebraic difference equations*, American Journal of Mathematics, vol. 55 (1933), pp. 505–514.

4. Drach, J. *Essai sur la théorie générale de l'intégration et sur la classification des transcendantes*, Annales de l'Ecole Normale Supérieure, (3), vol. 15 (1898), pp. 245–384.

5. Gourin, E. *On irreducible systems of algebraic differential equations*, Bulletin of the American Mathematical Society, vol. 39 (1933), pp. 593–595.

6. Hamburger, M. *Ueber die singulären Lösungen der algebraischen Differenzialgleichungen erster Ordnung*, Journal für die reine und angewandte Mathematik, vol. 112 (1893), pp. 205–246. See also ibid., vol. 121 (1899), p. 265, and vol. 122 (1900), p. 322.

7. Herzog, F. *Systems of mixed difference equations*, Transactions of the American Mathematical Society, vol. 37 (1935), pp. 286–300.

8. Kolchin, E. R., and Ritt, J. F. *On certain ideals of differential polynomials*, Bulletin of the American Mathematical Society, vol. 45 (1939), pp. 895–898.

9. Kolchin, E. R. *On the basis theorem for infinite systems of differential polynomials*, Bulletin of the American Mathematical Society, vol. 45 (1939), pp. 923–926.

10. ——— *On the exponents of differential ideals*, Annals of Mathematics, vol. 42 (1941), pp. 740–777.

11. ——— *On the basis theorem for differential systems*, Transactions of the American Mathematical Society, vol. 52 (1942), pp. 115–127.

12. ——— *Extensions of differential fields*, I, II, Annals of Mathematics, vol. 43 (1942), pp. 724–729; vol. 45 (1945), pp. 358–361.

13. ——— *Extensions of differential fields*, III, Bulletin of the American Mathematical Society, vol. 53 (1947), pp. 397–401.

14. ——— *Algebraic matric groups and the Picard-Vessiot theory of homogeneous ordinary linear differential equations*, Annals of Mathematics, vol. 49 (1948), pp. 1–42.

15. Lagrange, J. L. *Sur les solutions particulières des équations différentielles*, Oeuvres Complètes, vol. 4, pp. 5–108.

16. Laplace, P. S. *Mémoire sur les solutions particulières des équations différentielles et sur les inégalités séculaires des planètes*, Oeuvres Complètes, vol. 8, pp. 326–365.

17. Levi, H. *On the structure of differential polynomials and on their theory of ideals*, Transactions of the American Mathematical Society, vol. 51 (1942), pp. 532–568.

18. ——— *The low power theorem for partial differential polynomials*, Annals of Mathematics, vol. 46 (1945), pp. 113–119.

19. Poisson, S. D. *Sur les solutions particulières des équations différentielles et des équations aux différences*, Journal de l'Ecole Polytechnique, vol. 6, no. 13 (1806), pp. 60–125.

20. Raudenbush, H. W. *Differential fields and ideals of differential forms*, Annals of Mathematics, vol. 34 (1933), pp. 509–517.

21. ——— *Ideal theory and algebraic differential equations*, Transactions of the American Mathematical Society, vol. 36 (1934), pp. 361–368.

22. ——— *Hypertranscendental adjunctions to partial differential fields*, Bulletin of the American Mathematical Society, vol. 40 (1934), pp. 714–720.

23. ——— *On the analog for differential equations of the Hilbert-Netto theorem*, Bulletin of the American Mathematical Society, vol. 42 (1936), pp. 371–373.

24. Raudenbush, H. W., and Ritt, J. F. *Ideal theory and algebraic difference equations*, Transactions of the American Mathematical Society, vol. 46 (1939), pp. 445–453.

25. Ritt, J. F. *Manifolds of functions defined by systems of algebraic differential equations*, Transactions of the American Mathematical Society, vol. 32 (1930), pp. 369–398.

26. ——— *Differential equations from the algebraic standpoint*, American Mathematical Society Colloquium Publications, vol. 14, New York, 1932.

27. ——— *Algebraic difference equations*, Bulletin of the American Mathematical Society, vol. 40 (1934), pp. 303–308.

28. ——— *Systems of algebraic differential equations*, Annals of Mathematics, vol. 36 (1935), pp. 293–302.

29. ——— *Jacobi's problem on the order of a system of differential equations*, Annals of Mathematics, vol. 36 (1935), pp. 303–312.

30. ——— *Indeterminate expressions involving an analytic function and its derivatives*, Monatshefte für Mathematik, vol. 43 (1936), pp. 97–104.

31. ——— *On the singular solutions of algebraic differential equations*, Annals of Mathematics, vol. 37 (1936), pp. 552–617.

32. ——— *On certain points in the theory of algebraic differential equations*, American Journal of Mathematics, vol. 60 (1938), pp. 1–43.

33. ——— *Systems of differential equations*, I. *Theory of ideals*, American Journal of Mathematics, vol. 60 (1938), pp. 535–548.

34. ——— *On ideals of differential polynomials*, Proceedings of the National Academy of Sciences of the U. S. A., vol. 25 (1939), pp. 90–91.

35. ——— *On the intersections of algebraic differential manifolds*, Proceedings of the National Academy of Sciences of the U. S. A., vol. 25 (1939), pp. 214–215.

36. ——— *On the intersections of irreducible components in the manifold of a differential polynomial*, Proceedings of the National Academy of Sciences of the U. S. A., vol. 26 (1940), pp. 354–356.

37. ——— *On a type of algebraic differential manifold*, Transactions of the American Mathematical Society, vol. 48 (1940), pp. 542–552.

38. ——— *Complete difference ideals*, American Journal of Mathematics, vol. 63 (1941), pp. 681–690.

39. ——— *Bézout's theorem and algebraic differential equations*, Transactions of the American Mathematical Society, vol. 53 (1943), pp. 74–82.

40. ——— *On the manifolds of partial differential polynomials*, Annals of Mathematics, vol. 46 (1945), pp. 102–112.

41. ——— *Analytic theory of singular solutions of partial differential equations of the first order*, Annals of Mathematics, vol. 46 (1945), pp. 120–143.

42. ——— *On the singular solutions of certain differential equations of the second order*, Proceedings of the National Academy of Sciences of the U. S. A., vol. 32 (1946), pp. 255–258.

43. Strodt, W. C. *Systems of algebraic partial difference equations*, Unpublished master's essay, Columbia University, 1937.

44. ——— *Irreducible systems of algebraic differential equations*, Transactions of the American Mathematical Society, vol. 45 (1939), pp. 276–297.

INDEX

The numbers refer to pages.